Phase Contrast and
Interference Microscopy
for Cell Biologists

This book is gratefully dedicated to
Henry Cecil Waring Davis
B.Sc. (Lond.)
Biology Master at Sherborne School
whose stimulating and careful teaching
first kindled my interest in the
biological sciences.

Phase Contrast and Interference Microscopy for Cell Biologists

K. F. A. Ross

D.Phil. (Oxon.)

*Senior Research Associate, Department of
Medicine, University of Newcastle upon Tyne*

New York · St. Martin's Press · 1967

First published 1967

First published in
the United States of America in 1967

First published in Great Britain by
Edward Arnold (Publishers) Ltd.

Library of Congress Catalog Card No.: 67–28852

Printed in Great Britain by
William Clowes and Sons, Limited, London and Beccles

Preface

It was Mr. Francis Smith, the inventor of the interference microscope which is at the present time most extensively used for all kinds of investigations on cells, who, nearly three years ago, first expressed the opinion that there was a need for a book on the practical aspects of interference microscopy written expressly for cell biologists; he was kind enough to suggest that I ought to write it. After considering this carefully, I decided that such a book ought to include an account of the practical applications of phase contrast microscopy in cell biology also, because many of the cytological techniques which are applicable for use with interference microscopes were originally developed for use with phase contrast microscopes and have many varied applications with these less expensive and more generally available instruments.

This book, therefore, is addressed to those biologists and medical men who would like to know more about the capabilities and potentialities of phase contrast microscopes in investigations on cells of all types, and to those of them who would like to use interference microscopes for similar investigations but who have hitherto been discouraged from doing so by the somewhat esoteric nature of much of the existing literature on the subject. Almost all the existing treatises on interference microscopes imply that a considerable degree of mathematical aptitude and a knowledge of optics, such as are seldom possessed by medical and non-medical cell biologists, are necessary for their use; and they assume that their readers possess this knowledge. It is, of course, absolutely essential that certain basic optical principles are fully appreciated by all users of interference and phase contrast microscopes alike if these instruments are to be used discriminatingly, but the presentation of these principles in the existing literature has often been needlessly complicated. In this book, therefore, I have attempted to expound this essential theoretical background in a manner which assumes little more than a schoolboy's knowledge of the wave theory of the propagation of light, and I hope that by doing this I may encourage more cell biologists to use the techniques which I have described.

No technique or experimental approach in the field of cell biology is wholly satisfactory when used in isolation, and the use of phase contrast and interference microscopy is no exception to this rule. There is, however, no doubt in my mind that phase contrast and interference microscopy can illuminate a wide variety of cytological problems if appropriate experimental approaches are made. In this book I have tried to give an outline of the kinds of experimental approach that are most likely to be fruitful in a very wide variety of different sorts of cytological problems and I have illustrated each of these different experimental approaches with concrete examples. The emphasis has been more on the use of phase contrast and interference microscopes for making quantitative measurements on cells than on using them for qualitative observations, although these too are discussed; in this connection I have emphasized that comparative quantitative measurements made on cells under standardized conditions can often be every bit as biologically informative as any absolute quantitative measurements which are frequently subject to a variety of systematic errors that cannot always be precisely determined.

I have also been acutely aware that many cell biologists who may wish to use these instruments and techniques may have rather limited financial resources at their disposal; I hope that I have succeeded in indicating that the greater majority of the experimental techniques described in this book are in fact within the reach of those operating within the confines of quite a limited financial budget. In the first half of the book it is assumed that the reader has a phase contrast microscope and little else; Appendix I describes how even this may be made from an ordinary light microscope at considerably less cost than buying one commercially. In the later chapters it is assumed that one of the much more expensive interference microscopes is at the reader's disposal, but even here the emphasis has been placed on the use and limitations of the visual methods of measuring phase changes than on the marginally more accurate but much more costly densitometric methods.

At the end of the section devoted to phase contrast microscopy I have devoted almost a whole chapter to the applications of immersion refractometry in measuring corpuscular haemoglobin concentrations in the field of haematology. This is because, although these techniques would seem to be especially promising, it is my experience that they are almost unknown and untried by haematologists themselves. There are probably two reasons why this should be so; firstly, it appears as if all the publications on the subject have been in journals and books not read by haematologists, and secondly, the values which were originally obtained for corpuscular haemoglobin concentrations by the use of this method were somewhat suspect because they differed by several per cent from the values obtained by the classical haematological techniques. Now, however, largely as a result of the work of my very able former research student in Leiden, G. Galavazi, we have been able to establish that this latter discrepancy was due to a systematic error caused by an incorrect tonicity adjustment, and that when this is corrected or allowed for, closely comparable results may be obtained. I therefore hope that some haematologists, who alone have the knowledge and background properly to evaluate their efficacy, may be sufficiently interested to try out these techniques for themselves.

ACKNOWLEDGMENTS

It was Professor R. Barer who provided the initial and very considerable stimulus from which my interest in quantitative cytological techniques with phase contrast and interference microscopy originated; although my personal association with him at Oxford during 1952 and 1953 was brief, it was for me an extremely fruitful one and I therefore owe him a lasting debt of gratitude.

Subsequently, during a period of unavoidable financial stringency when I was a demonstrator and later an assistant lecturer at Wye College, it was due to the interest and active intervention of the Principal, Mr. D. E. Skilbeck, that I was enabled to obtain a grant from the London University Central Research Fund to buy one of the earliest commercially available models of the Smith interference microscope and I wish to thank him too. My greatest debt of all, however, is unquestionably to Dr. J. R. Baker, F.R.S., who not only supervised the work I did at that time with the interference microscope for an Oxford D.Phil. degree but acted as a guide, counsellor and friend, and has given me the benefit of his invaluable criticism and active encouragement over a far longer period. I also remember with gratitude the encouragement and interest of Professor J. F. Danielli, F.R.S., Professor Sir Alexander Haddow, F.R.S. and Professor W. G. B. Casselman when I subsequently worked at the Chester Beatty Cancer Research Institute in London and in the Charles Best Institute in Toronto, Canada.

Latterly, when I was directing the sub-department of Histology and Cytology in the Department of Zoology in the University of Leiden, Holland between 1960 and 1962, it was my lot to try to encourage others. This was made easy for me in that I was particularly fortunate in the keenness and ability of the Dutch research students who came to work with me. Of these, I am especially grateful to D. E. Jans, H. Berendes,

A. van der Eb and G. Galavazi and their work, especially that of G. Galavazi, is mentioned extensively in this book.

The people who have given me the benefit of skilled technical assistance over the last fifteen years are far too numerous to mention here and their help has been gratefully acknowledged in my previously published papers, but the very special help which I had from two chief technicians must be mentioned. Miss N. Lepper at Wye College (London University) and Mrs. K. Scheers-Dubbeldam at the sub-department of Histology in the Zoology Laboratory at Leiden, Holland, looked after all my needs and their help with my research and teaching in those two places was invaluable.

The entire manuscript of the book was typed by Miss P. Ruddick, with the valuable assistance of Mrs. A. Kharas and Miss Y. Riches in preparing parts of the preliminary drafts. Most of the figures were drawn by Mr. D. E. Jans and some of the others by Dr. J. T. Y. Chou.

Much of the text is based on papers and articles previously written and published by myself but relatively little has been transferred from any of these verbatim. I am, however, grateful for the permission of the Academic Press Inc. for their permission to reproduce parts of Chapters 3 and 5 and to the Editors of the *Journal of the Royal Microscopical Society* for similar permission to reproduce parts of Chapters 7 and 8. My other sources are fully acknowledged in the text. The original blocks for Plate II were provided by the University of Leiden and that of Plate I by the Muscular Dystrophy Association of Canada. Plate III was originally published in the Vickers magazine and is reproduced here by courtesy of Vickers Ltd.

Mr. Francis Smith not only originally suggested that I should write this book but has read the entire manuscript and given me the benefit of a great deal of detailed criticism and constructive comment. This has been of enormous value.

Finally, I would like to thank Dr. J. N. Walton, F.R.C.P., Director of this Muscular Dystrophy Research Unit, for providing very generous facilities and time for writing this book and for his friendly and active encouragement in my execution of this task.

The Muscular Dystrophy Group Research Laboratories   K. F. A. R.
Newcastle upon Tyne General Hospital, England
September 1966

Contents

6 QUANTITATIVE INTERFERENCE MICROSCOPY IN CYTOLOGY
I: MEASUREMENTS ON WHOLE LIVING CELLS, OR PORTIONS OF LIVING CELLS, AND ON CELLS IN HISTOLOGICAL SECTIONS

Introduction

The intention of this book is to describe and discuss some of the ways in which phase contrast microscopes and interference microscopes can be used in cytological investigations, and to explain some of the techniques and accessory equipment which have so far been developed in connection with their use in this field.

The definition and common properties of phase contrast and interference microscopes

The distinction drawn between phase contrast and interference microscopes is a somewhat artificial one since the two groups of instruments have many properties in common. Both demonstrate phase changes, or differences in optical path in the light that passes through microscopic objects as differences in contrast in the images that they form: in this sense both could justifiably be called phase contrast microscopes. Both, however, achieve this by causing two or more beams of light to interfere with each other, and thus with equal justification both can be called interference microscopes. This, indeed, has been done by Rienitz (1964) who, after reviewing the confusions of terminology that could have resulted if the conflicting definitions of various different authorities had been adopted, has concluded, with entire justification on optical grounds, that not only phase contrast microscopes, but also those employing dark-ground oblique and schlieren illumination ought to be included in any classification of interference microscopes. He also proposes the very useful and entirely unambiguous term 'the microscopy of phase objects' to embrace studies in which all these instruments are used. Smith (1966a) has suggested that *all* microscopes which achieve contrast by changing the phase relationship between the dioptric and diffracted components should be called 'phase microscopes', and that what are now called phase contrast microscopes should be called 'Zernike phase microscopes'. What are now called interference microscopes would then, in his definition, be called 'beam dividing phase microscopes'. It is, however, unlikely that this very sensible suggestion will ever now gain universal acceptance, as the present terminology has been in use too long. However, although the names 'phase contrast' and 'interference' are historical rather than strictly or comprehensively descriptive, their recognized common usage is justified in that it serves to distinguish two similar groups of instruments which nevertheless possess somewhat different characteristics and potentialities.

Although both kinds of microscopes are highly complex and sophisticated research tools (as indeed is the ordinary light microscope also), phase contrast and interference microscopes are both, to a greater extent than is perhaps generally realized, capable of being used for cytological investigations in a precise and discriminating manner by biologists, who need not possess the kind of specialized knowledge of optical theory necessary for a complete and full understanding of all the fine details of their design and operation once a few essential fundamental optical principles are fully grasped and understood. It is necessary to emphasize this because nearly all the treatises on the subject that have appeared hitherto have tended rather to convey the opposite impression, and this has undoubtedly in some cases discouraged some cytologists who have had no specialized training in physics from embarking on their use. This is regrettable because the full capabilities of these instruments for cytological research can, of necessity, only be fully explored by cytologists themselves.

Conversely, but equally regrettably, there has been a tendency for some biologists who possess a special knowledge of physics to become side-tracked into problems of pure instrumentation, or to spend a disproportionate amount of their time and ingenuity upon problems which can provide only rather limited biological information. It is therefore not wholly inappropriate at the outset of this book to attempt to define the aims and purposes of cytological research.

The aims of cytological investigations

Although before the invention of phase contrast and interference microscopes it is safe to say that more than 95% of the whole body of cytological knowledge was derived at second hand from the study of fixed and stained cells, the purpose of this fixation and staining was always to preserve and exhibit their structure and content in as life-like a manner as possible, so that the conclusions drawn from their study could be assumed to throw light upon the nature of these cells in their living state. The aim of such investigations, and indeed of all cytological investigations, can be therefore defined as follows:

1. To discover as much as possible about the morphology of living cells.
2. To discover as much as possible about the chemical nature of the substances that occur in living cells and relate their distribution to cellular morphology.
3. To discover in as great detail as possible the changes in morphology and distribution of cellular substances that occur in living cells of different types and functions and in different states of growth development and physiological activity.
4. From the foregoing to gain a detailed insight into every process of cellular metabolism.

From this it is clear that highly detailed knowledge about specific cellular regions and organelles is normally more valuable than more generalized information about cells as a whole, although usually it is more tedious to obtain. The need for this detailed knowledge stems directly from the extreme ultimate heterogeneity of cellular structures and the great complexity and subtlety of the chemical reactions of cellular metabolism, so that even parts of single molecules can often have a unique determinative significance in the context provided by a cellular environment.

Optical theory for practical ends

The writer of this book is very fully aware that many biologists and medical men who could find valuable uses for phase contrast or interference microscopy in their research on cytological problems have received comparatively little training in optics in their education as scientists, and it is rare for standard physics curricula to include any study of the microscopy of phase objects. It is therefore the intention of this book to include as much of this branch of physics as is essential for the full use of these microscopes for cytological research while excluding all aspects irrelevant to this end.

To achieve this a certain difference of emphasis has been necessary in treating phase contrast microscopy and interference microscopy. Phase contrast microscopes are now used by innumerable cytologists both for research and for routine investigations in many biological and medical fields; but it is probably true to say that the majority of their users do not appreciate enough of how these microscopes work to enable them to fully evaluate and interpret the images which they study with them. A cytologist using a phase contrast microscope soon becomes familiar with the characteristic image of, for example, a living fibroblast which typically shows clear sharp cell boundaries and nuclear boundaries, dark nucleoli and chromosomes, faint dark mitochondria and bright lipid droplets; but the full cytological implications of such an image are much more fully appreciated if one knows why these different regions and inclusions appear as they do. This is seldom explained in the instruction manuals supplied with commercial phase contrast microscopes, and one instance alone will suffice to show why such knowledge is valuable. Ten years ago there was a controversy among bacteriologists about the water content of bacterial spores. The resistence of spores to desiccation and heat led many authorities to believe that they contained very much less water than the vegetative cells which could be germinated from them; but some experiments which involved the bulk weighing and drying of vegetative cells and spores had indicated that both contained about 16% of water (Henry & Friedman, 1937; Friedman & Henry, 1938). It was eventually established from refractive index measurements made with an interference microscope that bacterial spores did in fact contain much less water than bacterial vegetative cells, and that the weighing and drying experiments had been misleading (Ross & Billing, 1957). It was, however, unnecessary to have used interference microscopy to have established that this was so. It could have been deduced at any time in the previous ten years from the familiar appearance of these spores and vegetative cells under a phase contrast microscope. Such bacterial spores under phase contrast normally appear in reversed contrast and this indicates that they are much more refractile, and hence much denser, than vegetative cells of the same dimensions (pp. 49 and 134 and Plates 3.1, 3.2).

Thus, in discussing phase contrast microscopy it has been necessary to include a simplified, but for most practical purposes adequate, description of how a phase contrast microscope works, along the lines of that first expounded by Osterberg in Bennett et al. (1951). Descriptions of this kind are not, however, so necessary for interference microscopes since most of the theoretical aspects of interference microscopy have been exhaustively written up (see, for example, Hale, 1958; Richards, 1963; Krug, Rienitz & Schultz, 1964) and the optical principles of individual instruments are always fully described in their instruction manuals. But since these descriptions are often both detailed and complex, the need here seemed to be more to simplify these accounts as far as permissible for the practical biologist and to exclude every complexity which is not strictly relevant to some aspect of the study of cells. Thus, by elaborating somewhat more than is customary in most purely practical accounts of phase contrast microscopy, and conversely simplifying the accounts of interference microscopy, it has been the intention that the optics of both classes of instrument are discussed on as elementary a level as is compatible with securing their effective use in practical cytological studies.

The importance of comparative measurements in quantitative investigations

By far the greater part of this book is concerned with the use of phase contrast and interference microscopes for *quantitative* cytological investigations because it is in these fields that potentialities of these instruments are greatest. The important thing to appreciate here, however, is that more frequently than not such quantitative measurements made in isolation are of little biological interest, but they can be of considerable importance when they can be compared with similar measurements made with standardized procedures on other cells of a different type or on similar cells undergoing different physiological activity. In other words, the absolute values of the measurements obtained are often of quite secondary importance compared to their value or *comparative measurements*. This is important because although some of the quantitative techniques described here undoubtedly have a high absolute accuracy, others may be subject to certain systematic errors difficult to quantify exactly. Properly interpreted, however, even these last are capable of yielding just as important and valuable information to the biologist as those whose absolute accuracy is above question.

Gradations in instrumental complexity and cost

The equipment required for many fundamental and detailed cytological investigations need not be very costly or elaborate, and in the first part of this book (Chapters 1–4) it will be assumed that the investigator only has a phase contrast microscope; but with this it is possible, once the phase contrast images are interpreted correctly, not only to

2

determine much of the detailed morphology of living cells but, as already mentioned, also to obtain a considerable body of quantitative information about them. As well as being valuable in itself, quantitative data of this kind can have considerable value in confirming and completing the picture derived from the evidence of other experimental approaches. Phase contrast microscopes can therefore, from time to time, be valuable auxillary research tools even in laboratories with rather meagre financial resources that do not ordinarily need to use them. For this reason an appendix has been included in this book containing instructions by which most ordinary research microscopes can be inexpensively adapted to provide a form of phase contrast with which critical qualitative and quantitative work can be performed.

In the latter part of the book, the reader is assumed to be able to afford apparatus which tends to become more expensive with each succeeding chapter. The considerably increased scope of investigations that become possible with the aid of interference microscopes is first discussed (Chapters 5–7), then later how this scope can be extended still further with the aid of auxillary equipment for measuring phase changes more accurately and with the help of microdensitometry (Chapter 8).

The very elaborate and costly phase change integrating devices which have been developed, e.g. by Mitchison, Passano & Smith (1956), Davies & Deeley (1956), Svensson (1957), King (1958), and still are being developed, will not be discussed for two reasons. Firstly, none of these developed as yet work completely satisfactorily over the full range of phase changes produced by normal cellular material, mainly because the non-linear relationship between phase changes and corresponding light transmissions has presented a particularly intractable problem, although one that is probably quite capable of solution.*

---

* Since this was written, Smith (1966b, 1967) and Lomakka (1965) have described entirely new integrating devices in which an electrically driven Sénarmont compensator is used with a double-refracting interference microscope, and the sinusoidally fluctuating light output is converted into an alternating voltage with an electrical phase proportional to the retardation of the specimen. An electronic system produces output signals which are proportional to the electrical phase difference between the voltage from the photo-detector and a phase-invariant reference voltage derived from the driven compensator. This results in a great extension of the effective linearity of the relationship between the phase change produced by an object and the final signal strength, and (in the Smith instrument) enables everything in the microscope field giving phase changes of up to nearly a whole wavelength (0°–356°) to be measured and integrated accurately.

By this notable achievement it would seem that it should be possible to make direct dry mass measurements on most, if not all, living cells mounted in aqueous

Secondly, integration, by its very nature, provides generalized rather than detailed information, so that even when all the problems are satisfactorily solved, it may well turn out that the cytological applications of such apparatus could be disappointingly limited. The author could, however, very well be wrong in holding this opinion. Smith (1966a) has pointed out that, although in medicine the regular weighing of a patient does not in itself provide any precise specific diagnostic information, it can provide valuable pointers to an individual's health and metabolism; the same argument is just as true of cells grown under standardized conditions, if they could similarly be weighed.

Full details of the optics and mode of operation of individual interference microscopes are also mostly omitted since this information is readily obtained from the appropriate instruction manuals in the case of all the commercially available models and, with the important exception of that of A. F. Huxley (1954), little cytological work of real note has been done with interference microscopes which have not been marketed commercially. Commercial interference microscopes are referred to throughout this work by the names of their inventors, and only secondarily by the name of the firm that manufactures them. This is in line with the general policy adopted by the author of attempting to assign the credit for each valuable development as far as possible to its originator. It should also be emphasized that the author's remarks on the relative merits of these instruments in Chapter 5, pp. 108–122, and elsewhere are simply his personal opinions based on his own particular experience; they have in no way been influenced one way or another by the altogether excellent personal relations he has with the representatives of most of the microscope firms in question.

---

media such as saline; this range of phase change embraces almost all those given by even the most highly refractile cell inclusions and the thickest cell regions. The cellular materials measured by the present writer, for example, that have given the greatest phase changes he has ever measured, are the larger lipid droplets in mouse ascites tumour cells (Ross, 1961a) and bacterial spores (Ross & Billing, 1957). The largest of the lipid droplets, $2 \cdot 5\ \mu$ in diameter, gave a phase change of $218°$ and the largest bacterial spores $130°$. Thus it would appear that, unless a cell contains lipid droplets larger than about $4\ \mu$ in diameter, or is thick enough to have several similarly highly refractile inclusions superimposed on each other, this device will give accurate values for its dry mass; but in some cases it may be necessary to flatten certain cells somewhat after making trial phase change measurements in the regions that give the highest phase changes. (Smith (1967) discusses the differences between his and Lomakka's instruments.)

Individual contributions to the development of practical phase contrast and interference microscopy in cytology

It will be appreciated that the number of individual workers who have contributed to the development of applications for phase contrast and interference microscopy to cytology is quite considerable and in the existing literature it is often by no means clear as to who was the originator of a particular idea or technique. Indeed, in a rapidly developing field of this kind it has been inevitable that a few of the experimental approaches and discoveries have been developed at almost exactly the same time by different investigators working quite independently (e.g. the 'bubble method' of Ambrose and Klug & Walker, p. 134). It has been the present writer's aim as far as possible to trace back each idea and contribution to its true originator and to assign the credit for the inception of each valuable development where it is rightly due. Consequently, the historical aspects of the subject have been discussed at some length and the original papers have been cited wherever possible: in some cases this information has been augmented by the writer's personal knowledge of the circumstances of a particular development. The present writer, however, is fully aware that such an attempt to set the record straight may be far from complete and he readily extends his apologies to anyone whose work has been inadvertently omitted, or wrongly ascribed.

This book is primarily intended as an introduction to the sort of experimental approaches likely to prove most fruitful in investigations in this field; it is the writer's opinion that these experimental approaches are best illustrated by the detailed discussion of actual cytological problems which have been investigated by these means rather than by a more generalized account, but this has inevitably necessitated some selection. The writer fully acknowledges that a disproportionate number of the illustrations of the applications of phase contrast and interference microscope to cytological studies are derived from his own work but the reasons for this are twofold. Firstly, naturally, these are the problems with which the writer is most intimately familiar and which are capable of being discussed in the necessary detail required to illustrate all the aspects of a particular experimental approach; secondly, publication delays could occur as a result of including exhaustive verbatim quotations from other people's work. This imbalance can be readily remedied by referring to the relevant books and papers of these other authors. It hardly needs emphasizing that the work omitted is in many cases just as good or better than that of the authors whose work is here discussed.

This book, therefore, is in no way a comprehensive review of *all* the cytological work in which phase contrast microscopy and interference microscopy have been employed, and in this rapidly developing field no such comprehensive review as yet exists. Richards (1963) has, however, compiled an extremely valuable bibliography in the instruction manual of the 'A. O. Baker' Smith interference microscope which includes almost all the cytological investigations undertaken with interference microscopes up to and including the year 1962. It appears that no such bibliography exists for cytological work done with phase contrast microscopy and, indeed, at the present time even the compilation of such a bibliography, let alone a full critical review of the literature, would be a task of very considerable magnitude.

Definition of cytology

Finally, it has unfortunately become necessary to define the words 'cytology', 'cytologist' and 'cytological' used throughout this work, since in recent years these words have acquired a new and restricted meaning which is not intended here. The word 'cytology' is derived from the Greek words κυτος, meaning a hollow object or cell, and λογος; for over a hundred years it has been used to mean 'the study of cells'. A 'cytologist', therefore, is one who studies cells. Now, however, in medical circles, it is used in a highly specialized sense to mean the specialist in that branch of human pathology who devotes his time to the study of the vaginal, bronchial, gastric and cystic epithelium in man for evidence of malignant disease; this is about as sensible as using the term 'geologist' exclusively for those who study sharks' teeth in the English chalk deposits of the Upper Cretaceous. Here the word 'cytology' and its derivatives are used in their original sense to denote the study of *all* cells; and 'cells' include all single-celled organisms and bacteria as well as the body cells of plants and animals.

I

The Properties of Cytological Phase Objects

1.1 The formation of visible images of fixed and living cells and the concept of phase change

In the nineteenth and early twentieth centuries, many staining techniques were developed to study cells and tissues under the light microscope, mainly because under ordinary microscope illumination unstained cells and tissues are practically invisible. Fixation was also extensively used because only relatively few regions in living cells could be satisfactorily stained with vital dyes and because fixation formed an essential part of the process by which tissues containing less accessible cells could be sectioned and examined without disintegrating. Some knowledge about the external and internal boundaries in living cells was also obtained by studying them with dark-ground illumination, but this was rather limited. By contrast, however, an enormous amount of detailed information was gained from the study of fixed and stained cells and this approach is still essential for the study of any new cellular material today; it is likely to remain so in the foreseeable future, although the development of cryostat techniques for the direct study of stained, deep-frozen sections has, in some cases, rendered the need for fixation, with its inevitable attendant artefacts, less necessary.

The examination of living cells by phase contrast or interference microscopy, however, has not only confirmed the findings derived from the study of fixed and stained material but quite frequently has provided interesting additional cytological information as well, and the proven value of the morphological examinations of all readily accessible living cells by phase contrast microscopy has led to this becoming a routine practice in many laboratories. In addition, quantitative information about the solid matter in living cells can be obtained by phase contrast and interference microscopy which may be impossible to obtain from studying them fixed and stained, although it is also true that the study of fixed and stained cells by densitometry and other techniques can sometimes yield unique quantitative information of a different kind. A further advantage of studying living cells by phase contrast or interference miscroscopy is that a succession of events can be recorded, thus adding an uninterrupted dimension of time to many cytological investigations.

The most striking property of phase contrast and interference microscopy is their ability to make unstained and almost transparent living cells appear very much as if they were selectively stained, and to understand this it is first necessary to give some explanation of why stained cells are visible and living unstained cells invisible. Fixed and stained cells are rendered visible because the stain absorbs some of the light, and the light emerging from these cells is to some extent diminished in amplitude in comparison with the light which passes only through the background. The eye is sensitive to such changes in amplitude and they are appreciated as a reduction in the cell's brightness and if, as is usual, some wave lengths are selectively absorbed, they are appreciated also as changes in colour. Fig. 1A is a diagram of an imaginary fixed and stained

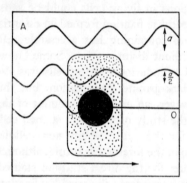 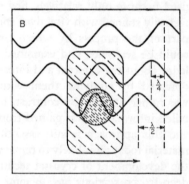

Fig. 1   A—The reduction in amplitude of waves of light passing through a stained cell. The waves passing through the full thickness of stained cytoplasm have been reduced to half the background amplitude and those passing through the centre of a very heavily stained circular-shaped inclusion have been completely absorbed and emerge with an amplitude of zero.

B—Retardations in phase in waves of light passing through a transparent living cell mounted in saline. The waves passing through the full thickness of the cytoplasm have been retarded by $\frac{1}{4}\lambda$ and those passing through the full thickness of a more highly refractile inclusion and some cytoplasm have been retarded by $\frac{1}{2}\lambda$.

cell mounted in a medium with a refractive index equal to that of its own material and containing a single very heavily stained inclusion. In this case, the pigment of the stain has absorbed the light (travelling from left to right) which has traversed its cytoplasm so that the amplitude of the light waves that have travelled through this region have been reduced to half its background value. Similarly, the amplitude of the light that has passed through the 100% absorbing inclusion has actually been reduced to zero, a state of affairs seldom approached in practice except in the case of staining with silver techniques or with other heavy metals. Fig. 1B (p. 2) is a similar diagram of light traversing an unfixed living cell mounted in an aqueous medium, such as physiological saline, with a lower refractive index than any of its own material, and containing an inclusion with a rather higher refractive index than its cytoplasm. In this case all the light waves traversing the cell emerge undiminished in amplitude since none of the light is absorbed by the totally unpigmented cell, but its quality has been changed in a different manner by virtue of the differences in refractive index between the cell contents and its environment. What has happened is that on entering the more highly refractile cellular material the light is slowed down, and the emerging waves are consequently displaced with respect to the wave that only went through an equivalent thickness of the mounting medium. Such a displacement is called a change in phase or optical path, and in this case the phase changes in the light passing through the cell are retardations in phase.

In Fig. 1B the waves of light traversing the cytoplasm alone are represented as having been retarded a quarter of a wavelength, and the waves that have gone through the cytoplasm and the more highly refractile inclusion have been retarded by half a wavelength, compared to the waves that pass through the background medium alone. Such changes in optical path or phase changes (usually denoted by the symbol ϕ) are commonly expressed either as fractions of a wavelength or in degrees, where a phase change of a quarter of a wavelength is 90°, half a wavelength 180° and a whole wavelength 360°. They can, of course, take the form of phase retardations, as in the present instance, or of phase advancements where light passes from a more highly refractile to a less refractile medium. In practice, the conditions represented in Fig. 1A and B are never completely realized, since all cells, however treated, contain some regions which change both the amplitude and the phase of the waves passing through them to some degree. Thus, the light passing through fixed and stained cells is almost always not only diminished in amplitude but retarded in phase as well, both because they contain regions of relatively high refractive index and because the stains themselves are refractile. The conditions represented in Fig. 1B are more nearly realized in practice than they are in Fig. 1A; but even unstained living cells absorb a little of the light that passes through them, so that here again the true picture is really one of both phase change and amplitude change.

Phase contrast and interference microscopes are both, in different ways, capable of turning differences in phase, like those illustrated in Fig. 1B, into differences in amplitude like those illustrated in Fig. 1A. In the case of phase contrast microscopes, the method by which this is achieved is essentially similar in all phase contrast microscopes, and an elementary explanation of the principles on which they operate is given in the next chapter. Interference microscopes, however, are much more diverse in their construction and mode of operation and employ such a variety of different optical principles to achieve their end that detailed descriptions of all of these are inappropriate to a work of this kind; some of the qualities of most of the commercially available interference microscopes suitable for cytological use are discussed from a practical standpoint in Chapter 5 (pp. 108–116).

Hale (1958) describes about 20 different interference microscopes, and Krug, Rienitz & Schultz in their extremely exhaustive and informative treatise (1964) no less than 40, but by far the majority of these are either not commercially available or are unsuitable for cytological investigations.

1.2   The nature of refraction and of the specific refraction increments of cell substances

Phase changes are created in light passing through transparent substances with differing refractile properties, and all matter capable of transmitting light at all, including, of course, all cells and their mounting media, are, to a greater or lesser extent, refractile. The refractile properties of different kinds of matter are commonly defined in terms of their refractive indices and, although the refractive index of a substance (commonly signified by the symbol n) is usually derived from a rather special situation, as a function, $(\sin i/\sin r)$, of the change in direction of the wave fronts of non-perpendicular incident light passing through a plane surface into that substance from air, this value can be used to determine the relative phase changes in the light entering it through any shape of surface and from any medium. Refractive indices are, in fact, equally well defined in terms of such phase changes.

It is these phase changes that are the direct result of refraction, and some understanding of the cause of refraction is now necessary since it holds several important implications of considerable relevance in cytological studies. A fuller treatment of the whole subject, based mainly upon the relationship between refractive index and density suggested by Gladstone & Dale (1858) and its subsequent modification in the light of electromagnetic optical theory by H. A. Lorentz (1880) and L. V. Lorenz (1880), has been given by Barer & Joseph (1954), but a less detailed presentation is probably sufficient here. The refraction of light can be considered as being the result of the interaction of the electromagnetic energy in the waves of the propagated light with that of the waves that they induce in the electromagnetic fields that constitute the bondings between the atoms of the molecules of any substance that they pass through. These induced waves can be imagined as adding themselves on to or subtracting themselves from the original propagated waves so as to cause them to become displaced and changed in phase. The extent to which this happens is dependent on both the numbers and on the nature of the electromagnetic bondings between the atoms of the refractile substances through which the light passes; but it is determined more by the total number of these bonds per unit distance than by their nature. Thus, generally speaking, it is true to say that the amount by which light is refracted depends principally on the total number of atoms in the molecules of the substances which it passes through, since this is fairly closely related to the total numbers of bondings by which they are joined to each other, and not on the sizes of the molecules that these atoms go to make up. Thus the refractive index of a substance can be expected to provide an indication of its overall density or concentration, since the concentration of a substance is dependent on the sum of the weight of all the individual atoms occupying a given space. This is true whether a substance having a certain concentration consists of relatively large numbers of molecules each containing a small number of atoms, or smaller numbers of molecules containing a great many atoms: in both cases, the overall numbers of interatomic bondings and hence the refractive indices of the substances will not be greatly different. This is especially true of the organic substances dispersed in an aqueous phase that are most commonly found in living cells, since the overall proportion of carbon, hydrogen, oxygen and nitrogen atoms that they contain, and also the nature of the bondings between them, differ very little because the larger organic molecules are frequently polymers of the smaller ones.

Thus, regardless of the size of its molecules, one might expect the refractive index of an organic substance to give an indication of its density or concentration, and this has in fact been experimentally verified. During the past 45 years many different workers have estimated how the refractive indices of numerous substances commonly found in cells have varied with their weight/volume concentration in aqueous solutions; in almost every case it has not only been found that the relationship is a strictly linear one over wide ranges of concentration, but also that the amounts by which the refractive indices of different substances increase over a given range of concentration differ very little. The actual rate of increase in the refractive index of a substance with its concentration in aqueous solutions (which must be expressed as weight/volume (w/v) concentrations, e.g. g/100 cc) is called the specific refraction increment (often also called the specific refractive increment) of that substance, and normally designated by the symbol α. This is defined as the amount by which the refractive index of a substance increases for every 1% rise in its w/v concentration.

Living cells contain protein, including lipoproteins, nucleoproteins and amino acids, nucleic acids, lipids, carbohydrates and inorganic salts dispersed in water; by weight the proteins greatly predominate. Table 1, which is based mostly on the compilations of Davies et al. (1954) and of Barer & Joseph (1954), shows a selection of typical values for the specific refraction increments of a number of these substances obtained by different workers over the last five decades. It has been found that these values do not vary significantly with temperature nor with pH over the ranges of temperature and pH commonly found in living systems. As might be expected they do vary in a linear manner with the wavelength of light used (Pederson & Andersen, quoted by McFarlane, 1935; Pederson, 1936) but even over the whole visible spectrum this variation amounts to less than 3 units in the fourth decimal place, and the differences between using, for example, white light or mercury green light for these measurements are for all practical purposes negligible.

The values for α shown in Table 1 and the entirely comparable values that can be found in the rather more extensive compilations of Davies et al. (1954), Barer & Joseph (1954) and Davies (1958), which for reasons of space have not been included here, all provide experimental confirmation of the theoretical predictions discussed above; they clearly show that the specific refraction increments of almost all the substances normally found in living cells differ by little, and those of the proteins, which by weight form by far the greater part of the cellular constituents, by very little indeed. The values obtained by Davies (1959) (by means of interference microscopy with Ambrose's and Klug & Walker's 'bubble' technique, p. 134) for the specific refractive increments of pure solid crystalline protein are of considerable interest since they indicate that the specific refraction increment of a protein, unlike that of many inorganic salts, is probably linear over its entire range of concentrations. This had previously been questioned (Barer & Joseph, 1954; Davies *et al.*, 1954) and is of importance in estimating the hydration of the very concentrated protein found in fixed cells or in dried cellular material such as bacterial spores.* Also of interest are the rather higher than average values for α given by tryptophane among the amino acids and by many pigmented proteins such as haemoglobins and haemocyanins. These all contain an appreciable proportion of conjugated double bonds in their molecules and their higher than normal refraction increments provide experimental evidence for believing that the actual nature of the chemical bonding, as well as the total number of bonds, affect the refractile properties of organic substances (p. 5). Substances of low molecular weight such as amino acids, sugars and inorganic salts have, for the same reason, predictably more variable specific refraction increments but they form only quite a small proportion of the total mass of material found in cells.

Apart from these minor deviations, the most striking thing about the values for the specific refraction increments of cellular constituents is that they differ from each other by so little. This means that, broadly speaking, the refractile properties of all the constituent substances of living cellular material are so similar that the refractive index of living protoplasm itself can in fact give a close indication of its total weight/ volume concentration. In the case of unpigmented proteins only very small errors would be involved if one were to assume that they all had specific refraction increments of 0·00185. When one includes the smaller molecules that also occur in cellular metabolizing systems, a slightly lower value would seem to be preferable, and a mean refraction increment of 0·0018 is now generally accepted for the constituents of

---

* It is, however, worth mentioning here that Goldstein (1965) cites evidence which suggests that very concentrated solutions of protein will tend to occupy less volume than might be expected: and that, consequently, the specific refraction increments of protein do in fact cease to be linear in the highest concentrations. His explanation of Davies' result here discussed would therefore be that the β-lactoglobulin contained some water of crystallization, and that proteins at these high concentrations do in fact have specific refractive increments which are appreciably less than 0·0018. Ross & Billing (1957), however, calculated the water content of bacterial spores from their refractive index measurements, assuming the then commonly held view that α for concentrated proteins (and other bacterial solids) was 0·0015, and found that over half their samples gave negative values for their water content, which is, of course, impossible. These values, +ve and −ve, were, however, small and could have indicated that the spores contained almost no water. A value of 0·0018 for α, on the other hand, indicated that these spores contained 14–23% of 'bound water' (see p. 133).

TABLE 1

Specific refraction increments of a selection of commonly found cellular constituents, derived from data obtained by various authorities here quoted

Substance	% concentrations from which estimates were derived	Wavelength of light used (mμ)	Specific refraction increment (α)	Reference
Proteins				
Bovine plasma albumin	0–50		0·00182	Barer & Tkaczyk (1954)
Human serum albumin	1·8–7·7	578	0·001862	Perlman & Longsworth (1948)
Bovine serum albumin	3·7–10·1	578	0·00187	Perlman & Longsworth (1948)
Horse serum albumin	2·9–8·5	white light	0·00183	Adair & Robinson (1930)
Egg albumin	dilute soln.	546	0·00182	Halwer et al. (1931)
Human serum globulin	3·3–17·0	white light	0·00186	Adair & Robinson (1930)
β-Lactoglobulin	dilute soln.	436	0·00189	Halwer et al. (1931)
β-Lactoglobulin	solid orthorhombic crystals		0·00191	Davies (1959)
β-Lactoglobulin	solid monoclinic crystals		0·00196	Davies (1959)
Human fibrinogen		589	0·00188	Armstrong et al. (1947)
Human haemoglobin	0·04–8·17	white light	0·001942	Stoddard & Adair (1923)
Sheep carboxy-haemoglobin	dilute soln.	white light	0·001945	Adair & Adair (1934)
Lobster haemocyanin	11·85	white light	0·002	Redfield (1934)
β-Lipoprotein (containing more than 75% lipid by weight)	dilute soln.		0·0017	Armstrong et al. (1947)
Nucleoprotein (tobacco mozaic virus)	dilute soln.		0·0017	Oster, quoted by Davies (1958)

Amino Acids				
Glycine		dilute soln.	0·0179	Adair & Robinson (1930)
Alanine		dilute soln.	0·0171	Adair & Robinson (1930)
Valine		dilute soln.	0·0175	Adair & Robinson (1930)
Tryptophane		dilute soln.	0·0025	Adair & Robinson (1930)
Nucleic Acids				
DNA	436	dilute soln.	0·0181	Brown et al. (1955)
DNA	436	dilute soln.	0·0020	Northrop et al. (1953)
RNA	436	dilute soln.	0·0194	Northrop & Sinsheimer (1954)
RNA		dilute soln.	0·0168	Davies & Wilkins, quoted by Davies (1958)
Carbohydrates				
Sucrose		2	0·0141	Handbook of Chemistry & Physics
Glucose		0–50	0·0143	Barer & Joseph (1954)
Starch		solid	0·0133	Handbook of Chemistry & Physics
Inorganic salts (in dilute solution)				
NaCl		5·25	0·0163	Handbook of Chemistry & Physics
KCl		10	0·0115	Handbook of Chemistry & Physics
CaCl$_2$		1·7	0·0021	Handbook of Chemistry & Physics

protoplasm as a whole. At first sight it would seem unlikely that living protoplasm, which is of course an immensely complex association of substances continually changing, could have a constant or easily determinable refraction increment, but by assuming that it has a refraction increment of 0·0018, it is possible to determine within fairly narrow limits the total overall per cent solid concentration of almost all the constituent substances that occur in any given region of a living cell from its refractive index. These refractive indices can in their turn be determined by the phase changes which are revealed with phase contrast and interference microscopes.

The important general conclusion, that it is possible to derive a mean value for the refraction increment of protoplasm from the specific refraction increments of all cellular substances, and its use in the evaluation of the hydration of a cell's contents, seems to have been first appreciated by Vlès (1921) who in his interpretations of the refractive index changes which he recorded in fertilized and dividing sea urchin eggs (p. 31) said, 'One knows that in a solution there is, as a rough approximation, a relationship between the refractive index of a solution, the concentration and molecular weight of the dissolved bodies, and the sum of their atomic refractions'. It was, however, Davies & Wilkins who appear to have been the first to formulate it explicitly and to present compiled data on the specific refraction increments of individual cellular substances in support of it at a meeting of the Cytochemistry Commission of the Society for Cell Biology in Stockholm in 1951; but the proceedings of this meeting, although occasionally quoted in the literature as a reference, were never actually published.

Later Barer (1952b) and Davies & Wilkins (1952) independently published letters in *Nature*, presenting the same general conclusion. Its great importance lies in the fact that it provides the foundations on which almost all the quantitative applications of phase contrast and interference microscopy depend, since these are primarily concerned with the measurement of concentrations and dry mass. The exact manner in which these principles are applied and just how these values can be derived from phase change measurements are discussed in subsequent chapters of this book.

2

Qualitative Phase Contrast Microscopy

2.1 A simplified explanation of the operative principles of a phase contrast microscope

It has already been stated that phase contrast and interference microscopes can turn the differences in phase change in the light passing through objects, which the eye is unable to appreciate, into visible changes in amplitude. Not surprisingly, a full exposition of how this is effected requires an elaborate mathematical treatment and, in the case of phase contrast, this has been done by its inventor, Zernike* (1934, 1935, 1942, 1946). A lucid but much simpler explanation of the mode of operation of phase contrast microscopes, quite adequate for most practical purposes, has been presented by Osterberg in Bennett, Jupnik, Osterberg & Richards (1951) and by Richards (1954). Its merits inclusion here, since some understanding of how phase contrast images are formed is essential for their correct interpretation.

Fig. 2A is a representation of a state of affairs similar to that in Fig. 1A, which is obtained when a stained object is examined by ordinary light microscopy. It shows two superimposed waves of light with no phase change between them, but of different amplitudes. The thin continuous line represents the wave *m* that travels through the background mounting medium before impinging on the object and the thicker continuous line, wave *o*, represents the same wave after having been reduced in amplitude by the molecules of the stain after passing through the object. In order to become reduced in amplitude some of the energy of the wave has been redistributed and it is normally converted into diffracted light which is scattered in all directions by the heterogeneous structure of the bondings between atoms of the molecules of the stained object. This scattering is not completely random,

---

* For an excellent appreciation of the remarkable work and versatility of this great Dutchman, see Barer (1966).

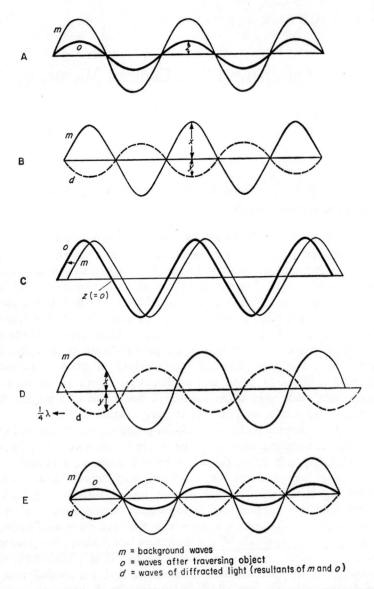

m = background waves
o = waves after traversing object
d = waves of diffracted light (resultants of *m* and *o*)

Fig. 2   Wave diagrams illustrating the behaviour of the direct and diffracted light in ordinary light microscopy with a stained object introducing an amplitude change A and B, and with an unstained object introducing a phase change C and D, and showing how in a phase contrast microscope the phase change can, by displacing the diffracted wave by $\frac{1}{4}\lambda$, be converted into an amplitude change, E.

however, and the sum of all the scattering can be considered as being equivalent to the single diffraction wave represented by wave *d*, which is drawn as a broken line in Fig. 2B. It can be seen that this wave is exactly 180° or half a wavelength out of phase with the background wave *m*, so that a trough in the former is opposite a peak in the latter and vice versa. The amplitude of the diffraction wave, created by the object, is such that wave *o*, the wave of reduced amplitude that emerges from the object, is the resultant of it and wave *m*: that is to say, the locus of points obtained by adding the positive or negative amplitudes of wave *m* and those of wave *d* at the same distances along the waves will trace out wave *o*. For example, in this figure the distance *x* minus the distance *y* equals the distance *z* which is the amplitude of the object wave. Thus an amplitude image of reduced intensity can be formed by the inter-action of the direct light represented by wave *m* and the diffraction light represented by *d*.

Fig. 2C is a representation of the equivalent state of affairs which one gets when an unstained phase-retarding object similar to the cell repre-sented in Fig. 1B is also examined by ordinary light microscopy. In this case wave *o* is represented as having been retarded about 45°, or one eighth of a wavelength, as a result of having passed through the more highly refractile object, but is still of the same amplitude as the wave travelling through the background medium before it impinged on the object. Again, light has also been diffracted when passing through the object and once again the position and amplitude of the resulting dif-fraction wave *d* is such that the object wave *o* is the resultant of wave *m* and wave *d* (e.g. $x - y = z$), but this time the diffraction wave *d* is con-siderably less than 180° out of phase with the background wave *m* as well as being of different amplitude.

In fact, the diffraction wave *d* is very nearly 90° or one quarter of a wavelength out of phase with the background medium wave: it can be immediately appreciated that if it were possible to retard this diffraction wave by another quarter of a wavelength, one would then get the state of affairs illustrated in Fig. 2D which is, in this case, indistinguishable from that in Fig. 2A and B for a stained object. In other words, if one could separate the light directly transmitted by a transparent micro-scopic object and the light diffracted by it and retard the phase of the latter by, say, a quarter of a wavelength with respect to the former, the two waves will interfere with each other to produce visible changes in amplitude; this is in fact what Zernike achieved with the phase contrast microscope.

Fig. 3A shows in a diagram of the essential optics of a phase contrast microscope how this is achieved. The design of a phase contrast microscope is essentially the same as that of an ordinary light microscope as far as the condenser, objectives and eyepieces are concerned. It differs only in having a special diaphragm, most usually ring-shaped and called an annulus,* at some position between the light source and the condenser,

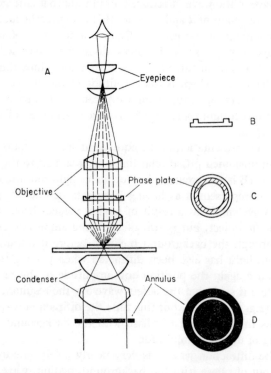

Fig. 3   A—The paths taken by the directly transmitted light (continuous lines) and the light diffracted by an object (broken lines) through an ordinary Zernike phase contrast microscope, showing sectional views of a ring-shaped sub-stage annulus in the front focal plane of the condenser and a ring-shaped +ve phase plate in the back focal plane of the objective. (The pencil of rays entering the eye from the Huygenian eyepiece has been drawn so that it diverges slightly instead of being parallel, as normally drawn in these optical diagrams, because it has been very recently established by Baker (1966) that the human eye is normally almost always focused for near vision when looking down a microscope.)

B—Sectional view of a −ve phase plate which could be substituted for the +ve phase plate shown in A.

C—Plan view of phase plate.

D—Plan view of sub-stage annulus.

* Sometimes also called a 'light form' (see Fig. 7A).

and in having a plane surface of glass specially etched* with a configuration similar to that of the diaphragm. This is called a phase plate and is situated in some point above the front lens of the objective. The most common practice is for there to be a ring-shaped annulus in the front focal plane of the condenser and a similar ring-shaped phase plate in the back focal plane of the objective; their plan views are illustrated here in Fig. 3B and C. When properly adjusted the ring-shaped image of the annulus is brought to a focus in the plane of the ring-shaped area on the phase plate and is made to correspond with it. Under these circumstances it can be appreciated that all the light directly passing through an object placed in the object plane, shown by continuous lines in Fig. 3A, will pass only through the ring-shaped area of the phase plate which is indicated by shading in Fig. 3C. This ring-shaped area has a slightly different thickness to the rest of the phase plate: most commonly it is made slightly thinner so that the light passing is advanced by a quarter of a wavelength or 90°, more than that passing through the rest, as in Fig. 3A. This is known as a 90° +ve phase plate; but 90° −ve phase plates, where the ring-shaped area is correspondingly thicker, are sometimes used, as shown in section in Fig. 3D (and occasionally phase plates which introduce phase changes other than that of a quarter of a wavelength).† As all the light directly transmitted through the object, corresponding to wave *o* in Fig. 2C, passes through the special ring-shaped area of the phase plate, it follows that the only light which can pass through the rest of the phase plate must be light diffracted by the object corresponding to wave *d* in Fig. 2D. However, this area in a +ve phase plate is made thicker so that this diffracted light is retarded a quarter of a wavelength compared to the directly transmitted light. Thus, with the aid of the annulus and phase plate, one arrives at the state of affairs illustrated in Fig. 2E where, because the diffracted light

---

* It is now unusual for the phase step to be produced by etching. The most common method is to evaporate a dielectric layer over the main portion of the phase plate which has been covered with an annular-shaped mask (Smith, 1966a).

† The notation derived by Bennett *et al.* (1946) to describe the optical path differences and absorptions induced by different kinds of phase plates has much to recommend it; if phase contrast microscope manufacturers had used it to define their products, much of the present-day confusion about the optical properties and capabilities of their instruments could have been avoided.

It is particularly important, however, that phase plates should continue to be described as +ve or −ve, since all phase contrast microscopists know, or should know, what these terms mean. Some sections of the trade however are beginning to use ambiguous and imprecise terms such as 'objectives producing bright phase contrast' (a phrase used to designate −ve phase contrast objectives by one manufacturer and +ve phase contrast objectives by another), and it is sincerely to be hoped that this trend will not continue.

has been artificially retarded a quarter of a wavelength compared to the direct light, the two wave fronts interfere with each other and, on recombination, form images with variable amplitudes of objects that had originally only induced phase changes.

2.2 The relationship between the phase change given by an object and the intensity of its phase contrast image

In the example illustrated by Fig. 2C–D, an object giving a phase retardation of about one eighth of a wavelength has resulted in a final image with only about half the intensity or brightness of the background, since the amplitude of the image forming waves have been reduced to this amount by the waves of the direct light and diffraction light acting antagonistically, and objects giving very small phase changes always produce, in varying degrees, a reduction in the brightness of the image compared to that of the background when +ve phase plates are used. A similar treatment applied to objects giving larger phase changes, however, show that the waves of the direct and diffracted light can reinforce each other and actually produce images brighter than the background and cases of these are shown worked out in Bennett et al. (1951). Thus the relationship between the phase change given by an object and the relative brightness of its image is not a linear one—an object does not automatically appear darker the greater the phase change it produces, but for a non-absorbing 90° +ve phase plate it actually takes the form shown in Fig. 4, redrawn from Barer (1952a). Here the level of background intensity is indicated by the horizontal line and the ordinate represents the brightness of the object in multiples of this. It can be seen that an object giving a phase retardation or +ve phase change will appear darker than the background provided the phase change is less than 90° and an object giving a phase retardation of 45° will appear maximally dark. An object giving a phase change of exactly 90°, however, will appear neither bright nor dark but will appear at exactly the same intensity as the background and therefore be invisible in spite of being a phase-retarding object under a phase contrast microscope. Objects giving +ve phase changes of 90°–360° will appear bright or 'reversed' and maximally so if their phase change is 225°. With objects giving phase changes of more than a full wavelength, 360°, the cycle is repeated. Objects giving −ve phase changes will conversely appear bright provided these phase changes are less than three quarters of a wavelength, and if greater than this they can appear dark. This can often be seen in the case of air

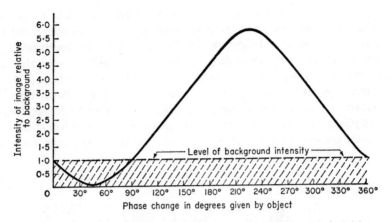

Fig. 4 Curve showing the relationship between the phase change produced by an object and the intensity of its image when viewed under a phase contrast microscope with an ordinary 90° +ve phase plate with an absorption of zero. (Redrawn from Barer, 1952a)

bubbles included in preparations mounted in aqueous media or in balsam. The centres of such bubbles can appear dark and their thinner, more peripheral regions, giving less phase change, bright; but in this case the effect is accentuated by the tendency of such bubbles to act as lenses and form images of the annulus (p. 24).

In practice, however, totally transparent non-absorbing 90° +ve phase plates are seldom employed in phase contrast microscopy since, for one thing, being invisible, they are very difficult to line up satisfactorily to correspond with the image of the annulus.* Instead, it is the practice to make the ring-shaped area of the phase plate rather darker than the rest by applying to it a coating of light-absorbing material. The effect of this, apart from making the phase plate visible for alignment, is to enhance the contrast in the images of many small microscopic objects by still further reducing the brightness of objects giving small phase changes, and the extent to which this happens depends on the absorption conferred on this part of the phase plate.

Thus, not only is the relationship between the phase change given by an object and the brightness of the image not linear, but the exact relationship can only be known if the amount and sign of the phase change produced by the phase plate and its absorption are all known (Barer,

* The American Optical Co., Buffalo, N.Y., U.S.A. market a +ve phase contrast objective with zero absorption which they call a 'B-minus contrast objective', and which they recommend for examining objects that give both phase and amplitude changes, and objects that give relatively large phase changes.

1952). Fig. 5 shows the relationship, over a range of just under one third of a wavelength, between the phase change given by an object and the intensity or relative brightness of its image for non-absorbing, 25% absorbing and 75% absorbing, phase plates. It will be seen that the higher the absorption of the phase plate the less is the range of phase changes given by an object which will produce images darker than the background; although within those ranges, the higher the absorption of the phase plate the darker will be the image of such an object at the particular phase change that gives maximum darkness. The practical result

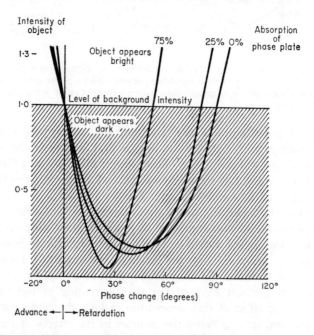

Fig. 5   Curves showing the relationship between the phase change produced by an object and the intensity of its image when viewed under phase contrast microscopes with ordinary 90° +ve phase plates with absorptions of zero, 25% and 75%. Ordinate and abscissa as in Fig. 4. (From Ross, 1961b, based on Barer, 1952)

of this is that, in general, the contrast of the images of objects giving small phase changes will be much enhanced by using phase plates with a high absorption, and cellular images in particular will appear pleasantly contrasting. For this reason most manufacturers of phase contrast microscopes equip them with phase plates that are heavily absorbing, usually in the range 70–90% absorption, but for reasons which will be discussed in the next section it is questionable whether this trend has been altogether desirable.

The consequences of all this are that the images of living cells seen under a phase contrast microscope will not entirely correspond to the familiar images of similar cells in fixed and stained preparations under an ordinary light microscope. Thin tenuous pseudopodia, for example, which are barely visible when stained, will show up quite conspicuously under a phase contrast microscope since the small phase changes which they give will form dark phase contrast images; but highly refractile lipid droplets will often appear actually brighter than the background because they frequently give phase changes of more than a quarter of a wavelength. Other objects giving appreciable phase changes will be totally invisible even under a phase contrast microscope if these phase changes are such as to result in their appearing at the same intensity as the background. For instance, it can be seen from Fig. 5 that if a 70% absorbing 90° +ve phase plate is used, the image of an object giving a phase change of just over 53° will match the background and appear to match the intensity of the background in exactly the same way as an object giving no phase change at all. Such a match is called a 'false match point' while an object giving a zero phase change gives a 'true match point' to the background intensity. The distinction between these two conditions is important in immersion refractometry (see Chapter 3).

Manufacturers do not often publish the percentage absorptions of the phase plates in the objectives which they use in their phase contrast microscopes, but these data can usually be obtained on request.* It is essential to know the absorption of the phase plate before a curve similar to those illustrated in Fig. 5 can be constructed for the particular phase contrast objective being used: such a curve is necessary if the phase contrast image of a cell is to be interpreted as fully as possible. More complete data for obtaining such curves are given by Barer (1952a) but one important point by which such curves are defined is the 'false match point', also called a 'secondary match point' by Osterberg & Carlan (1958) (i.e. the phase change, ϕ, at which the image of a phase-retarding object will match the background intensity). This can be obtained from the following formula.

* It is, however, unfortunately true that many manufacturers do not measure the absorptions of their phase plates with very great precision, and Smith (1966a) considers that such absorptions are in fact rarely known more accurately than to within $\pm 5\%$ of the stated absorption. This means that, unless the absorptions of the phase plates actually being used can themselves be measured densitometrically, the methods presented here must be considered as providing a useful approximation of the phase changes indicated by different image intensities rather than a precise evaluation.

$$\phi = 2 \times \tan^{-1} \frac{\mathrm{I}}{\sqrt{\left(\frac{\mathrm{I}}{\mathrm{100}-A}\right)\mathrm{100}}} \tag{1}$$

where A is the percentage absorption of the phase plate

Another point can be defined by the phase change given by an object which will result in a maximally dark image (which will have exactly half the value obtained by eqn. 1) and the amount by which this image will appear darker than the background. The latter value can be deduced from the curve in Fig. 6 (also reproduced from Barer, 1952a). From these two points (and of course the 'true match point' of the same intensity as the background at zero phase change) parabolic curves

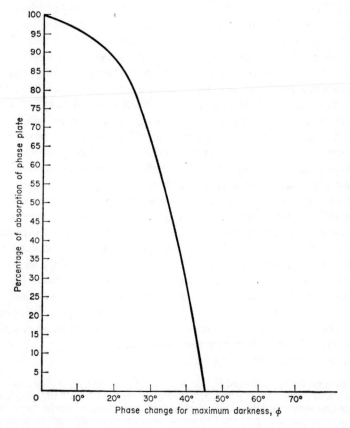

Fig. 6   Curve showing the phase change given by an object which will give a maximally dark image with 90° +ve phase plates of different absorptions. (Redrawn from Barer, 1952a)

can be constructed showing the relationship between the phase change given by an object and the intensity of its image for 90° +ve phase plates of any absorption, which are quite adequate for all practical purposes.

2.3 The 'halo' and 'shading off' optical artefacts

The non-linearity of phase change and image brightness is not, however, the only difficulty which has to be borne in mind when interpreting the phase contrast images of cells, because striking and even more important optical artefacts are introduced by the incomplete separation of the directly transmitted and diffracted light which is inherent in the

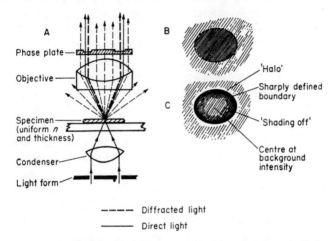

Fig. 7   A—A typical Zernike phase contrast system showing how the light passing directly through the specimen and the light diffracted by the specimen is incompletely separated. Some of the diffracted light passes through the phase ring in the phase plate along with the direct light (represented by the heavy dotted line).
B—The image of a retarding object of uniform refractive index and thickness (such as that shown in cross-section in A) as it would appear if the direct and diffracted light could be completely separated: and as it does, in fact, appear under most kinds of interference objectives.
C—The actual appearance of the image under the phase contrast system, showing the 'halo' and 'shading off' optical artefacts induced by the incomplete separation of the direct and diffracted light.

phase contrast system. Fig. 3 shows how the direct and diffracted light is separated in a phase contrast microscope, but Fig. 7A shows that in fact this separation is incomplete, since the light diffracted by the object is diffracted in all directions, and inevitably some of it passes through the ring-shaped area of the phase plate and adds itself to the directly transmitted light which has been confined to this area. This in fact produces an unresolved reversed image of the object superimposed on its principal image: the results of this are twofold, best described as the 'halo' and 'shading off' optical artefacts.

Wolter (1950) in his mathematical treatment of phase contrast images has described these effects more explicitly but it is their practical consequences that are principally of concern to the cytologist. The principal result of the 'halo' effect is to produce a bright halo around the image of each cell and every object within each cell that appears in darker contrast than the background. Conversely, dark halos surround objects which appear bright. These halos are especially prominent at boundaries between regions giving markedly different phase changes, provided of course they are not so different as to approach the condition of 'false match point' (p. 19), although, even here, some halo is normally visible. Their effect is often to obscure the internal detail of cells that contain many highly refractile granules closely crowded together, such as mammalian liver cells, because the halos around these bodies can altogether mask and obscure the morphological details of adjacent structures. The boundaries of cells closely packed together can be similarly obscured, and for this reason phase contrast microscopy has limited usefulness for examining sections unless they are either very thin or mounted in highly refractile media. On the other hand, they often appear to emphasize the contrast between the image of a thin cell and its background This may in fact be an optical illusion because, on theoretical grounds, the contrast should be better if the halo could be eliminated (Smith, 1966a), but it does help to make the excessively thin edges of a cell or pseudopodia more visible than they would otherwise be.

The 'shading off' effect (called by Wolter, 1950, and Barer & Joseph, 1954, the 'zone of action' effect) is less obvious in many cells owing to the differences in their thickness and internal refractile properties but can be easily appreciated in the flat relatively empty squamous or 'pavement' human oral epithelium cells that are so often used on test objects by cytologists using phase contrast microscopy. It is, however, best explained by considering a hypothetical phase object of uniform thickness and refractive index like that illustrated in section in the object plane in Fig. 7A. If there were no 'halo' effect and no 'shading off' effect, the object would, if its phase change were such as to give a dark image, appear very much as in Fig. 7B, uniformly dark all over and not surrounded by a halo, and such an image is in fact given by an interference microscope (Chapter 5). In practice under a phase contrast microscope it appears as in Fig. 7C, not only surrounded by a bright halo but with the internal intensity or brightness of its image increasing as one passes from the outer boundary inwards, until at some distance within, the internal structure of the object appears at background intensity. This shading off of the expected dark appearance of the image is not exhibited to any appreciable extent by very small objects such as bacteria, and is of course modified and often obscured by variations in the shape and thickness of cells being examined. In ordinary spherical cells giving a uniform cytoplasmic and nuclear phase change and containing few refractile inclusions it is more than counteracted by the fact that the phase changes in the light passing through their centres are much greater than that of the more tangential light passing through their more peripheral regions, but with red blood corpuscles lying in the object plane it is actually enhanced by their biconcave shape.

In general, it can be said that the 'halo' and the 'shading off' effects together tend to emphasize edges and boundaries where appreciable differences of phase change occur in the images of heterogenous phase objects such as cells, although not quite as much in the case of darkground illumination, which can be regarded as the extreme form of phase contrast where the phase plate is made 100% absorbing and all the direct light is excluded for the image plane. In this case, it is in practice only the sharp phase boundaries which show up at all, and always brighter than the background, with their brightness depending in a non-linear manner upon these differences in phase change. The images given by interference microscopes, on the other hand, tend to give a much truer representation of such phase boundaries, and for this reason the images of edges giving small differences in phase change are not rendered nearly so conspicuously as under phase contrast. This is the principal reason why experienced phase contrast microscopists using interference microscopes for the first time are often disappointed with the non-contrasting nature of the image.

2.4 The advantages of using low absorbing phase plates in the evaluation of cytological phase contrast images

Actually the popularity among the majority of cytologists using phase contrast microscopy of very contrasting cell images is a somewhat mixed blessing, since it is obtained by using phase plates with high absorptions. These not only limit the range of phase change over which the cell contents will appear dark, but they increase the 'shading off' or the 'halo' effects; the latter in particular obscure much cell detail. In theory the 'halo' as the 'shading off' effects could be reduced without diminution of contrast by making the ring-shaped stop below the condenser and the ring-shaped region of the phase plate as narrow as possible, but there is a limit to how far this can be done without requiring an immensely powerful source of illumination and making the system excessively difficult to line up. The alternative is to use low absorption phase plates and while it is true that the overall contrast of phase contrast images obtained with these is appreciably lower than with the more commonly used higher absorbing phase plates, this is relatively unimportant compared to the fact that the cell images are a truer representation of what is really there. Almost the only firm which markets an instrument with low absorption phase plates is W. Watson & Sons Ltd. of Barnet, England,* which manufactures a phase contrast microscope developed by Baker and his collaborators in 1948–9 (Kempson et al., 1948, Baker et al., 1949) which is described in Appendix I. These workers made careful and comprehensive tests of the most suitable sizes and absorptions of phase plates in the course of the development of their system. They found that low absorbing phase plates reduced the halos quite appreciably and finally decided on using 25% absorbing phase plates in preference to the 65–95% absorbing plates used by almost every other manufacturer. Two photomicrographs (Plate 2) of locust spermatocytes, taken by the author in 1955 and not hitherto published, may serve to illustrate this point.

Plate 2.1 shows a group of cells taken with a 4 mm (90° +ve) phase contrast objective with a standard Watson 25% absorbing phase plate, while Plate 2.2 is a photograph of the identical field taken with a similar 4 mm objective at exactly the same plane of focus, equipped with a 70% absorbing phase plate supplied by Watson & Sons Ltd. at the author's request. It can be seen immediately that the detail of the chromosomes in particular is definitely clearer in Plate 2.1 than in Plate 2.2. This is not a question of resolution; it is simply due to the reduction, with the lower absorbing phase plate, of the obscuring halos immediately adjacent to the chromosomes and other structures.

2.5 The 'defocused annulus' optical artefact given by lenticular phase objects

An optical artefact inherent in the phase contrast system to which hitherto insufficient attention has been paid, and which may very well be

* But see footnote on p. 17.

of greater importance than the 'halo' and 'shading off' optical artefacts in the study of cells, has been brought to the attention of the writer by Smith (1966a). Cells are frequently either lens-shaped themselves (very commonly spherical) or they contain inclusions which are lens-shaped and, if such bodies have refractive indices which are different to their surrounding media, they will act as lenses. A lens of this kind will defocus the image of the annulus of a phase contrast microscope so that the optical system will fail to function for its internal structure. The Zernike phase contrast system was evolved from a technique for examining and testing astronomical mirrors (Zernike 1934a, b) where such defocusing effects did not arise, but most real microscopical objects, including cells, have significant thicknesses and, with the semi-coherent illumination associated with phase contrast, this results in artefact 'images' of defocused levels of the specimen being superimposed upon the true in-focus image, which makes for difficulty in interpretation.

This could very well account, even more than the 'halo' and 'shading off' optical artefacts, for the difficulty that every phase contrast microscopist experiences in distinguishing the internal detail in spherical cells mounted in media of markedly different refractive index to that of the cellular material, and for the fact that the internal structure of such cells becomes much more visible when the refractive index of the mounting medium approaches that of the cell (p. 28).

2.6 The qualities of phase contrast images of cells

Although it is practically impossible to evaluate the individual effects of the non-linearity of intensity and phase change and of the halo, shading off and defocusing optical artefacts in the image of every cell viewed under phase contrast, a knowledge of these factors help enormously in interpreting the image. Indeed, after all that has been said, it is still true that the most striking thing about phase contrast images of living cells is their similarity to the images of the same cells seen in fixed and stained preparations under ordinary light microscopy and not their differences. Enough has now been said, however, to emphasize the importance of these differences to attaining correct morphological interpretations.

2.7   Discoveries in the field of cell morphology by phase contrast microscopy

Since phase contrast microscopes can, in spite of these limitations, show up a surprising amount of morphological detail in living cells which is capable of structural interpretation, it may be asked why the development of phase contrast microscopes has not led to many more striking scientific discoveries in this field than it has. The short answer is that the study of fixed and stained cytological preparations in the preceding century was so thorough and so exhaustive that there really was not very much of universal application left to discover. Flemming, for example, had worked out the full and complex story of the appearance and behaviour of chromosomes during cell division in 1882 and other organelles that show up conspicuously under phase contrast, such as nuclear boundaries and nucleoli, had been stained and described earlier. Even so, new morphological discoveries in the field of cytology revealed by phase contrast microscopy have been by no means negligible, especially when a sequence of events in the activities of living cells has been recorded by a succession of still photomicrographs, or more completely by time-lapse cinemicrography. This is particularly true of the behaviour of organelles that are normally difficult to fix satisfactorily, such as mitochondria, and a striking example is provided in one of the earliest records made with a phase contrast microscope, namely the cine film of meiosis in grasshopper spermatocytes made by Michel in 1941. This film (which is still readily available for hire from Vickers Instruments Ltd., York, England, for the benefit of student instruction) shows the mitochondria aggregating peripherally to the chromosomes on the equator of the spindle during metaphase and moving rapidly and dramatically towards the poles upon the appearance of the cleavage furrows, a fact now well-established but unknown before phase contrast studies. The appearance of transitory polar bulges in the cell membrane during telophase, known as 'bubbling', the curious rotatory movements of nucleoli and contractile movements in mitochondria are among other discoveries of this kind, many of which are as yet unexplained.

2.8   The accessibility of living cells for study by phase contrast or interference microsopy

One strong reason favouring the study of fixed and stained preparations of cells in preference to studying them in the living state lies in the fact that by fixing and sectioning almost every cell is accessible for studies of this kind, whereas undamaged living cells, suitable for study by phase contrast or interference microscopy, are often much less accessible. Cells that live naturally isolated in body fluids such as blood corpuscles are, of course, completely accessible for live study, and so are many cells grown in artificial media in tissue culture; but cells forming compact tissues are often difficult to separate intact, and sometimes this is impossible if a lot of connective tissue is present. With animal cells, careful teasing and microdissection can achieve a lot, however, and the most remarkable preparations of this kind are perhaps the intact living single muscle fibres (50–100 μ in diameter) obtained from frogs by Huxley & Niedergerke (1954) and used in their famous studies of the width changes in the A- and I-bands during the contraction of a single sarcomere by interference microscopy. Some animal tissues are only loosely bound with connective tissue, such as the cells of germinal epithelium in the seminiferous tubules of mouse testes (van den Broek, 1961) or the cells of certain solid mouse carcinomas (Ross, 1961a) and can be effectively separated intact by a glass homogenizer, such as the simple and extremely effective device which was made by Mr. Joseph Kopp of 70–73, 35th Road, Jackson Heights, 72, Long Island, U.S.A. This consisted of a ground glass plunger, about 1 cm in diameter, working in a ground glass test-tube-shaped cylinder very carefully made so that the clearance between the cylinder and plunger was between 40 and 60 μ. When a small piece of solid tissue was placed in the cylinder together with about 1 ml. of saline, and the plunger was pushed down and withdrawn once only, it was almost completely broken up into a murky suspension which contained a remarkably high yield of separate intact cells.

Greatly extended cells such as nerve cells and muscle fibres do not have to be intact over their whole length in order to retain most, if not all, of their qualities of viability in situ, although their physiological function may, of course, be temporarily impaired if any part of them is cut or injured. The fact that nerve axons and muscle fibres can regenerate from portions containing nuclei, however, suggests they are still in every sense living cells after such peripheral injuries, and consequently the cell body region of neurons and long lengths of muscle fibres can often be examined satisfactorily by phase contrast or interference microscopy without resorting to the almost impossible task of dissecting them in their entirety (p. 136).

In general, it can be said that a surprising number of cells commonly found in animal tissues can be removed intact or with negligible injuries

4

and examined separately under phase contrast or interference microscopes if care and ingenuity are used: but the cells in some tissues bound
together with tough collagenous extracellular matrices are virtually
inaccessible. Trypsin digestion has been used to separate some of these,
but it is doubtful whether the process really leaves the cells wholly
unimpaired and more work certainly needs to be done to establish this.
Some cells capable of being isolated alive for examination are nevertheless difficult to study by phase contrast or interference microscopy
because they contain many refractile inclusions closely crowded together, e.g. mammalian liver cells and salivary gland cells: but these can
sometimes be spread out by gently squashing them between slide and
coverslip, or in a suitable cell compressor such as that designed by
Goldacre *et al.* (1957) so that much internal detail previously obscured
by halos becomes discernible (see, for example, Berendes & Ross,
1963, and p. 167).

The cells of higher plants are often difficult to study by phase contrast
microscopy since the extracellular matrices of their thick cellulose walls
hold them firmly together and the watery vacuoles they contain often
produce sharp external and internal phase boundaries. Pectin is sometimes used to separate these cells but its use is subject to the same
doubts as the use of trypsin. However, things like the streams in the
protoplasm in the thin-walled hairs of *Tradescantia* can be dramatically
demonstrated, and some truly remarkable studies have been carried out
by Bajer on mitosis in relatively thin-walled and unvacuolated meristematic cells. Lower plants such as yeasts and fungal mycelia on the other
hand are extremely suitable objects for study and the latter, in particular,
are profitable subjects for immersion refractometry (see p. 52).

2.9   The use of special mounting media as an aid to the study of cell morphology

Finally, it must be pointed out that the phase contrast picture of the
morphological detail of many cells can be made much plainer and more
easily discernible if the phase changes at their edges can be reduced by
reducing the difference in refractive index between the cells and the
media in which they are mounted, because this also has the effect of
considerably reducing any obscuring halos. The methods by which this
is done are described in the next chapter on immersion refractometry,
but although this is primarily a quantitatve technique it should be
emphasized that in many instances its use also greatly facilitates qualita-

tive investigation both with phase contrast and interference microscopy. The cells in Plate 2, for instance, are immersed in isotonic bovine plasma albumin with a refractive index only a little lower than that of their cytoplasm, which has probably contributed more than any other factor to the visibility of their internal detail.

3

Quantitative Phase Contrast Microscopy
1: The refractometry of individual living cells

3.1 The historical development and basic principles of the technique of immersion refractometry of living cells

The refractometry of living cells is no recent development. It has been attempted by a variety of methods and with varying success for nearly 80 years. Almost all the established methods for measuring the refractive indices of crystals and other transparent inanimate objects have, at one time or another, been employed. One of the oldest methods of all was de Chaulne's apparent depth method, by which the top and bottom of an object is focused in turn and its refractive index calculated from the amount by which the fine adjustment had to be moved to obtain each focus and the refractive index of the mounting medium. Its use for the refractometry of cells was suggested by Pfeiffer (1931) and successfully employed by Frederikse (1933) to measure the refractive indices of different regions in a specimen of the very large amoeba, *A. verucosa*, streaming between a specially marked slide and coverslip. The validity of this method has, however, been criticized by Galbraith (1955). As a variant of this approach, Pfeiffer (1938) measured the angle of total internal reflection in incident light shone on to aggregations of lamprey fibroblasts grown in tissue culture and teased tissues from snails and flatworms.

Other workers used spherical and cylindrical cells as lenses, measured their focal lengths and deduced their mean refractive indices from these. This method had been used for measuring the refractive indices of drops of extracted cellular constituents by Nageli & Schwendener as far back as 1867. It was, however, apparently first used on intact cellular material by Senn (1908) to measure the refractive indices of the phalli and the cells in the palisade tissues of various plants. Vlès (1921) used spherical fertilized sea urchins' eggs as lenses to measure their refractive indices during their development up to the appearance of the first cleavage furrow and again after two blastomeres had been formed; Pfeiffer (1930) employed the same technique to measure the refractive indices of the spores of some unspecified strains of the fungi *Mucor* and *Saccharomyces*. The most careful and critical study of this kind was, however, that carried out by Castle (1933) who measured the refractive indices of the cylindrical hyphae of the fungus *Phycomyces* in an attempt to relate this to its phototrophic behaviour.

A different approach again was that of Pfeiffer (1938) who measured the distance between the poles of the hyperbolic figures obtained under polarized light when cells were placed upon a selection of correctly cut and orientated biaxial crystals of different substances. He was able to deduce the cell's refractive indices from these measurements and the known optical properties of the crystals that he used; with this method he measured the mean refractive index of the plasmodia of the *Badhamia utricularis* cells of the mesenchyme of *Helix* and an unspecified amoebocyte. He also made measurements on *Amoeba verucosa* and obtained comparable measurements with those of Frederikse (1933) who used the apparent depth method. In addition, Pfeiffer (1951), in an attempt to study the changes in refractive index occurring in cell division, used an ingenious (although unsuccessful) method related to immersion refractometry which might be called insertion refractometry. Taking advantage of the many different kinds of glass now manufactured, he inserted a succession of microneedles made of glass of different refractive indices into the dividing cells of *Glyceria* pollen mother cells, *Tradescantia* staminal hair cells, *Nereis* eggs and cells from the glandular tissue of *Palaemon*. He was able to judge by the presence or absence of a Becke line (the bright line which appears at the boundary of two regions of different refractive index under ordinary microscope illumination; it moves towards the region of higher refractive index when the distance between the objective and object is increased and vice versa) whether the refractive index of their contents was the same or different from that of the inserted microneedle. The values he obtained, however, were very high, and in some cases so high as to approach closely the values for the refractive indices of coagulated protein (1·53–1·54); it seems possible, as suggested by Barer (1953a), that the cell contents immediately in contact with the glass needles coagulated and formed a thin surface deposit of protein precipitant upon them. This would have amounted to no more than a local injury, leaving the actual processes of cell division unaffected, but it would have seriously affected the appearance of the Becke line.

It would appear that with the exception of Vlès (p. 10) none of these workers appreciated the significance of their refractive index measurements as an indication of cellular hydration and only three of them, Vlès (1921), Pfeiffer (1951) and Castle (1933), attempted to relate their measurements to any cellular physiological activities. In every other case, the refractive index seems to have been recorded simply as if it were a physical constant; all the methods described except the last (Pfeiffer's microneedle insertion method) had the disadvantage that they tended to give only average values for the refractive indices of cellular contents, which in many cases may be quite unrelated to the actual refractive index of any single cellular constituent. This last difficulty does not apply if immersion refractometry is used, since this enables at least the refractive index of the cytoplasm and sometimes other regions to be measured as well; this method, too, has been employed for a very long time.

In the field of mineralogy, methods of measuring the refractive indices of homogeneous crystals by examining them microscopically when immersed in liquids of similar refractive index, have been employed for over 100 years and, according to Pfeiffer (1951), were initiated by Toepler. Crystals, or other homogeneous transparent objects, are examined in a succession of mounting media, usually oils, of different refractive indices; when two such fluids are miscible, a continuous range of media of intermediate refractive index can be made and used. Various optical criteria have been used to detect the presence of small optical path differences, or phase changes, that occur in the transmitted light passing through the crystal when its refractive index is different to the mounting medium, notably the presence of a bright 'Becke line' at the boundary of the object in convergent light with central illumination and the appearance of an asymmetric border shadow under oblique illumination. The absence of such appearances in any one of the mounting media normally indicates that the object has a refractive index very close to that of the particular fluid in which it is immersed; under these circumstances the crystal will appear almost invisible. The refractive index of the mounting medium can then be measured in a refractometer.

Living cells, like crystals, are also usually transparent, and frequently contain quite large amounts of optically homogeneous cytoplasm and other homogeneous material. Similar immersion methods have actually been used to measure their refractive indices for over 70 years. Vlès (1911) anticipated the investigations which the present writer and Barer

& Tkaczyk carried out in 1952 in order to establish the necessary properties of suitable immersion media for living cells. He pointed out that the immersion media for living cells 'must not in any way change the protoplasm so as to alter the refractive index of the cell'; this in effect means that they must be non-toxic, incapable of penetrating cells, and not cause changes in cell volume. This seems to have been appreciated by Exner who as early as 1887 mounted living muscle fibres of the beetle *Hydrophilus* and of an unspecified mammal in liquid paraffin, solutions of egg albumin and in the aqueous humour extracted from the eyes of freshly killed mammals. He used oblique illumination as an optical criterion for determining when the fibres had the same refractive index as the mounting medium and obtained values for their mean refractive index closely comparable with those obtained by Huxley & Niedergerke (1958) and the present writer & Professor Casselman (1960) for living muscle fibres from frogs and mice.

Faure-Fremiet (1929) also used immersion refractometry to measure the refractive indices of the pseudopodia of living amoebocytes and he observed that the mounting media '...should be free from any toxic action whatever, and that their molecular concentration should be near to that of the normal physiological medium of the cells in question'. He mounted the amoebocytes of the starfish *Asterias* in sugar solutions of nearly the same tonicity as sea water, and those of the earthworm *Lumbricus* in solutions of acacia gum dissolved in 0·7% saline, which has the same tonicity as that of earthworm's blood. He examined the cells so mounted with a microscope using vertical illumination and was able to determine from the presence and the nature of the interference fringes in pseudopodia whether the refractive index of the mounting medium was higher or lower. From their absence he inferred that the refractive indices of the mounting media and pseudopodia were the same. This elegant method of showing up small refractive index differences was admirably suited to the material in question, i.e. thin homogeneous sheets of protoplasm in contact with a glass surface, but it is not satisfactory for thicker regions or for the curved surfaces of a spherical cell and cannot be applied to living cells in general.

The development of the Zernike phase contrast microscope from around 1941,* however, provided an instrument that is capable of showing up small optical path differences, or phase changes, in a wide variety of different kinds of living cells more strikingly and critically

---

* References to investigations which foreshadowed the concept of phase contrast microscopy prior to Zernike are given by Bennett (1946).

than any previous optical system. In 1952, Professor R. Barer and his colleagues at Oxford—the present writer and Dr. S. Joseph (né Tkaczyk) —developed a method of measuring the refractive index of the cytoplasm of living cells by immersion refractometry, using phase contrast microscopy and isotonic solutions of bovine plasma albumin as immersion media (Barer & Ross, 1952; Barer, Ross & Tkaczyk, 1953).

This originated in the chance observation by Barer and the present writer early in 1952 of an earthworm amoebocyte suspended in a drop of the animal's own blood taken from one of its pseudo-hearts by means of a fine pipette and mounted under a phase contrast microscope employing an ordinary 90° +ve phase plate. Barer was immediately struck by the unusual appearance of this cell because, instead of appearing typically darker than the background field, the cytoplasm of this cell appeared markedly bright or 'reversed' in contrast. The present writer then suggested what subsequently turned out to be the correct explanation: that the respiratory pigment (erythrorcurin) which, in the case of the earthworms is dissolved directly in the blood fluid and not contained in separate red blood corpuscles, was actually sufficiently concentrated in the blood fluid for the latter to have a higher refractive index than the cytoplasm of the amoebocyte. This was later proved when a preparation containing another similar bright-looking amoebocyte in a sample of earthworm's blood was irrigated with 0·7% saline and kept under continuous observation as the blood fluid was replaced. The cytoplasm of the amoebocyte was seen first to become less bright, then to match the background so that the cell became almost invisible, and finally to reappear with the characteristic normal dark appearance given by cells so observed when mounted in saline. A repetition of this experiment is illustrated in Plate 1.

It was Barer, however, who appreciated the full implications of the experiment; he suggested that by immersing any other cell in a succession of protein solutions similar to the protein of earthworm's blood and finding one in which this cytoplasm appeared neither dark nor bright, but matched the intensity of the background field, it would be possible to measure its refractive index by placing another drop of this solution in a refractometer. Subsequently, the present writer and Tkaczyk (who about two years later changed his name to Joseph) made the method really work by establishing the correct tonicities and pH for these protein immersion media; a very full account of the technique finally developed was eventually published in a series of excellent papers by Barer & Joseph (1954–5). The sequence of photomicrographs of a living chick myoblast immersed in a succession of isotonic saline/protein media of ascending refractive indices, illustrated in Plate 9, provides a good illustration of this experimental approach.

3.2 The significance of refractive index measurements as an indication of cellular hydration

Nearly all the substances that are commonly found dissolved or finely dispersed in an aqueous phase in living protoplasm (of which proteins, lipoproteins and amino acids normally form by far the greater part) have very similar specific refraction increments, which do not deviate appreciably from 0·0018 (see Chapter 1). From this it follows that the w/v concentration of the total solids in the cytoplasm, and other regions of living cells containing water soluble substances with similar refraction increments, C_s, can be obtained from the formula:

$$C_s = \frac{n_c - n_w}{0 \cdot 0018} \qquad (2)$$

where n_c is the refractive index of the region of the cell being measured, and n_w is the refractive index of water (usually taken as 1·333 at room temperature).

It is often extremely convenient to express this relationship graphically so that refractive index measurements can be converted rapidly into values for the approximate percentage w/v solid concentration; Fig. 8 shows a suitable graph for this purpose. This covers the ranges of refractive index normally found in living cells and bacterial vegetative cells and includes the highest concentrations obtainable of the more frequently used immersion media. The hard line indicates refractive index plotted against the percentage of cell solids, assuming a refraction increment (α) of 0·0018. The broken line is a similarly plotted relationship for a refraction increment of 0·0019 which is a closer approximation of the specific refraction increment of haemoglobin, and is therefore applicable in the special case when the refractive indices of red blood corpuscles are being measured (see Chapter 4, p. 63). It will be noted that because it is the intention of the writer that this graph should be used by the reader for converting refractive indices into solid concentration, the background co-ordinate lines have been left in. Indeed, the present writer can see no real object in the current practice in most scientific publications of omitting these lines, which are often very helpful in checking the exact values of any point with relation to the ordinate and abscissa scales.

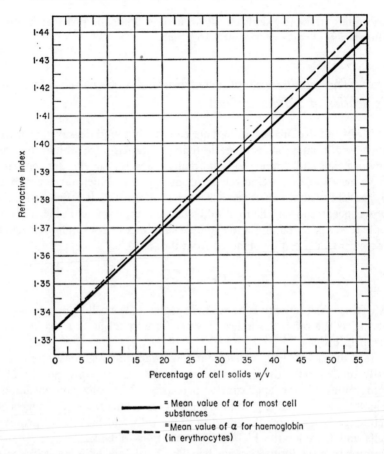

= Mean value of α for most cell
substances

= Mean value of α for haemoglobin
(in erythrocytes)

Fig. 8 Graph, derived from eqn. 2, for the quick conversion of measurements (at 20°C) of the refractive indices of cell substances dispersed in an aqueous phase into total solid concentrations expressed in g/100 ml. **This graph is reproduced on a larger scale inside the cover for more convenient practical use.**

An approximation of the water concentration in various regions of living cells can also be obtained from refractive index measurements but this is not just 100 minus the percentage concentration of cell solids, because the specific volumes of proteins and some other water soluble substances occurring in living cells are less than one. One gram of dry protein, for example, does not occupy 1 cc, but approximately 0·75 cc. Consequently, the w/v percentage water concentration in a protein solution, C_w is given by the formula:

$$C_w = 100 - 0·75C_s \tag{3}$$

where C_s is the w/v percentage solid concentration. Since protein is the principal solid constituent of protoplasm an approximation for the water concentrations can be obtained in this way (for example, the values for the water content of bacterial spores obtained by Ross & Billing, 1957), but such values will be less accurate than those of the percentage solid concentrations since they are derived from a second set of assumptions. It is important to realize that, although quite a number of non-proteins occurring in protoplasm have similar refraction increments, they do not necessarily have similar specific volumes.

3.3   Necessary requirements for and preparation of suitable immersion media

As has already been mentioned (p. 33) liquid mounting media for the immersion refractometry of living cells and organisms must be non-toxic and must not penetrate the cells nor cause any alteration in cell volume. Their refractive indices must also be capable of being continuously variable over a range covering the refractive indices of the cytoplasm, and of any other optically homogeneous regions in living cells and organisms that are adjacent to their surface and therefore accessible to measurement by immersion refractometry. Such variations can only be achieved by mixing two substances of different refractive indices in varying proportions—either two miscible liquids or a solid dissolved in a liquid in varying concentrations. To match the refractive indices of every kind of viable cell and micro-organism, the refractive indices of these media should be continuously variable over a range extending from little above that of water (1·333 at room temperature) up to values approaching those of dried proteins (e.g. *c.* 1·540 for some bacterial spores). No single mixture of suitable substances is capable of compassing the whole of this range. Mixtures of some animal and vegetable fats and oils are suitable for a restricted part of the higher end of this range, and are sometimes helpful for the measuring of the refractive indices of bacterial and fungal spores, but the greater majority of animal and plant cells, bacterial vegetative cells and protozoa have cytoplasmic refractive indices lower than 1·420 and can be measured in aqueous solutions of suitable solid substances.

A very full account of the necessary properties of such solutions and of the various substances tried by Professor Barer, the present author, and others is given by Barer & Joseph (1955a), but the most notable thing is that very few substances appear to fulfil all the exacting conditions mentioned above. Quite a number of reputedly non-toxic manufactured preparations, containing molecules that are undoubtedly large enough to be incapable of passing through normally constituted cell membranes in life, such as peptones, dextran, polyvinyl-pyrollidone and some polyglucose preparations, appear to penetrate almost all living cells either immediately or only a short time after the cells are mounted in them; it is by no means always clear why this happens. In all probability, in most of these cases, the preparations in question contain traces of toxic substances that have a lytic effect on cell membranes when the solutions are of sufficient concentration for their refractive indices to exceed that of the cytoplasm of the cells being measured.

The present account need only be concerned with the substances that form solutions in which a large variety of different cells appears to remain in a completely viable condition for long periods in a wide range of concentrations. Although there are many preparations of proteins and other non-toxic substances with large molecules that need to be tested, several have now been exhaustively investigated and found to fulfil these conditions satisfactorily.

3.3.1   Bovine plasma albumin immersion media

Of the successful immersion media made from aqueous solutions of solids the one that has been most extensively used in the last 13 years, by Professor R. Barer and his colleagues, the present writer and a number of other workers (e.g. Mitchison, Passano & Smith, 1956; Allen, 1958; King & Roe, 1958; Keohane & Metcalf, 1959), is bovine plasma albumin, fraction V, manufactured by the Armour Laboratories, Kankakee, Illinois, U.S.A. (and also obtainable from the Armour Laboratories, Eastbourne, England). This dissolves equally readily in distilled water or saline to form solutions of concentrations up to about 50% w/v, or a refractive index of 1·424. The following remarks apply particularly to these bovine plasma albumin solutions but are, for the most part, just as true when solutions of other substances are being used.

3.3.2   Adjustment of the tonicity of the immersion media

For measuring the refractive indices of fresh-water protozoa and organisms such as fungi and bacteria that do not appear to shrink or swell in solutions of quite widely different tonicity, the fraction V powder can be dissolved in distilled water. For the refractometry of animal tissue cells, however, it is necessary to make the solutions isotonic with the body fluid of the animal in question in order that their volume should remain unchanged, and this means that the powder must be dissolved in a solution of salt of the right concentration.

Tonicity has been defined succinctly by Barer & Joseph (1955a) in the following manner: 'Two solutions are said to be isotonic for a given type of cell if (i) they are compatible with life, and (ii) the cell volume is the same in each solution.' The concentrations of saline solutions generally accepted as being isotonic with the tissue fluids of various animals are usually based on determinations of the ionic content of the animal's blood or lymph, but it is important to point out that for many animals this is entirely unknown, and it is wrong to assume that the tonicity of the fluids of closely related phylogenetic groups of animals are necessarily the same. If the tonicity of the body fluids of a particular animal is unknown, it is best, if it can be done, to compare the size of spherical cells from the animal in question in that animal's blood or the tissue fluid in immediate contact with the cells, and in salt solutions of varying concentrations until one is found in which no alteration of cell size is apparent.

This method was used by the present writer in 1952 to determine the concentration of saline necessary as a solvent for bovine plasma albumin to produce solutions isotonic for various tissue fluids; as it is a method that can be recommended for adjusting the tonicity of any new immersion medium that may be tried, it will be described here in detail.

The spherical primary spermatocytes from the ovo-testis of the snail, *Helix aspersa*, were used, although other spherical cells that show little size variation in the population, such as spermatocytes from the testis of *Locusta* would be equally suitable. The tonicity of the blood of *Helix aspersa* is generally stated to be equivalent to that of a 0·7% solution of sodium chloride (Pantin, 1948) and the sizes of the cells in this and in the uncontaminated blood of the snail are the same (Ross, 1953). The diameters of 50 primary spermatocytes (with the coverslip supported so as to ensure that no cells were compressed), were measured mounted in this 0·7% NaCl solution, and also in lower concentrations down to 0·1% NaCl; the size distributions of the cells measured are shown as histograms in Fig. 9. The vertical dotted line in each histogram represents the modal value for the diameter of these cells in isotonic 0·7% NaCl (just under 19 μ). It will be seen that considerable swelling occurs in NaCl solutions of 0·2% and below. Similar cells were then mounted in a 20% solution (w/v) bovine plasma albumin fraction V powder dissolved in distilled water, and as the dry powder contains only a little free salt (between ½% and 1% according to the maker's specifications) such a solution might be expected to be hypotonic for the cells in question. The diameter of the cells in this solution were measured as before, and their size distributions compared with those in the hypotonic solutions already measured.

It will be seen from Fig. 9 that the amount of swelling of the cell population indicated that a 20% solution of the bovine plasma albumin

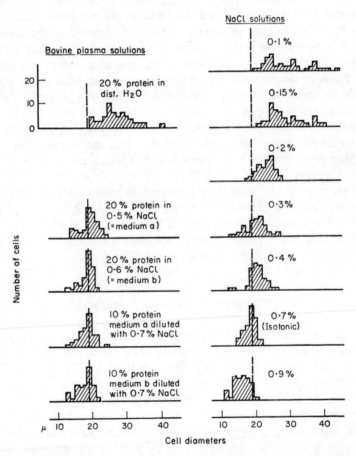

Fig. 9 Histograms showing size distributions of living primary spermatocytes of *Helix aspersa* in hypotonic, isotonic and hypertonic sodium chloride solutions, and in hypotonic and isotonic saline/protein solutions of different concentrations. Fifty cells were measured in each preparation. (From Ross, 1954c)

in distilled water had a tonicity between that of a 0·2% and a 0·1% NaCl solution and almost exactly equivalent to a 0·15% NaCl solution. This meant that, in order to make up a 20% solution of the bovine plasma albumin isotonic with the cells in question, it was necessary to dissolve the powder in a NaCl solution with a concentration of between 0·5% and 0·6%. Fig. 9 also shows that the size distributions of the cells in 20% solutions of bovine plasma albumin, fraction V, dissolved in 0·5% and 0·6% NaCl approximated extremely closely to those in (isotonic) 0·7% NaCl, and these solutions can therefore all be regarded as isotonic. As might be expected, the size distributions of the cells in 10% solutions of the above saline/protein media diluted with 0·7% NaCl were the same again and these solutions also were isotonic (see Fig. 9).

The salt content of the Armour bovine plasma albumin, fraction V, varies very little in individual batches of the product and the foregoing experiments provide the data necessary for making up solution of any required tonicity. One simply needs to assume, for the purpose of tonicity adjustment, that the dry powder contains approximately 0·75% of salt. Thus, to make up a 20% solution of the powder isotonic with mammalian blood and body fluids, usually assumed to be equivalent to that of a 0·9% NaCl solution, one dissolves the powder in 0·7% NaCl; to make a 40% solution of the same tonicity one dissolves the powder on 0·5% NaCl. Isotonic dilutions of these media to any required refractive index can then be made by adding (in this case) 0·9% NaCl. It is of interest to find that the estimate of 0·75% of salt in the dry powder, based on the experiments described above, is in good agreement with the measurement of depression of freezing point made by Dick (1954, quoted by Barer & Joseph, 1955a), which showed that a 10% solution of the powder in distilled water has a tonicity equivalent to that of a 0·08% sodium chloride solution.

Cell measurements of the kind described above are strongly to be recommended for adjusting the tonicity of any new immersion media that may be tried for the refractometry of living cells, as the technique of measuring 50–100 cell diameters with a micrometer or image-splitting eyepiece is not as lengthy or tedious as might appear. It is usually only necessary to make such measurements on 3–5 such suspensions in order to determine the equivalent tonicity of the substances investigated.

Most cells stay alive and apparently unaffected in the simple solution of bovine plasma albumin and sodium chloride described above, except that it is highly advisable to add a trace amount of calcium ions to the salt solutions, since their presence seems to be essential for the proper metabolism of the cell membrane. 0·02 ml of a 10% $CaCl_2$ solution added to 100 ml of NaCl solution is adequate for the purpose; this has been done in all the experiments described here.

3.3.3   Adjustment of the pH of the immersion media

Solutions of Armour's bovine plasma albumin in distilled water and in the simple saline solutions described above are all markedly acid, having a pH of about 5, and while a large number of cells seem to be unaffected by this acidity, it is often desirable to adjust the pH of the medium to approximate more closely to that of the body fluid of the animal from which the cells have been taken. This is necessary, for example, in the refractometry of mammalian muscle fibres which in acid media usually go into a state of tonic super-contractions (Ross & Casselman, 1960). This can be done by dialysing the protein solutions against a suitable saline containing a phosphate buffer (Barer & Joseph, 1955a) but a simpler and no less effective way, if high concentrations of protein are not required, is to use isotonic sodium bicarbonate as a diluting medium. For example, one can make up a 40% solution of bovine plasma albumin, fraction V, suitable for mammalian material by dissolving the powder in 0.5% NaCl (plus a trace of $CaCl_2$) in the manner described above and diluting it with 1.3% $NaHCO_3$. Solutions so made with concentrations of 25% and below have a pH of between 6·8 and 7·2, the protein itself acting in some measure as a buffer. The pH of the dilution required for refractometry can be measured by a meter.

3.3.4   Practical details of making and storing the solutions

Solutions of Armour's bovine plasma albumin are best made by adding the powder in small quantities to the water or saline in a small beaker or flat-bottomed specimen tube and stirring at each addition with a glass rod; it is easiest to use a refractometer to determine when the required concentration is attained. Solutions of concentrations higher than 25% w/v are very viscous and froth considerably as the powder goes into solution and, although this may result in some of the protein becoming denatured, this does not appear to have any adverse effect on the solutions as immersion media. It does mean, however, that these concentrated solutions need to stand for an hour or more before becoming free of air bubbles and if they are required immediately it is advisable to centrifuge them. The solutions can be stored for more than a week in small corked specimen tubes, if they are placed in a refrigerator at 0° to 5°C when not in use to retard the growth of any contaminating organisms. It is advisable to check their refractive indices if they have not been used for several days as evaporation and condensation on the side of the specimen tube sometimes occurs. These protein solutions are, of course, ideal culture media for some fungi and bacteria and the

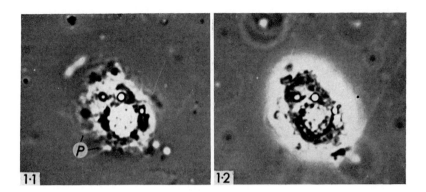

Plate 1 Photomicrographs illustrating a repetition of the experiment originally performed by Barer & Ross in January 1952. This experiment led to the development of the technique for the refractometry of living cells by examining them, immersed in protein solutions, with a phase contrast microscope. (See p. 34.)

1.1—An amoebocyte from the blood of an earthworm of the genus *Allolobophora* mounted in a slightly diluted solution of the earthworm's blood, photographed under a 4 mm +ve 90° phase contrast objective. Parts of the cytoplasm at the edges of this cell, and the pseudopodia indicated by *P*, appear brighter than the background. This naturally occurring 'reversal' would have been even more marked if the blood could have been taken directly from the earthworm's circulation, but with the small individual used here this was not possible. Instead, the pseudo-hearts were cut into, and the blood allowed to spill into a small region of the coelomic cavity which had previously been mopped as dry as possible with cotton wool. The resulting mixture of blood with a little coelomic fluid had a refractive index of 1·368, equivalent to that of an 18% solution of the respiratory pigment; this is higher than that of the cytoplasm of the amoebocyte.

1.2—The same amoebocyte photographed under the same phase contrast objective after the blood fluid surrounding the cell had been replaced with 0·7% saline drawn under the coverslip with a fragment of filter paper. The cytoplasm and pseudopodia of the amoebocyte now appear darker than the background and the whole cell is surrounded by a bright halo characteristic of that given by strongly phase-retarding objects, under the phase contrast objectives. (See p. 21.)

Plate 2.1 and 2.2   Phase contrast photomicrographs of a suspension of locust spermatocytes, spermatids and developing spermatozoa mounted in a saline/protein medium with a refractive index of 1·3535, in which the spermatocytes mostly appear with their cytoplasm matched or in bright (reversed) contrast, and the spermatids and spermatozoa appear dark. 2.1 is taken under a +ve 90° 4 mm phase contrast objective with a 25% absorbing phase plate. 2.2 is the identical field taken at exactly the same focus under a similar 4 mm phase contrast objective with a 70% absorbing phase plate. It will be noted that the bright and dark halos around the unmatched cells under the objective with the lower absorbing phase plate in 2.1 are less pronounced than in 2.2, and that many of the internal details in the cells indicated by arrows are more clearly discernible in 2.1 This is not due to any increased resolution in the ordinary sense, but to the reduction of the 'halo' optical artefact in the phase plate with lower absorbtion. (See Chapter 2, p. 21.)

2.3 and 2.4 are photomicrographs of a group of spermatocytes (numbers 1–6 in Table 1) mounted in a saline/protein medium with a refractive index of 1·3530 and taken under the same 4 mm two-phase contrast objectives as for 2.1 and 2.2. In 2.3, which is taken under the objective with the 25% absorbing phase plate, the cytoplasm of all these cells appears matched to the background except for that of cell 1. In 2.4, which is taken under the objective with the 70% absorbing phase plate, the cytoplasm of cells 3 and 4 (and perhaps that of cell 2 also) appears dark. This shows that more heavily absorbing phase plates are rather more critical for immersion refractometry by matching. (A surge in the mounting medium fluid took place during the few minutes that elapsed between the two photomicrographs 2.3 and 2.4 so that in 2.4 cells 1 and 4 have shifted slightly from their former position.) (See Chapter 3, p. 50.)

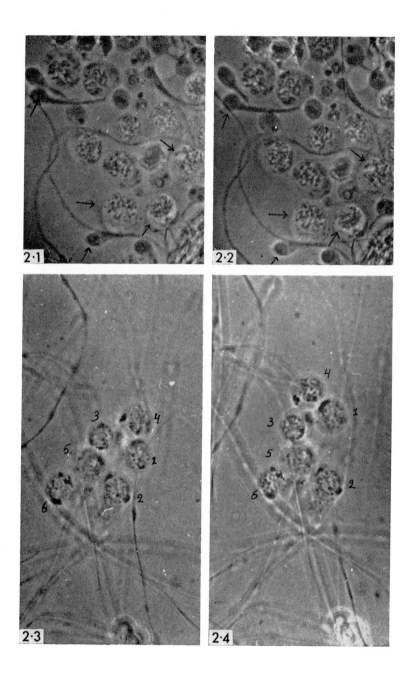

Plate 3.1 and 3.2   Phase contrast photomicrographs, taken with a 2 mm phase contrast objective with a +ve 90° 25% absorbing phase plate of the vegetative cells and spores of *Bacillus cereus*.

3.1—The vegetative cells, showing their typical dark appearance under +ve phase contrast microscopy.

3.2—The spores at the same magnification as 3.1. The centre of each spore shows up in bright (reversed) contrast to the background indicating that the phase changes in the light passing through this region is much greater than that passing through the middle parts of the vegetative cells illustrated in 3.1. From this one can conclude that the spores (which have smaller diameters than the vegetative cells) have both higher refractive indices and a lower water content than the vegetative cells. (See Introduction, p. xvi and pp. 49 and 134.)

3.3–3.7—Photographs and photomicrographs illustrating the centrifuging experiment carried out by Ross, Morris, Hall & Monks (1957) to determine whether there was any correlation between the age and the refractive index or density (and hence the Hb concentration in) a red blood corpuscle: 3.5—a specimen of isotope-labelled blood (the sedimented corpuscles from Case 1 in Table 5) being introduced into a centrifuge tube containing a saline/protein solution with a refractive index of 1.3810, n which it had been found that under a phase contrast microscope almost exactly 50% of both dark and bright erythrocytes from this specimen had been visible; 3.6—after introducing this blood it shows an equal tendency to rise and fall in the solution; 3.7—after centrifuging at low speed the corpuscles are apparently uniformly dispersed. 3.3—A phase contrast photomicrograph of a sample of blood taken from the top of the centrifuged specimen illustrated in 3.7, shows a preponderance of the brighter, less dense erythrocytes.   3.4—A similar sample taken from the bottom of the centrifuged specimen, shows a preponderance of heavier, dark denser cells. In 3.3 and 3.4, R = a reticulocyte and L = leucocytes. Both these types of cells have lower refractive indices than normal erythrocytes and therefore appear bright here. (See Chapter 4, pp. 79–80.)

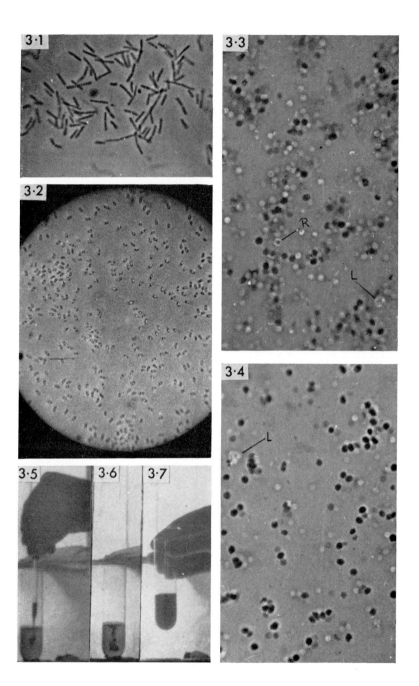

Plate 4.1   Diagram of a locust spermatid containing a spherical *nebenkern* mounted in a medium with the same refractive index as its cytoplasm. The phase retardation due to the *nebenkern* alone is indicated.

4.2—Diagram of a compact, slightly compressed, group of similar spermatids to that shown in 4.1 mounted in saline. The phase retardation due to the *nebenkern* alone is again capable of being measured by using an adjacent area of cytoplasm as a reference point.

4.3–4.8—Photomicrographs, taken in mercury green light with a Smith interference microscope with a 2 mm 'double focus' objective, of the living spermatids of *Locusta migratoria*, containing *nebenkerns*. 4.3—Two isolated spermatids mounted in 0·9% NaCl, with the analyser goniometer set at 110°. Internal cell structures are obscured. 4.4—A group of similar isolated spermatids mounted in isotonic bovine plasma albumin with a refractive index (1.366) rather higher than that of their cytoplasm, with the analyser set at 112°. The cytoplasm looks paler than the background, indicating (at this analyser setting) an acceleration in phase. The internal cell structures show up plainly and are dark, indicating a retardation in phase. 4.5—An isolated group of spermatids mounted in an isotonic bovine plasma albumin solution of the same refractive index (1·354) as the cytoplasm, with the analyser goniometer set at 149° to give a maximally dark field. Only the cell inclusions are visible and the *nebenkerns* (*n*) show up bright. 4.6—The same group of spermatids as in 4.5 with the analyser goniometer set at 111°. At this setting, the centres of some of the *nebenkerns* appear maximally dark. The rotation of the analyser from the position shown in 4.5 represents a phase change of 76°. 4.7—A compact group of spermatids mounted in 0·9% NaCl, under slight compression, with the analyser goniometer set at 149°, to give a maximally dark (cytoplasm-filled) field. 4.8—The same preparation as in 4.7 with the analyser goniometer set at 112°, making the centres of the *nebenkerns* appear maximally dark. The rotation of the analyser from the position shown in 4.7 represents a phase change of 74°. (See pp. 152–156.)

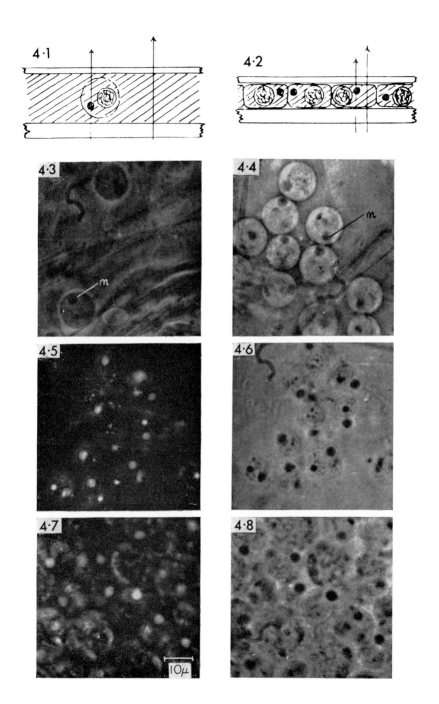

4·1

4·2

4·3

m

4·4

m

4·5

4·6

4·7

4·8

10μ

Plate 5.1 Photomicrograph, taken with a Smith interference microscope, of a preparation of living neurones of *Helix aspersa*. A large neurone is shown with a cell body, N, and an axon, A. The latter contains several groups of triglyceride droplets, T. The middle group indicated consists of 5 droplets in a row, apparently touching each other. The cell body contains phospholipid droplets, P.

5.2—An interpretation of the submicroscopic structure of protoplasm by Schmidt (1939). V, a vacuole with aqueous contents surrounded by a bimolecular phospholipid lamella. Between these droplets, P and T, is a protein framework which holds in its meshes water and other substances.

●— phospholipid and related substances

Ε triglyceride.

⊥┬⊥ protein molecules

o water molecules

· ions

5.3—Electron micrograph of a row of triglyceride droplets in the axon of a neurone of *Helix aspersa* (from Chou & Meek, 1958).

5.4—Electron micrograph of a phospholipid droplet in a neurone of *Helix aspersa*, showing the concentric lamellar structure which had previously been inferred from refractive index measurements (from Chou & Meek, 1958). (See pp. 164–166.)

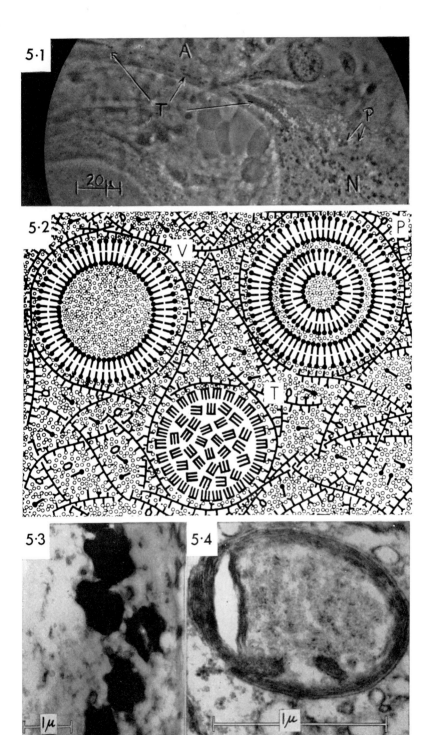

Plate 6.1 Photomicrograph, reproduced from Ross (1957) of some bacteria from a yoghourt culture mounted under a Smith interference microscope and lying on or near the image of the strip comparison area in a Smith half-shade eyepiece. The analyser of the microscope was adjusted so that the part of the thicker specimen of *Lactobacillus bulgaricus* that lay across the image of the strip, b–c, *appeared* to match the parts lying outside it, a–b and c–d. (The remaining bacteria in the picture are a specimen of *Streptococcus*, an encapsulated *Diplococcus* and a second, moribund specimen of *L. bulgaricus*.) (See pp. 184–187.)

6.2—A microdensitometer trace along the line A–B in 6.1. The part of the bacillus b–c lying inside the image of the strip is shown to be actually markedly darker than the parts a–b and c–d that lie outside the image of the strip.

6.3—Photomicrograph of similar short specimens of *L. bulgaricus* under a Smith interference microscope without a half-shade eyepiece, with the analyser adjusted so that the centres of the bacilli *appear* to match the background field. (See pp. 187–188.)

6.4—A microdensitometer trace along the line A–B in 6.3. The centre of the bacillus can be seen to be actually rather darker than the background.

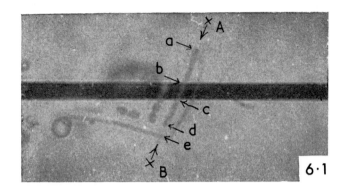

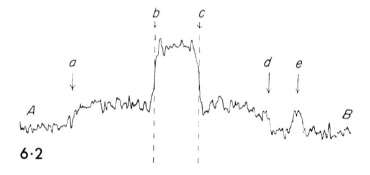

6·2

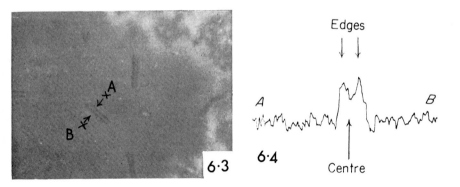

6·4

Plate 7.1   A photomicrograph (at $2\frac{1}{2}$ times the magnification of Plate 6.1 and 6.3) of part of a very long specimen of *L. bulgaricus* under a Smith interference microscope and half-shade eyepiece and partly lying over the very small comparison area left after scraping away part of the metal on the surface of the half-shade eyepiece prism. The analyser of the microscope has been adjusted so that the part of the bacillus lying outside the comparison area appears to match the part a–b that lies within it, except for the brighter image formed by the scratch (s in 7.2). (See pp. 188–189.)

7.2—The same bacillus as illustrated in 7.1, photographed under the same conditions and at exactly the same analyser setting, but with the prism of the half-shade eyepiece moved slightly so that part of the image of the bacillus lies over the image of the uninterrupted part of the half-shade strip. This part of the bacillus, a–b, now appears rather brighter than the rest of the bacillus owing to the optical illusion caused by the adjacent very dark regions of the half-shade strip. The small comparison area, with its scratch, s, is now clear of bacterial images and shows up conspicuously.

7.3—A microdensitometer trace along the long axis of the bacillus illustrated in 7.1 from A–B. No significant differences can be seen in the parts of the trace lying within the comparison area, a–b, and the parts that lie outside it, except at the point of the scratch, s.

7.4—A microdensitometer trace along the long axis of the bacillus illustrated in 7.3 from A–B which again shows no change as it crosses the image of the half-shade strip.

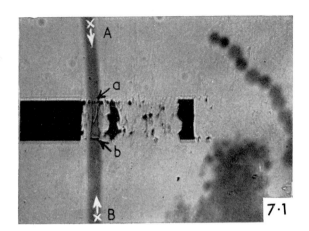

7·1

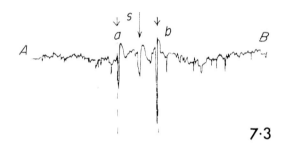

7·3

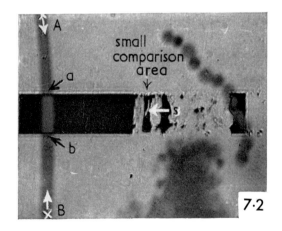

small comparison area

7·2

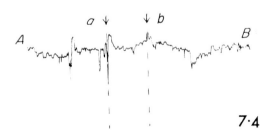

7·4

Plate 8.1 Photograph (taken by Mr. D. E. Jans) illustrating the Perspex constant temperature chamber constructed around the author's Smith interference microscope by Mr. A. Taylor of Taylor Industries Ltd. of Rowlands Gill, Co. Durham, England, from the author's modification of a design of Professor P. J. V. Pulvertaft. The access doors and the heating coils, h, the thermostat, t, and the thermometer, T, on the microscope stage can all be plainly seen. Superimposed on the interference microscope, and supported entirely by the Perspex case is a cine camera with a magnetic shutter connected to a simple non-electronic time-lapse mechanism, both of which are manufactured by W. Vinten Ltd. of Bury St. Edmunds, England. (See p. 207.)

8.2—A conversion of a 60-year-old Watson 'Student' microscope stand for phase contrast microscopy which was used by the author at Wye College when his financial resources for research were unavoidably stringently limited. The simple tin lamp housing, which was constructed in the college farm workshop, with the annulus, a, cut from black paper, the surface aluminized mirror, m, and a Watson fluorite phase contrast objective, σ (the only expensive item which needed to be purchased) are all plainly visible. (See p. 209.)

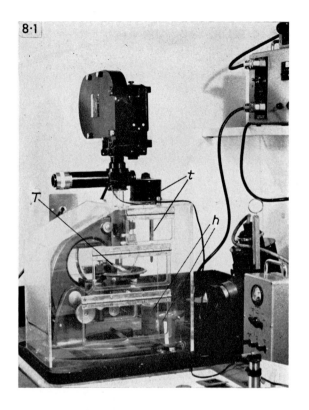

8·1

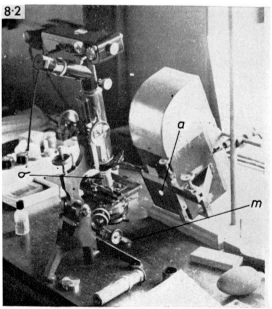

8·2

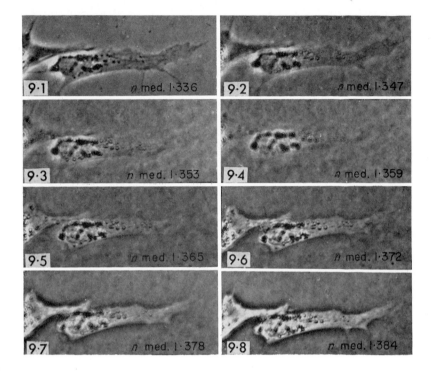

Plate 9 Photomicrographs, taken with a 4 mm +ve 90° phase contrast objective, of a living chick myoblast growing in a one-day-old culture, mounted in the culture fluid, 9.1, which had a refractive index of 1·336, and in a succession of isotonic saline/protein media, 9.2–9.8, of increasing refractive index. In 9.1, 9.2 and 9.3 the cytoplasm of this cell appears darker than the background, indicating that these mounting media had lower refractive indices than the cytoplasm. In 9.5, 9.6, 9.7 and 9.8, the cytoplasm conversely appears bright or 'reversed', indicating that these mounting media have higher refractive indices than the cytoplasm. In 9.4, the cytoplasm is all but invisible, indicating that it must have a refractive index very close indeed to that of this mounting medium, 1·359.

The entire succession of photomicrographs were taken within the space of 20 minutes, during which time the mounting medium was replaced 7 times in the culture chamber. The cell exhibited no visible signs of deterioration at the end of this period, which is rather longer than that normally needed to measure cytoplasmic refractive indices by this immersion method.

It can also be seen that the visibility of the various cell regions and inclusions varies with the mounting media. The nucleus, for example, is especially conspicuous in 9.5 and 9.6, while the lipid droplets are clearer in 9.1. (See p. 35.)

chances of accidental contamination by spores of these organisms vary greatly with laboratory conditions. However carefully the glassware itself may be cleaned, spores are always liable to fall into the solution from the air while it is being dissolved. Although the presence of small amounts of fungal mycelia and bacteria in the media often appears to leave other cells mounted in them unaffected, the use of contaminated solutions cannot be recommended for refractometry. It is, therefore, advisable not to make up more solution at one time than one needs for a few days' experimental work and, if this is stored in a refrigerator, special sterilization of glassware is not necessary. In some air-conditioned laboratories solutions so stored and opened only occasionally remain clear and free of organisms for many weeks, but this is unusual. Detergents such as 'Teepol' should never be used for cleaning slides or glassware since even traces have a powerful lytic action on living cells and can give rise to very misleading results.

3.3.5   The refractometry of the immersion media

An ordinary Abbé refractometer is very suitable for measuring the refractive indices of the immersion media and is capable of measuring liquids with a wide range of different refractive indices very accurately. A small 'pocket' refractometer working on the same principle but covering a more restricted range (1·333 to 1·420) is manufactured by Bellingham & Stanley Ltd. of Hornsey Rise, London. This instrument is relatively inexpensive (about £15) and is quite accurate enough for biological purposes since it measures refractive indices accurately to the nearest 0·0005. It can be obtained either directly calibrated in refractive indices or (more usually) in per cent sucrose (g/100 g of solution), with a conversion table into refractive indices which can conveniently be plotted on a graph similar to that of Fig. 8 (p. 36). They are also capable of measuring the refractive indices of very small drops of fluid: about 0·001 ml or less.

All commonly used refractometers have built-in yellow filters with a transmission spectrum equivalent to the mean of the two sodium lines (589 mμ) and are calibrated for this wavelength. As phase change measurements with the interference microscope are usually made in mercury green light with a wavelength of c. 540 mμ, it has been suggested that this could constitute a source of error. H. S. Bennett and others, however, have investigated this, and have concluded that for bovine plasma albumin solutions with refractive indices between 1·334 and 1·420 the error in refractive index measurement will not exceed 0·001 even in the highest concentrations. Consequently, for practical purposes

6

of immersion refractometry of living cells this error can normally be ignored but it may have to be taken into account if other immersion media with higher refractive indices and different dispersions are used.

The temperature in most laboratories in temperate climates seldom fluctuates by more than 5° from 20°C, and this fluctuation will not affect refractive index measurements by more than 0·0001 when solutions with refractive indices lower than 1·420 are being measured. Consequently, it is seldom necessary to correct for this, unless a warm stage is being used.

The author has found that a drop of a fairly dilute suspension of cells in a bovine plasma albumin solution, sufficient to include up to about ten separate cells in a single microscopic field when a 2 mm objective and a × 10 eyepiece are used, can be placed in a refractometer, and will give a refractive index reading that is indistinguishable from that given by the mounting medium alone. This is extremely useful because it means that two drops of the suspension can be taken from a pipette in quick succession and placed one in the refractometer and one on a side and this prevents any errors due to mixing or evaporation.

3.3.6 Preparation of specimens

If a drop of cell suspension in a solution of low refractive index (e.g. saline) is added to a protein solution of higher refractive index, the refractive index of the mixture will be slightly lower than that of the original protein solutions; the maximum effect of this dilution error is discussed in the next chapter (p. 68). Normally, however, it is convenient to add only a very small drop of the suspension to an excess of the protein, and if the volume of the added suspension is only 1% of that of the protein solution, or less, the error is negligible. Even when very concentrated protein solutions (e.g. 40%) are used, 0·01 ml of a cell suspension containing, say, 90% by volume of fluid of a refractive index equal to water, when added to 1 ml of the protein solution will lower the refractive index of the resulting mixture by less than 0·0005, and the error will be less than this if lower concentrations are used.

The length of time that cells may stay alive in these protein media is conditioned more frequently by the way in which the preparation is mounted than on the presence of the mounting medium itself. The most usual way to make preparations for examination is to cover them with a coverslip, supporting it if necessary to prevent large cells from being squashed, although the presence of tissue debris is usually sufficient to prevent this. The protein right at the edge of the coverslip in contact with the air soon dries to form a very thin crust and this prevents any further evaporation of fluid for several hours and supports the edges of the coverslip so as to prevent further squashing. It also, unfortunately, acts as an effective barrier to the diffusion of oxygen and carbon dioxide so that after about an hour the cells often deteriorate. If, however, the preparation is ringed round with some immiscible liquid, such as liquid paraffin, immediately after it is made, and while the protein at the edge of the coverslip is still wet, oxygen and carbon dioxide can readily diffuse through the two liquids. Joseph (1954) has observed cells dividing in protein media for as long as three days when mounted in this manner.

3.3.7   Evidence for the viability of the immersed cells

The evidence for the continued viability of cells mounted in the saline/protein media described above has been discussed at some length by Barer & Joseph (1955a). Briefly, apart from the fact that the cells remain the same size and show no obvious morphological changes, this is based on the continued mobility of motile cells such as amoebocytes, spermatozoa, ciliated epithelia and of motile protozoa in these media (although often at a decreased rate in the more viscous high concentrations of proteins), the continued growth and division of cells of bacteria and fungi, and the fact that animal tissue cells may be observed undergoing normal divisions in these media. The latter, which provides the most striking evidence that the cells are not adversely affected, was observed by the present writer in 1952 in the course of his study of the changes of refractive index of the cytoplasm of the dividing spermatocytes of *Locusta migratoria* (Ross, 1954b).

3.3.8   The practical limitations of bovine plasma albumin immersion media

Although Armour's bovine plasma albumin, fraction V, is by far the most useful mounting medium so far found for immersion refractometry, there are some cells for which it may not be suitable, particularly those that have cell membranes with peculiar permeability properties, such as cells that imbibe proteins by pinocytosis, and this has not as yet been sufficiently investigated. Allen, in the course of his studies of amoeboid movement by interference microscopy (Allen, 1958), attempted to use bovine plasma albumin as an immersion medium but found it unsatisfactory as it was taken in by pinocytosis. It is obvious that protein solutions cannot be used for the refractometry of cells that are capable of actively and rapidly assimilating protein through their membranes. The possibility of the protein having serological lytic effects on the cell membranes of certain types of cells is also one that cannot be entirely disregarded.

3.3.9   Immersion media other than bovine plasma albumin, fraction V

The author's experience with media other than Armour's bovine plasma albumin, fraction V, is rather limited, but several other workers have used other substances dissolved in saline and found them satisfactory for many kinds of living cells. Of protein, Professor Barer and his colleagues found that human plasma albumin, dialysed commercial egg albumin, carboxy-haemoglobin and Armour's bovine plasma globulin, fraction II, were satisfactory for all the cell material on which they were tried. The latter forms solutions with a pH close to 7·0 and so no pH adjustment should be necessary in making up its solution.

Armour's highly purified microcrystalline bovine plasma albumin is much more expensive than fraction V and its solutions, which also have a pH of about 5·0, appear to have practically no advantages over the latter as immersion media. A cell measurement test of the kind described above (p. 39) does, however, indicate that it has only about half the salt content of fraction V, and this may be useful if fairly concentrated solutions are required for the refractometry of some fresh water protozoa sensitive to hypertonicity.

Of non-proteins Barer & Joseph (1955a) have found that solutions of acacia gum (or 'gum arabic'), a polysaccharide with a MW of about 200,000, either in its commercially available form or when further purified, were excellent immersion media for many cells. (It was first used on amoebocytes by Faure-Fremiet in 1929.) Rather surprisingly, it appears to penetrate the cell walls of all bacteria and this cannot be simply an effect of the high concentrations necessary for their refractometry since fungal mycelia in similar concentrations appeared normal. Red blood corpuscles in concentrated solutions also appeared grossly distorted and it is therefore an unsuitable medium for haematological studies. Recently Mayhew & Roe (1965) have reported that solutions of this substance have a lytic effect on mouse ascites tumour cells which they attribute to the fact (which they were able to demonstrate with the P.A.S. test) that its molecules attach themselves very readily to the surface of these cells. These particular ascites tumour cells characteristically have many tiny pseudopodia or processes on their surfaces, and probably the polysaccharide from the gum gets entangled with these and accumulates so as to interfere with the cell membrane's metabolism. The solutions of acacia gum have a markedly acid pH, c 4–0, unless this is adjusted.

Allen (1958) used a polyglucose product manufactured by Du Pont Nemours of Wilmington, U.S.A. which seemed to show considerable promise for refractometry, since in addition to the properties shared by bovine plasma albumin it appeared not to be taken into *Amoebae* by pinocytosis. Unfortunately, the manufacture of this product has, temporarily at least, been discontinued and a rather similar polyglucose product 'Fycoll' manufactured by Aktieselskabet Pharmacia of Copenhagen, Denmark, recently investigated by the writer, seems to have a toxic action on living cells and is unsatisfactory.

To sum up, one can say that there is a considerable need for more work to be done in investigating new media that might be useful for the refractometry of certain kinds of living cells and in understanding why, unaccountably, some substances that would appear to be suitable do not work. Armour's bovine plasma albumin is, however, entirely satisfactory for most types of cytological investigations.

3.4 The appearance and interpretation of the phase contrast image

The matching method of using a phase contrast microscope to measure the refractive indices of living cells immersed in media of the same refractive index can be used for the refractometry of the cytoplasm of living cells, when this is optically homogeneous and relatively free from large granular inclusions, and for peripherally placed organelles of specialized cells, such as sperm tails, cilia and pseudopodia. It can also be used for measuring the refractive indices of whole cells that are themselves optically homogeneous, such as enucleate red blood corpuscles and many species of bacteria. The method cannot be used for the refractometry of cytoplasmic inclusions, or of other bodies located deeply within cells, unless they happen to have the same refractive index as the surrounding cytoplasm, as is often the case with the clear regions in nuclei.

It is dependent on the fact that when any of these homogeneous regions of living cells are surrounded by a medium with a refractive index equal to their own, there is no optical path difference, or phase change, in the light passing through them and the adjacent medium, and under a phase contrast microscope they will exactly match the background field in relative brightness or intensity, and will therefore be practically invisible. When the refractive indices of the medium and object are only a little different, however, the latter will appear appreciably brighter or darker than the background.

Most commercially marketed phase contrast objectives have 90° +ve phase plates (which means they are constructed so that the diffracted

light is retarded one quarter of a wavelength behind the directly transmitted light) and, if these are used, a homogeneous object will appear
darker than the background if its refractive index is slightly greater than
the mounting medium, and brighter than the background, or 'reversed'
if its refractive index is slightly less than the background. Negative
phase plates, however, in which the diffracted light is advanced
relative to the direct light, are also sometimes used and with those the
opposite is true. This, if one knows the characteristics of the phase
plate in the objective one is using, one can usually tell at a glance whether
the refractive index of the mounting medium is higher or lower than
the object being measured.

With ordinary +ve phase contrast objectives, an object which causes a
retardation of phase in the light passing through it relative to that
passing through the background, through having a higher refractive
index than the mounting medium, will appear darker. One that causes
an acceleration in phase, as a result of having a lower refractive index
than the mounting medium, will appear bright, although, for reasons
that have already been explained (pp. 16–19), this is only true when the
phase differences involved are smaller than about a third of a wavelength in most cases, or half a wavelength at the most. Fortunately,
the phase changes produced in the peripheral region of living cells
mounted in saline or protein media are usually appreciably smaller than
this.

The great advantage of phase contrast microscopy for immersion
refractometry lies in the way in which small phase changes in the light
passing through objects caused by small departures of refractive indices
from that of the immersion medium show up so strikingly as differences
of brightness or intensity, but for objects giving relatively large phase
changes, these differences of intensity may be very misleading if not
interpreted correctly. For this it is desirable to know all the characteristics of the phase plate being used. Although it is most probable that
this will be a 90° +ve phase plate it is still necessary to know the absorption of the phase plate if the intensities of the cell and its background are
to be related to a curve such as those shown in Fig. 5 (p. 18). In
particular it is important to be able to distinguish between a 'true match
point' indicating a zero phase change in the light passing through the
cytoplasm and the 'false match point' which may be given by a region
of the cytoplasm which actually has a higher refractive index than the
mounting medium if the light passing through it happens to be
retarded by a certain value (e.g. 53° in the case of a 75% absorbing
+ve 90° phase plate). In practice, however, this does does not usually

present serious difficulties since a falsely matched region of this kind in a cell will almost always appear surrounded by a darker region caused by the lower phase changes given by light passing through its thinner more peripheral regions. If any doubt remains a 'false match point' can be distinguished from the match of a zero phase change for, if the phase change is further increased by mounting the object in a medium of lower refractive index, it will appear brighter than the background, and conversely it will appear darker in a medium of higher refractive index, whereas with a match at zero phase change the opposite is true.

Indeed, curves relating the intensities of the image and its background, such as those in Fig. 5 (p. 18), can sometimes provide quantitative data of considerable biological interest even when matching by immersion refractometry is not employed. For example, Plate 3.2 shows the spores *Bacillus cereus* mounted in water under a 2 mm 25% absorbing, 90° +ve phase contrast objective. Their centres show up brighter than the background and, as they obviously do not have lower refractive indices than water, this must mean that the phase change in the light passing through them is appreciably greater than 82° (or 0·227 of a wavelength). Plate 3.1, taken with the same objective and on the same scale, shows the vegetative cells of the same organism similarly mounted and appearing dark, indicating that the phase change in the light passing through them is considerably less than 82°. As the maximum diameters of the spores and the vegetative cells are nearly the same, this means that the spores must be considerably more refractile than the vegetative cells (Ross & Billing, 1957).

3.5 The accuracy of immersion refractometry

All ordinary phase contrast objectives are capable of showing in this way phase differences of as little as 7°, or about a fiftieth of a wavelength, quite clearly (Oettlé, 1950). As the phase change in light passing through an object, compared to that passing through an adjacent region of the mounting medium, is proportional to the product of the difference between the refractive index of the object and mounting medium and the object's thickness, and the thickness of homogeneous regions of living cells that are measured by immersion refractometry are seldom less than 5 μ thick, this means that refractive index differences of 0·0018 (equivalent to 1% of cell solids) can be detected without difficulty. Consequently, it is normally true to say that when the cytoplasm of a cell mounted in a suitable medium appears to match the background when examined under a phase contrast microscope, its refractive index must be within 0·002 of that of the mounting medium. It may be considerably nearer to it than that, although the refractive indices of thinner objects such as bacteria or flagella cannot be measured so accurately. Taking 0·0018 as the mean refraction increment of cell solids, this means that the solid content of the cytoplasm of living cells can usually be measured to the nearest 1%, or more accurately than this if a thicker region is measured. This degree of accuracy is usually well within the limits of variability normally found in the refractive indices of the cytoplasm of individual cells, and so is entirely adequate for almost all practical purposes.

Barer (1956a) suggests that a refractive index match accurate to the nearest 0·001 or ½% of solid can be obtained with most phase contrast microscopes, but this may not be true of those employing rather low absorbing phase plates. It is certainly true that the accuracy with which a match in refractive index can be obtained is increased by using phase plates with a higher absorption. That this is theoretically true can, of course, be readily appreciated from the differences in the steepness of the curves in Fig. 5 (p. 18); in 1955 the present writer investigated it practically by comparing the appearance of the same groups of locust spermatocytes and spermatids mounted in matching protein media successively under 25% absorbing and 70% absorbing 90° +ve phase contrast objectives. The results, shown in Table 2, demonstrated that 7 out of the 14 cells which had appeared to have their cytoplasm matching the background under the 25% absorbing objective, appeared under the 70% absorbing objective with their cytoplasm actually slightly phase advancing or phase retarding. This can be seen in the photographs of some of these cells shown in Plates 2.3 and 2.4.

In spite of this, however, it must be emphasized that even a low absorbing phase plate, such as the 25% absorbing one used here, normally enables refractive index measurements to be made which are well within the limits of the biological variation of cytological material; the advantages that they confer in making fine internal cellular detail more discernible (p. 24) normally more than outweigh the small quantitative inaccuracies.

3.6   Some cytological problems investigated by the immersion refractometry of living cells

The wide variety of different investigations in which phase contrast microscopy has been employed for the immersion refractometry of individual cells in the course of the last twelve years are rather too numerous for them all to be discussed individually here. One of the earliest was a study by the present writer of the changes in the water content of the cytoplasm and clear nuclear sap of dividing cells (Ross, 1954b). This

TABLE 2

The recorded appearance, under a 25% absorbing and a 70% absorbing +ve 90° phase contrast objectives of the same spermatocytes and spermatids of *Locusta migratoria* mounted in isotonic bovine plasma albumin media with refractive indices close to that of the mean refractive index of their cytoplasm

Cell no.	Appearance of cytoplasm with a 25% absorbing plate	Appearance of cytoplasm with a 70% absorbing plate
Cells in a protein solution of n 1·3530		
(a) Group of 6 isolated cells (photographed)		
1	perceptibly dark	appreciably dark
2	matched	matched
3	matched	perceptibly dark
4	matched	perceptibly dark
5	matched	matched
6	matched	matched
(b) Eight cells at edge of testis debris		
1	bright (secondary spermatocyte)	markedly bright
2	perceptibly dark	distinctly dark
3	matched	matched
4	matched	perceptibly dark
5	dark (spermatid)	markedly dark
6	matched	perceptibly dark
7	matched	perceptibly dark
8	? perceptibly bright	matched
Cells in a protein solution of n 1·3535		
(a) Group of 4 isolated cells		
1	matched	perceptibly dark
2	perceptibly dark	perceptibly dark
3	? perceptibly bright	distinctly bright
4	matched	matched
(b) Group of 5 rather scattered cells		
1	matched	perceptibly dark
2	matched	matched
3	bright	bright
4	matched	matched
5	? perceptibly bright	distinctly bright

showed that the concentration of total solids in these regions fell during prophase by about one third its value in the resting cell (from around 11% to around 7%) concurrently with the chromosomes first making their appearances as discrete dense bodies, so that probably this indicated a redisposition of the solid material in the cell at this time.

Dick (1958) used immersion refractometry with phase contrast microscopy in a thorough and extremely interesting investigation of the solid concentration in cultured chick fibroblasts in media of differing tonicity. He irrigated these cells grown in a special perfusion chamber of his own design (Dick, 1955) with a succession of bovine plasma albumin solutions with varying salt content. He found that if they were maintained at blood temperature the volume of these cells (the reciprocal of the concentration of their contents) was linearly related to the osmotic pressure of the solutions in which they were mounted over a wide range of different tonicities, but that they all had slightly more water in them than had been predicted on theoretical considerations.

A number of very interesting observations in the field of mycology made mainly by Joseph in 1952–3 are briefly reported by Barer (1956a) and seem to indicate a considerable potentiality for immersion refractometry in this field. Not unexpectedly, spore germination was found to be accompanied by a considerable amount of hydration as demonstrated by a drop in refractive index, and the reverse process was demonstrated in at least one instance of the formation of ripe spores. In the rows of spores formed and forming on the conidiophores of some *Penicillia*, a regular gradient in refractive index was found from the newly formed ones adjacent to the mycelia, which had a relatively low solid content of around 25%, and the most distal ripe ones which contained about 50% of solid material. Striking differences were also found in the conjugating progametangia derived from the 'plus' and 'minus' strains of *Absidia glauca*, the solid content being considerably higher in the latter. In the same publication, Barer (1956a) lists a number of measurements of the solid content of the ectoplasm, flagella and cilia of a selection of protozoa, some measurements on different spermatozoa and the solid content of a variety of different bacteria whose vegetative cells nearly all contain between 25% and 35% of solid material. The haematological applications of the technique also appear to show considerable promise and will be discussed in the next chapter.

A few general conclusions can be drawn from the considerable number of measurements made by the writer and others on metazoan tissue cells. Apart from highly specialized cells like spermatozoa and red blood corpuscles, their cytoplasmic refractive indices do not vary very greatly and the solid concentration in the cytoplasm of most resting tissue cells is seldom found to be higher than 16% or lower than 11% w/v. The solid concentration in cells taken from any one particular tissue of a given animal varies less, rarely by more than 3% w/v. van den Broek & Ross (1961, unpublished), for example, found a maximum variation of only 2% in the solid content of the cytoplasm of all the intact living cells, i.e. the spermatocytes, spermatids, Sertoli cells and interstitial cells which they obtained from mouse testes by means of a Kopp glass homogenizer (p. 27) and this was found to be true of material obtained from mice of widely different ages. The hyaline part of the nuclei in resting cells is found surprisingly often to have a refractive index identical with that of the cytoplasm, e.g. in cultured myoblasts from chick and mouse (Ross, 1964) and in mouse ascites tumour cells (Ross, 1961a). This may be because nuclear membranes are almost certainly much more permeable to large molecules than cell membranes. In many cells, however, the nuclear sap appears slightly brighter than a matched cytoplasm, signifying that it induces a slight phase advance in the light passing through it and is slightly more aqueous than the cytoplasm. This difference may become even more marked at the onset of cell division. It is rare, on the other hand, to find living cells with nuclear sap that has an appreciably higher refractive index than the cytoplasm.

Enough has been said to indicate that immersion refractometry with phase contrast microscopy can provide a lot of extremely interesting information and insight into the physiological activities of cells, and it is often very profitable to carry out investigations of this kind even when the main line of an investigation is by other methods, such as the examination of fixed and stained material. In those cases, such an investigation may not always justify the purchase of an expensive phase contrast microscope and it is for this reason that instructions for inexpensively converting an ordinary light microscope for this purpose are included in the appendix, p. 209.

3.7 Problems connected with the penetration of immersion media

One aspect of immersion refractometry not discussed so far, which deserves mention, is its use on sections of fixed and dead cells. When a cell is dead, its cell membrane becomes permeable to quite large molecules and the globular protein molecules of bovine plasma albumin can readily penetrate into the cell so that the cytoplasm of a cell mounted in a saline/protein medium sufficiently concentrated for it to appear bright when the cell is alive, will, when the protein passes in, appear dark. This was suggested by Barer & Joseph (1955b) as a criterion for cell death. It is at least as reliable and more obviously explicable than, for instance, the effect of Janus Green, which stains only the mitochondria in living cells, and the whole cytoplasm when they are dead.

Around 1954, Barer & Joseph made another interesting observation on the effect of bovine plasma albumin solutions on fixed cells (Barer, 1955a, 1957). They found that when preparations of fixed cells that had been dividing were mounted in fairly high concentrations of their protein media, their cytoplasm predictably appeared dark but that the dense chromosomes which appeared in some of them presented a bright 'reversed' appearance. When similar cells were mounted in xylene, however, which had a much higher refractive index than the protein solution, approaching that of fixed protein, every part of these cells, including the chromosomes, appeared dark. At first they were at a loss to account for this anomaly, but then they realized that it could be explained if the protein molecules in the bovine plasma albumin were too large to penetrate between the meshes of the fixed precipitated material of the chromosomes. Xylene, on the other hand, being a much smaller molecule, penetrated easily and consequently gave a true refractometric picture of this chromatic material as having a higher refractive index than xylene. Photomicrographs of this are to be found in Barer (1955a).

This, however, suggests a way in which pore size in fixed material might be investigated by optical means, using molecules of various sizes and seeing if they penetrated, and studies on these lines have indeed been done more recently by Goldstein (1965), by Galjaard (1962) and Galjaard & Szirmai (1965). Just occasionally the penetration properties of bovine plasma albumin into the denser regions of living cells may provide insight into their submicroscopic structure too, and a case of this is discussed in connection with the polytene chromosomes of Diptera, investigated by Berendes & Ross (1963), in Chapter 7 (p. 167).

In 1956 Barer, Joseph & Esnouf suggested using penetrative properties of bovine plasma albumin to distinguish between intact cells and free nuclei by suspending both in a rather concentrated saline protein solution (c. 30%). The cytoplasm of the intact cells under these conditions appears bright and the cells themselves, being less dense than their mounting medium, tend to float up with the plane of the coverslip, while the naked nuclei are penetrated by the protein and appear dark and sink to the plane of the slide. Centrifugation of such a sample in a medium of this kind could lead to the almost complete separation of intact cells and nuclear fragments (p. 76).

4

Quantitative Phase Contrast Microscopy
2: Applications of immersion refractometry in haematology

4.1 The significance of measuring the refractive indices of red blood corpuscles

As well as being used for measurements on individual cells, the techniques of immersion refractometry described in the previous chapters can also be used to obtain information about cell populations in which the individual cells show a wide variation in refractive indices. This involves a slightly more elaborate approach, including the use of cell counts to establish the range and the nature of the distribution of cellular refractive indices, but these data can be of considerable biological interest and throw light on a variety of physiological and pathological processes.

In the field of haematology in particular the potentialities of the use of the phase contrast microscope in the immersion refractometry of cell populations seem to the author so very promising as to merit a separate chapter. Indeed, it may seem rather surprising that these potentialities have been so little explored by haematologists to date because several papers have appeared in which at least some aspects of these applications have been described (Barer, Howie, Ross & Tkaczyk, 1953; Barer & Joseph, 1955b; Ross, Morris, Hall & Monks, 1958; Keohane & Metcalf, 1959; Ross, 1961b); this can be explained by the fact that all of these have been published in journals or books not normally read by clinical haematologists. Although it is undoubtedly true that these techniques could be used for diagnosis, no claim can be made for their superiority over existing routine diagnostic methods except in a very few doubtful and difficult cases, such as the one cited on p. 77. Their real potentialities lie more in the field of haematological research, for it is certainly true that with the aid of immersion refractometry considerable insight can be gained into the progress of blood disorders and the processes of their therapy that is not attainable by employing 'classical' methods.

This is because immersion refractometry enables one to measure the refractive index and hence the total solid concentration in the clear regions of any individual cell. In the case of mammalian red blood corpuscles their internal structure is normally almost completely homogeneous and at least 95% of their total solid material, including the material of the stroma, consists of haemoglobin (97% in the case of human red blood corpuscles according to Ponder, 1948). Therefore the refractive index of a red blood corpuscle is related almost exactly to the haemoglobin concentration. It is therefore possible to determine in a sample of blood not only a value for the mean corpuscular haemoglobin concentration of the sample, which can be obtained by well-established 'classical' haematological techniques from the values for the haemoglobin in the sample and the packed volume of the red corpuscles after the sample has been centrifuged in a haematocrit tube (p. 64), but also the complete range and distribution of the corpuscular haemoglobin concentrations in the individual cells of the whole population. Thus it can be appreciated that this technique unquestionably provides more information about the blood picture as a whole. The experimental procedures involved in its use and some of the problems that they have been applied to, and the conclusions that it is possible to draw from them, will now be discussed.

4.2 The presentation of data derived from the refractometry of cell populations

The two main problems involved in using phase contrast microscopy for the immersion refractometry of red blood corpuscles, additional to those already discussed in the previous chapter, are the more general problems of measuring the refractive indices of cell populations and presenting these data as informatively as possible, and the special problem of correctly adjusting the tonicity of the relatively concentrated mounting media that are required so as to avoid any changes in the volume of the corpuscles.

As already mentioned (p. 53) the cytoplasmic refractive indices of non-dividing metazoan epitheliocyte and mechanocyte tissue cells usually show only small individual variations in cells of the same kind, and in these cases it is possible to find a medium in which the cytoplasm of the majority of the cells appears matched. This, however, is certainly not true of all cells; the individual refractive indices of a sample of normal mammalian red blood corpuscles, for example, seldom vary by less than 0·011, and the maximum variation in the refractive indices of bacterial populations can be greater than this. In these cases, in all mounting media with refractive indices between the limits of that of the cell populations, both bright and dark cells will be visible in addition to those that appear matched. The kind of appearances one gets on examining samples of mammalian red blood cells under a phase contrast microscope with an ordinary +ve 90° phase plate when they are mounted in media of different refractive indices are illustrated in Fig. 10A–D. In

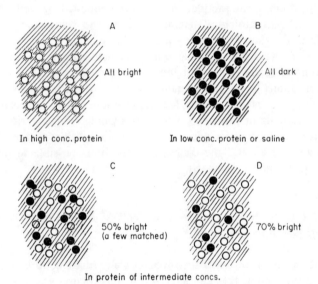

Appearance of red blood corpuscles under phase contrast

A — All bright — In high conc. protein

B — All dark — In low conc. protein or saline

C — 50% bright (a few matched)

D — 70% bright

In protein of intermediate concs.

Fig. 10   The appearance of human red blood corpuscles under phase contrast (using a 90° +ve phase plate) in different protein concentrations.

saline alone or in saline/protein solutions of low refractive index all the corspucles appear dark, and in saline/protein solutions of high refractive index they all (except for an extremely small proportion of dead cells which have consequently become permeable to the protein, see p. 70) appear bright. In similar media with refractive indices intermediate between these, however, both dark and bright cells can be found, together with a small proportion of corpuscles that match the background field almost exactly and are consequently nearly invisible (Fig. 10C). Within the range of the refractive indices of the media in which both bright and dark cells are visible, solutions of higher refractive index will contain more bright-looking cells and vice versa. Thus in Fig. 10 the medium giving the appearance of a field of corpuscles illustrated in Fig. 10D will have a higher refractive index than that giving the appearance illustrated in C.

In cell populations which show a wide range of variation in the refractive indices of individual cells such as these populations of red blood corpuscles, it is of interest to know the upper and lower limits of the refractive indices of the cell population, the mean refractive index of the population, and whether or not the variations of refractive index of the population approximates to that of a statistician's 'normal distribution'. By making suspensions of the red blood corpuscles in a series of saline/ protein solutions with closely spaced refractive indices it is possible to estimate the upper and lower limits and the nature of the distribution of the refractive indices of the cells in the population. The most immediately obvious way of doing this is by making counts of the relative numbers of matched corpuscles in each preparation and plotting this against the refractive indices of the mounting media in which they occurred. If the distribution of the corpuscular refractive indices within the population approximates to that of a 'normal distribution' such a record might be expected to give a characteristic symmetrical bell-shaped curve such as that illustrated in Fig. 11A. This is, of course, the familiar way to present data of this kind. In practice, however, it is almost impossible to estimate the proportion of matched cells in such a population with any real accuracy, both because they are nearly invisible and are liable to be missed and because they almost never form more than a very small proportion of the cells in any particular field, so that an extremely large number of cells would need to be counted before statistically significant values could be obtained.

It is, on the other hand, a relatively easy and simple matter to count the numbers of dark and bright cells in each suspension and this can be done with much greater accuracy. These values can be used to obtain exactly the same information if they are plotted against the values for the refractive indices of the mounting media in the form of integrated distribution curves. An integrated distribution curve of this kind, showing the proportion of cells having higher or lower refractive indices than the media they are mounted in, and equivalent to the more familiar cell refractive index distribution curve illustrated in Fig. 11A, is shown in

7

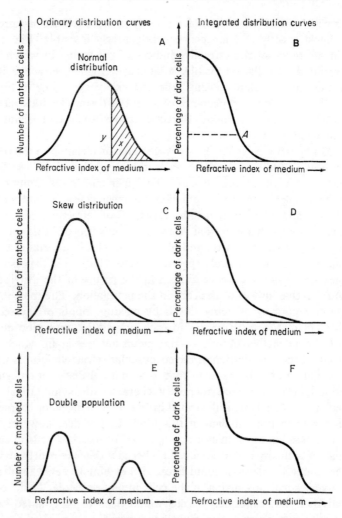

Fig. 11 *Left*—Ordinary population distribution curves. *Right*—the corresponding integrated distribution curves, of bright, dark and matched cells immersed in media of different refractive indices.

A and B normal distributions; C and D positively skew distribution; E and F discontinuous double population.

(Point *A* on B represents $\dfrac{\text{area } x}{\text{area } x+y}$ on A)

Fig. 11B. If, as in this case, the more familiar type of curve takes the form of a symmetrical bell-shaped curve typical of the 'normal distribution' frequently encountered in biometric studies (Fig. 11A) the equivalent integrated distribution curve will be characteristically regularly and symmetrically S-shaped. If enough points are plotted it is theoretically possible to draw a distribution curve of the first type from the integrated distribution curve of the second type because the slope of the latter is related to the height of the former. In practice this is unnecessary, however, because with a little experience it is possible to interpret the refractive index values shown in these integrated distribution curves and visualize the distribution of the actual refractive indices of the cells in the population. The asymmetric S-shaped curve illustrated in Fig. 11D, for example, represents an asymmetric or 'skew' distribution of corpuscular refractive indices, represented by Fig. 11C. Such distributions are found in some cases of pernicious anaemia and in certain other conditions (pp. 73, 84). An integrated distribution curve with a completely flat portion in it like the one illustrated in Fig. 11F indicates the presence of two entirely separate populations of high and lower refractive indices (Fig. 11E), since over the entire range of refractive indices where the curve is flat the proportion of bright- and dark-looking cells remains unchanged, and therefore there must be no cells at all in the population having these particular refractive indices. An interesting example of this is the case of pernicious anaemia treated with vitamin B_{12} discussed on p. 74.

The counting technique worked out by Ross & Tkaczyk in 1952 (and subsequently used by Barer, Howie, Ross & Tkaczyk, 1953; Ross, Morris, Hall & Monks, 1958; Ross & van der Eb in 1960; and Ross & Galavazi in 1961) involved making separate counts of the bright, dark and matched cells in each preparation. It was found easiest and quickest for two people to collaborate in making these counts. An observer at the microscope examined the cells in a succession of different fields and classified each in one of three categories, 'plus' for dark-looking corpuscles that gave a +ve phase change, 'minus' for bright-looking corpuscles and 'zero' for those that appeared matched, while his collaborator recorded this differential count upon squared paper. When exactly 100 or 200 squares were filled up the counting was stopped and the matched 'zero' corpuscles were first added up and half the total assigned to each of the other two categories (dark and bright), then the percentage of dark and bright cells was arrived at immediately. Essentially the same results would have been obtained, however, if the matched cells had been ignored entirely and it was also found quite possible for a single observer to complete the counts alone with the aid of a differential cell counter or with two or three separate unit counters.

The counts necessary for investigations of this kind are not as tedious as many kinds of routine haematological counting techniques, and the six to eight counts of cells mounted in different media required for constructing an integrated distribution curve of the kind shown in Figs. 14–16 and 18 can be done with practice in considerably less than an hour. Approximate estimations of the percentages of dark and bright cells are also quite informative, and were found to correspond quite closely to subsequent counts (see Fig. 18).

4.3 The tonicity of immersion media and its effect on corpuscular size and corpuscular haemoglobin estimations

The immersion refractometry of red blood corpuscles necessitates the use of very much more concentrated solutions of bovine plasma albumin than are needed for refractometry of ordinary cells. This poses a number of problems if the tonicity of the saline/protein solution used as immersion media to match the refractive indices of the corpuscles is to be adjusted so as to ensure that no changes occur in these cells' volumes. This is due both to the fact that it is difficult to predict the degree of ionization of the protein molecules themselves and the osmotic effect that they will exert in these more concentrated saline/protein solutions, and because some dispute still exists over what concentrations of saline are truly isotonic with mammalian red blood corpuscles. For humans, it is commonly accepted that a 0·9% NaCl solution is isotonic with the blood and tissue fluids and 'normal' saline of this tonicity is almost universally used in physiological and clinical studies on human and mammalian material; but Ponder (1948) considers that a 1% NaCl solution is, in fact, more nearly isotonic for human red blood corpuscles, and some recent experimental evidence obtained by Galavazi in 1961–1962, which will be discussed below (p. 66), certainly suggests that this latter figure may turn out to be more nearly correct for both human and some other mammalian corpuscles.

Correct tonicity adjustment is especially critical in the case of red blood corpuscles since they are exceptionally sensitive to small changes in the concentration of salts in the media they are mounted in, and readily shrink or swell and change their shape if this is not of exactly the same tonicity as that of the natural blood fluid. Not unnaturally any changes in their volumes resulting from this will result in a change in their refractive indices. In practice, small departures from isotonicity in the saline/protein mounting media used for immersion refractometry do not appear to matter very much provided a completely standardized procedure is used so that all the results obtained with it are fully comparable with each other. As was emphasized in the Introduction (p. xvii), important conclusions of considerable biological interest and significance can almost always be obtained from such comparative measurements. In all the work on erythrocytes described in this chapter, the tonicity of the saline/protein immersion media was adjusted to be nearly equivalent to a 0·8% sodium chloride solution by making up a 40% protein solution in 0·5% NaCl and diluting it with 0·8% NaCl, so the results obtained are, in fact, comparable with each other. All these media were thus made deliberately slightly hypotonic, because, according to Ponder (1948), the corpuscular swelling resulting from small deviations in the direction of hypotonicity is appreciably smaller than the corpuscular shrinkages which are caused by an equivalent degree of hypertonicity. Therefore, in view of the uncertainty about the osmotic effect of any ionized protein molecules, it seemed better to err on the low side.

It could, however, immediately be appreciated that in these media the corpuscles had swollen, and their contents had become more hydrated, for two reasons. Firstly, the corpuscles did not appear as regular biconcave discs as they do in whole blood, but more like squashed tennis balls or gastrulae, and such shapes often assumed by them when they begin to swell; secondly, the values for the mean corpuscular haemoglobin concentration obtained by the immersion refractometry of blood samples in these solutions were always several per cent lower than those obtained by haemoglobinometry and haematocrit measurements.

To obtain values for the percent haemoglobin concentration in any matched corpuscles measured by immersion refractometry it is, of course, necessary to use a slightly higher value for the specific refraction increment of their contents than the value of 0·0018 ordinarily used for living protoplasm because, as was explained in Chapter 1, the specific refraction increments of haemoglobins and certain other pigmented proteins are nearer to 0·0019. This value is therefore used and the value for haemoglobin concentration in a corpuscle can be obtained from its refractive index by using the dotted line in a graph presented in Fig. 8, p. 36. The mean corpuscular haemoglobin concentration of a sample of blood can therefore be obtained from the refractive index of the solution in which exactly 50% of both dark and bright cells are visible; or this value can be determined almost equally satisfactorily by interpolation when the percentages of dark and bright cells in media with different refractive indices above and below this particular value are plotted graphically on an integrated distribution curve.

The 'classical' method of obtaining a value for the mean corpuscular haemoglobin concentration in a sample of whole blood employed by haematologists is from an estimation of the total haemoglobin concentration in an unsedimented sample (which can be obtained by various colourimetric or densitometric methods in common use), and an estimation of the ratio of the volume of packed corpuscles to the total volume of a sample after it has been centrifuged at moderate speeds in a graduated centrifuge tube called a haematocrit. The mean corpuscular haemoglobin concentration (MCHC) is given by the formula:

$$\text{MCHC} = \frac{\begin{array}{c}\text{Haemoglobin concentration of an unsedimented}\\ \text{sample in g/ml}\end{array}}{\text{Volume of packed corpuscles in ml/100 ml}} \quad (4)$$

The value for the mean corpuscular haemoglobin concentration of normal human blood most usually quoted is 34% ±2% (Ponder, 1948; Wintrobe, 1951).

Fig. 12, however, shows the distribution of corpuscular refractive indices of twelve normal subjects measured, in 1952, by immersion refractometry in these slightly hypotonic saline/protein immersion media made by the standardized procedure already described, and plotted as integrated distribution curves. It will be seen that the total range of the refractive indices of the corpuscles in these subjects ranged from 1·379–1·394, or from 23·5–32% of haemoglobin, and the mean refractive indices of the corpuscles in these subjects ranged from 1·383–1·387 or from 26–28·5% haemoglobin. It can thus be immediately appreciated that because these values, which can be considered as being equal to 27% ± 1·5%, are 7% lower than the generally accepted value of 34% ±2% established by haemoglobinometry and haematocrit, it is virtually certain that the tonicity of the immersion media in which these corpuscles were measured was too low and caused them to swell so that their contents became more dilute.

Fortunately, Galavazi (1961) devised a most ingenious and elegant technique for estimating the actual change in corpuscular volume caused by using those hypotonic media; this will undoubtedly enable saline/protein solutions of the correct tonicity to be made. Galavazi's technique depended on making haematocrit measurements of the corpuscular volumes in blood diluted with their saline/protein solutions and comparing them with the predicted corpuscular volumes if the blood had been diluted with its own plasma fluid instead. The details of his method are as follows. He used a long, rather wide, precision-made capillary tube of constant diameter, with a large rubber bulb to suck up fluids attached to it. He first sucked in a certain volume of the whole blood of

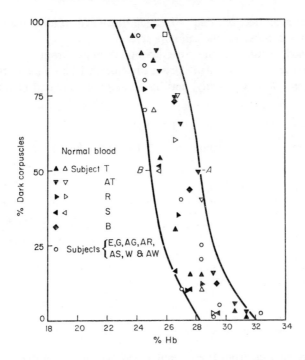

Fig. 12 Distribution of haemoglobin concentrations in the corpuscles from normal blood samples from 12 normal individuals in Oxford in 1952. (From Ross, 1954c)

a mouse and measured the length of the column from meniscus to meniscus. He then sucked in a small amount of air to separate two columns of fluid followed by a column of dilute saline/protein solution with a refractive index of 1·346 (which is approximately equal to the measured refractive index of mouse plasma) and the length of this column, again measured from meniscus to meniscus, was made as nearly as possible three times the length of the column of whole blood.

Both fluids were then expelled from the capillary tube into a small glass receptacle and thoroughly mixed by sucking them up and expelling them again fifty times to form a mixture of accurately known volumetric composition. This was then transferred to a haematocrit tube and centrifuged to determine the packed cell volume. A sample of the whole blood undiluted was then similarly centrifuged in a haematocrit tube and the reading obtained was multiplied by the measured dilution of the first specimen. This product is directly comparable with the actual packed cell volume obtained in the mixture with saline/protein solution, and any differences between them will be indicative of volume changes in the corpuscles induced by the saline/protein.

Galavazi performed the experiment on blood from three separate mice of the strain N.H.R.I. (from the Suddentache Versuchtier farm, Tüttlingen, West Germany) and his results are tabulated below.

TABLE 3

Results from Galavazi's dilution method for determining the tonicity of blood suspensions

(a) Haematocrit reading on whole blood	(b) Dilution ratio in mixture of blood and saline/protein	(c) Product $a \times b$	(d) Haematocrit reading on mixture	(e) Increase in cell volume $\frac{(d-c)}{c}$
43·9	1/3·34	13·1	15·8	21%
39·1	1/3·83	10·2	11·7	15%
39·3	1/2·36	16·2	19·0	14%
			mean increase	17%

It can be seen from these results that the mean volume of the corpuscles were, on average, 17% larger in the hypotonic saline/protein immersion media than in the whole blood. Therefore, the mean corpuscular haemoglobin concentrations measured in the 'classical' way by haemoglobinometry and haematocrit may be expected to be 17% higher than those that were measured by immersion refractometry; the correction factor can be applied to all these measurements. When this is applied to the case of the blood of the twelve normal human subjects, referred to on p. 64, who appeared by immersion refractometry to have a mean corpuscular haemoglobin concentration of 27%, this value becomes 31·5% which accords very closely with the generally accepted value of 32% ±2% for the mean corpuscular haemoglobin concentration in normal human blood. Fig. 13 shows values for the mean corpuscular haemoglobin in mice, residing at various altitudes, obtained in 1962 by Galavazi and the present writer by immersion refractometry and by the 'classical' (haemoglobinometry and haematocrit) method which is represented by solid dots joined with a continuous line. The lower broken line (joining the crosses) is the uncorrected results obtained by refractometry and the upper broken line is the same measurements after the correction for a 17% increase in corpuscular volume has been

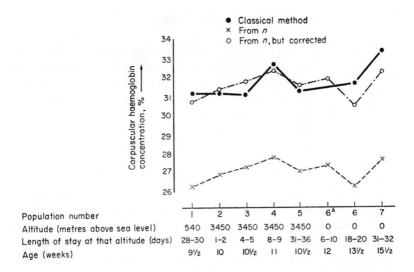

Fig. 13   Values for the mean corpuscular haemoglobin concentrations in 7 different populations of mice (5 of which are shown in Fig. 21) obtained by Galavazi in 1961 by using the 'classical method' (haemoglobinometry and haematocrit), and by immersion refractometry before and after applying the volume correction factor determined by Galavazi in 1962. (From Galavazi, 1963)

made. It will be seen that this corresponds extremely closely with the line representing the values obtained by the classical method.

Although this has not yet been done, it is obviously desirable that more concentrated saline/protein solutions should be made and tested by Galavazi's method until a concentration is found which causes no change in corpuscular volume. This would both eliminate the need to apply a correction factor when translating refractive index measurements into values for corpuscular haemoglobin concentration and eliminate the (admittedly not very likely) possibility of differential shrinkages and swellings occurring in non-isotonic saline/protein media of different refractive indices. Such solutions will certainly have to be more hypertonic than the ones that have been used hitherto and it may turn out that solutions isotonic with a 1% NaCl solution will achieve this. According to the freezing point determination obtained by Dick and discussed by Barer & Joseph (1955a) such solutions can be made by making a 40% solution of Armour's bovine plasma albumin in 0·7% solution of NaCl and diluting this to required refractive indices with 1% NaCl.

4.4   Some practical details of technique

The practical details of the method of making the suspensions of red blood corpuscles in the immersion media used for all the investigations here described are as follows: small drops of fresh whole blood were obtained from normal human subjects by means of finger pricks and from mice from a small incision in the ventral side of the tail. The first exuded drop of blood was discarded and the second was sucked up with a fine, glass pipette (which had been drawn out to nearly capillary dimensions over a gas flame). A tiny drop of it was immediately expelled into an excess of the saline/protein mounting medium in a solid watch glass or embryo dish, and then thoroughly mixed with it by stirring with a small glass rod and sucking up and expelling the suspension several times with another coarser glass pipette. One drop of this solution was then placed on a clean slide, covered with a coverslip, and examined, and another was at the same time placed in a refractometer and its refractive index measured. The latter procedure was found to be justified because experiments showed that, at the dilutions used, the refractive indices of the saline/protein solutions before and after the admixture of the blood did not differ significantly (see p. 44).

4.5   The dilution error

In this context it is profitable to consider the actual change in refractive index induced in the immersion medium by the addition of the plasma contained in the drop of blood. According to Barer & Joseph (1955a) the concentration of solids P' in the final mixture is given by the formula:

$$P' = P - \frac{lv}{V}(P-p) \tag{5}$$

where P is the concentration of solids in the saline/protein medium, p is the concentration of solids in the cell suspension (i.e. in the plasma), V is the volume of the drop of saline/protein, v is the volume of the drop of cell suspension (the whole blood) and l is the proportion of liquid in the cell suspension. In this case the accepted value for the solid content of plasma is 7% w/v and, since in normal blood the packed cell volume as measured by haematocrit is about 45%, the proportion of liquid l, even allowing for trapped plasma in between the sedimented corpuscles, is unlikely to exceed 60%. The maximum concentration of the saline/

protein medium P used in the refractometry of red blood corpuscles is normally about 33% w/v and the volume of a drop of saline/protein in the watch glass V normally exceeded 0·3 ml. The volume of the added drop of blood v never exceeded 0·01 ml and was usually nearer half this size so that the value v/V was never greater than 1/30 and was probably usually nearer to 1/60. Consequently when P is 33% the lowest value for P' calculated for formula is found to be 32·47%; this means that the very maximum error introduced by the dilution of immersion medium was around $\frac{1}{2}$% of solid, or an error in refractive index measurement of 0·0009 and this can to all practical intents and purposes be disregarded. The error due to this was even less when pathological specimens of blood were examined since in them the corpuscles had settled to form nearly plasma-free sediments in specimen tubes of venous blood brought from the hospital.

4.6   Effect of anticoagulants on the refractive indices of blood samples

As just mentioned, pathological specimens of blood can rarely be examined absolutely fresh from finger-prick samples but are usually available in the form of samples of several ml collected several hours before being examined. Such specimens, of course, need the addition of an anticoagulant if they are not to clot and become useless in the meantime. And so, at the suggestion of Dr. J. B. Howie who subsequently supplied all the pathological samples, an investigation into the effect of anticoagulants was initiated. To investigate the effect of anticoagulants, a venous sample from a normal subject (Dr. Howie) was treated with three commonly used anticoagulants—heparin, citrate and oxalate added in the concentrations shown in Table 4. Suspensions of these were then examined in media of relatively high refractive index in which all the corpuscles normally appeared bright; the presence of an appreciable proportion of dark cells was taken as indicating autolysis (p. 70). From Table 4 it can be seen that when these were examined within a few hours of the specimen being taken in a saline/protein medium with a refractive index of 1·388 (which was just higher than the upper limit of the range of refractive indices found in normal subjects, see p. 64) all the corpuscles appeared bright whichever anticoagulant was used, but after the specimens had been left at room temperature for 24 hours an appreciable amount of autolysis began to occur. This was most marked in the specimens in which citrate had been used as an anticoagulant and least

TABLE 4

Effect of anticoagulants on a sample of normal human blood
(*Subject H 26/9/52 ♂*) *freshly prepared, and autolysis after storage*
Percentage of bright cells (estimated approximately)

Time	Refractive index of mounting medium	Heparin— 1 mg of heparin (= 100 international units added to 1 ml of blood)	Citrate— 0·4 ml of 35% sodium citrate added to 1·6 ml of blood	Oxalate— 6 mg of ammonium oxalate and 4 mg potassium oxalate added to 5 ml of blood
Freshly prepared	1·3980	100%	100%	100%
	1·3880	100%	100%	100%
After 24 hours at room temp.	1·3960	100%	98%	98%
	1·3865	90%	75%	85%
After 6 days at room temp.	1·3980	98%	95%	95%
	1·3885	90%	40%	80%

marked in the specimens in which heparin had been used, and these effects were even more marked after the specimens had been left at room temperature for 6 days. One can therefore conclude that, if a specimen cannot be examined immediately after withdrawal, heparin appears to be the best anticoagulant in arresting autolysis.

4.7   *The detection of autolysis in stored blood*

The problem of autolysis in samples of stored blood at blood transfusion centres could be investigated by using exactly the same approach. This blood is normally stored at or near 0°C and it was found that, even over as short a period as 24 hours, storing at this temperature resulted in slightly smaller proportions of cells exhibiting a drop in refractive index than when identical samples were left at room temperature or incubated at 37°C. Over longer periods of time a progressively greater proportion of dark-looking, apparently permeable and therefore dead, cells appeared. At present, it is the common practice in blood banks at transfusion centres to discard all stored blood more than 3–4 weeks old. The rectitude of this practice is certainly not questioned but with this technique it should be possible to arrive at an estimation of the relative rates of autolysis in stored samples of blood. Experiments with transfused animals and animals' blood could possibly be used to relate the amount of autolysis in a sample to its actual efficacy in transfusion.

4.8 The refractometry of red blood corpuscles as an aid to diagnosis and research into pathological conditions

When in 1952 the technique of immersion refractometry of red blood corpuscles was being developed by Barer, Ross & Tkaczyk, they were especially fortunate in enlisting the interest and assistance of Dr. J. B. Howie, then at the Department of Haematology, The Radcliffe Infirmary, Oxford (and now at the University of Dunedin, New Zealand) in using it for a preliminary investigation of the range and distribution of corpuscular refractive indices in samples of blood from patients suffering from a variety of common pathological conditions. In all, blood from 23 different cases was so examined and the corpuscular refractive indices plotted as integrated distribution curves; the results obtained were sufficiently interesting to merit more than just a passing mention. A brief summary of Dr. Howie's clinical notes on each case discussed below is to be found in Appendix II (p. 216).

In most of these cases the distribution of the values for their corpuscular refractive indices showed some significant departure from those characterized by the 12 normal individuals illustrated in Fig. 12. In this figure, the upper and lower limits of the normal range as represented respectively by the two curves A and B, and these curves are reproduced for purposes of comparison on all the subsequent figures (Figs. 14–16 and Fig. 18) which represent the distribution of corpuscular haemoglobin concentrations in the pathological blood specimens.

4.8.1 Iron deficiency anaemia

It was hardly surprising that, as reported by Barer, Howie, Ross & Tkaczyk (1953), the most striking departures from the normal were found in five untreated cases of established iron deficiency anaemia of varying severity, which are illustrated in Fig. 14. From this, it can be seen that the distribution of their corpuscular refractive indices was almost all below the normal range and especially low in the more acute cases (see Appendix II). It can also be seen that characteristic integrated distribution of corpuscular haemoglobin concentrations given by each individual was essentially the same shape and width as those given by normal individuals, but the refractive index values were all lower than normal so that the curves are displaced to the left of the normal limits. These findings indicate that almost every corpuscle had less haemoglobin in it than normal, which accords well with the fact that iron deficiency anaemia is characterized by hypochromatism, low total haemoglobin values, a more or less normal cell count and, of course, low values for mean corpuscular haemoglobin concentration.

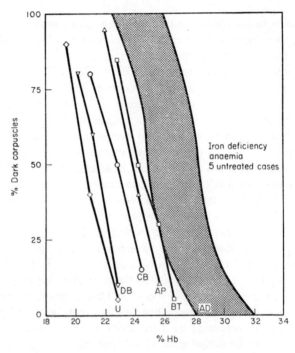

Fig. 14   Distribution of corpuscular haemoglobin concentrations in untreated iron deficiency anaemia: 5 samples, showing varying degrees of hypochromatism. (From Ross, 1954c)

4.8.2   Untreated pernicious anaemia

Three untreated cases of pernicious anaemia, by contrast, had corpuscular refractive indices which lay almost entirely within the normal range (i.e. between the curves A and B in Fig. 12), but unlike the cases of iron deficiency anaemia, the range of corpuscular refractive indices found in each of these patients was appreciably more extensive than was found in any single normal individual (see Fig. 15). The lower ends of these ranges were nearly as low as the lowest values found in any of the normals, but in two cases out of the three (AF and D) the upper end of these ranges included a small but significant proportion of corpuscles with higher refractive indices than were ever found in the normal individuals, and these cells were clearly hyperchromic. Thus it appears as if the integrated distribution curve of the corpuscular haemoglobin concentration in cases of pernicious anaemia can be distinguished from those of normal individuals, but it is less easy to suggest an explanation for these differences than in the cases of iron deficiency. It is almost certainly naïve to suggest that the tendency towards hyperchromatism was

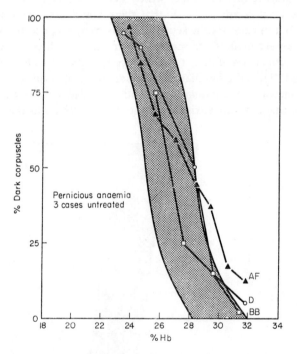

Fig. 15 Distribution of corpuscular haemoglobin concentrations untreated in pernicious anaemia: 3 samples, showing a wider scatter than normal and a tendency towards hyperchromatism. (From Ross, 1954c)

an adaptation to increase the oxygen-carrying capacity of the corpuscles in a disease which is chiefly characterized by a low erythrocyte count, because, for one thing, it is doubtful whether the oxygen-carrying capacity is appreciably increased in corpuscles with higher haemoglobin concentrations in them than normal, but this possibility cannot be entirely discounted.

4.8.3   *Pernicious anaemia undergoing treatment—evidence of double populations*

Extremely interesting results were, however, obtained in two cases of pernicious anaemia (AN and D) which had been under treatment with vitamin B_{12} for 7 and 10 days respectively; these are shown in Fig. 16. The 'node' or flat region in each of these integrated distribution curves indicates clearly the presence of two distinct cell populations in both these samples: one with refractive indices typical of untreated cases and the other with refractive indices which were appreciably lower.

In case D, it seems probable that these populations were not quite separate, but in case AN the separation was complete, because when the corpuscles were mounted in media with refractive indices from $1\cdot377$ to $1\cdot383$ the proportion of bright and dark cells in the population remained unchanged. Thus the familiar distribution curve of corpuscular haemoglobin concentrations equivalent to this integrated distribution curve would, in this case, approximate to the double curve illustrated in Fig.

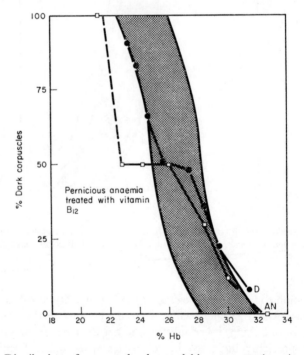

Fig. 16   Distribution of corpuscular haemoglobin concentrations in pernicious anaemia after treatment with vitamin B_{12}: 2 samples, showing evidence of double cell population. (From Ross, 1954c)

11E. The most probable interpretation of the presence of these two cell populations in these cases undergoing treatment was that the population with the higher refractive indices represented the residual microcytic corpuscles typical of the untreated anaemia, while the populations with the lower refractive indices were composed principally of corpuscles newly formed in the bone marrow under the influence of the vitamin B_{12} which had passed into the general circulation. It is well known that such newly formed cells often contain a high proportion of reticulocytes, and in this connection it is of interest to find that in case AN the reticulocyte count was as high as 37·8% which was fairly closely comparable with the proportion of the whole population with lower refractive indices than were found in any normal blood specimens. It would appear probable that reticulocytes (which are immature red blood corpuscles containing recognizable nuclear remnants in fixed and stained smears) have less haemoglobin in them than normal fully mature blood corpuscles. Nine years later, Galavazi & Ross in 1961 obtained convincing evidence to suggest that, in mice, a very high proportion of the reticulocytes can actually be recognized alive when examined by phase contrast microscopy when the corpuscles are mounted in these nearly matching saline/ protein media, and that they had rather lower refractive indices than normal corpuscles (p. 80; Plate 3.3 and Fig. 19).

In case AN, the discontinuity in refractive index between the two distinct populations was so great (from 1·377 to 1·383) that when a sample of the blood was mounted in a saline/protein solution with a refractive index in the middle of the range, 1·380, the corpuscles showed a tendency to separate according to density and the bright-looking corpuscles, which were of course lighter, lay in the plane of the coverslip and the heavier dark-looking corpuscles sank to the plane of the slide. When a larger sample of this blood was introduced into a centrifuge tube, filled with an excess of this medium and centrifuged, the corpuscles separated completely into two fractions (see Fig. 17), the upper fraction consisting almost entirely of bright-looking corpuscles, with low refractive indices and densities, and the bottom fraction almost entirely dark-looking corpuscles with high refractive indices and densities. (The separation was not absolute because, in packing, a few of the denser corpuscles were carried up with the less dense and vice versa.) This experiment suggested a method by which later the present writer, in collaboration with a team of haematologists and physicists at the Kent and Canterbury General Hospital, was able to investigate whether the age of a red blood corpuscle in any way affected its refractive index and density (p. 79).

8

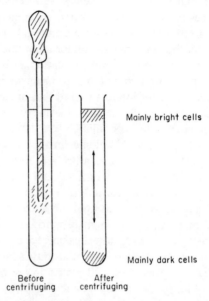

P.A. after treatment with vitamin
B₁₂ centrifuged in bovine plasma
of intermediate concentration

Mainly bright cells

Mainly dark cells

Before   After
centrifuging   centrifuging

Fig. 17   The effect of centrifuging a sample of blood from Case AN (see Fig. 16: pernicious anaemia treated with vitamin B_{12}) in a protein medium of intermediate density (refractive index 1.3800) showing partial separation of two cell populations.

4.8.4   Spherocytosis and atypical iron deficiency anaemia

It would certainly seem that as this technique may be especially valuable in investigations of the changes which occur in red cell populations day by day during the process of therapy, it could be profitable to carry out investigations on conditions other than iron deficiency and pernicious anaemia as well. Blood from a single case of spherocytosis (haemolytic jaundice), for instance, was found to have a large proportion of corpuscles with higher refractive indices than normal and the integrated distribution curve given by this particular case is shown in Fig. 18. This indicates high corpuscular haemoglobin concentration and is in accord with the findings of Guest & Ponder (quoted by Ponder, 1948) that the mean corpuscular haemoglobin concentration (measured by the 'classical' method) can in these cases be as high as 40% compared to the normal value of 32%.

One more pathological case needs to be described because at the time of its examination by immersion refractometry it had not been diagnosed with certainty. The blood in this case, C, resembled pernicious anaemia in that the corpuscular diameters were larger than normal, but not in any other respect (see Appendix II, p. 217). Examination of a sample by immersion refractometry showed a wider variation in corpuscular refractive indices than normal, together with an appreciable proportion of cells with lower than normal refractive indices (Fig. 18). The case

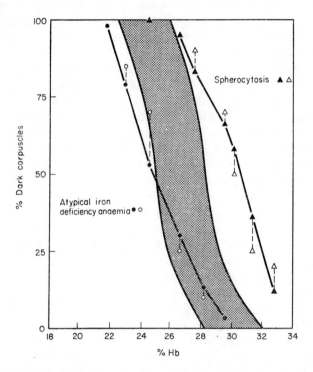

Fig. 18 Distribution of corpuscular haemoglobin concentrations in two pathological conditions. *Right*—A single case of spherocytosis (acholuric jaundice) showing marked hyperchromatism. *Left*—A single case in which diagnosis was decided by immersion refractometry—an atypical iron deficiency anaemia. In both cases the percentages of dark cells were first estimated approximately and then counted and in each sample both points are plotted. Approximations are represented by open symbols. (From Ross, 1954c)

was therefore diagnosed as an atypical case of mild iron deficiency anaemia, for this condition is usually microcytic. The patient responded well to iron treatment and, after a further month, his blood picture was normal.

4.8.5   Other investigations

The only other investigation which was done in 1952 in collaboration with Dr. J. B. Howie was a comparison of normal and foetal blood. The latter was taken from the umbilical cords of 5 new-born babies, treated with heparin and examined within 24 hours of birth. All had corpuscular refractive indices which lay within the normal adult range. Therefore, it seems probable that although foetal haemoglobin is different from adult haemoglobin in chemical composition, the concentration in the corpuscles is the same.

The cases mentioned above are rather few in number, but are discussed at some length since they are fully documented. They are not, however, by any means the only investigations that have been made on pathological samples of blood with the refractometric technique. In 1957–58, the present writer collaborated in Toronto with Dr. E. A. McCullough at the Ontario Cancer Institute in a similar investigation of 15 cases of pernicious anaemia and iron deficiency anaemia, and obtained distributions of corpuscular refractive indices which were in every way comparable with those described above; the clinical notes for these cases are now unfortunately no longer available. A much more extensive investigation is also reported by Barer (1957) to have been carried out by himself and Miss F. M. Gaffney around 1955 on the distribution of corpuscular refractive indices of some 500 samples of normal and pathological blood which included cases of iron deficiency anaemia, erythroblastosis foetalis, spherocytosis, haemolytic anaemia and pernicious anaemia; but although they seem to confirm the general picture these, too, have been incompletely reported, and only the means and the upper and lower limits of the distributions in individuals exhibiting the highest and lowest values for each condition have been published. These are expressed in percentages of haemoglobin with the mean of the normal distributions lying at 31·5%. This value is probably correct, but if these workers had used the bovine plasma albumin immersion media of incorrect tonicity used three years earlier by Barer, Howie, Ross & Tkaczyk, the mean refractive index of normal blood would have indicated a haemoglobin concentration of only about 27%. It would indeed be interesting to know whether these workers anticipated the tonicity adjustment arrived at by Galavazi (1963) (see p. 64) in arriving at their new value for the mean.

4.9   Does the haemoglobin concentration in red blood corpuscles alter with their age?

Nine years ago the writer collaborated with Drs. Morris, Hall & Monks at the Kent and Canterbury General Hospital in using immersion refractometry and Barer's technique of differential centrifugation in a protein medium (p. 79) to determine whether or not there was any relationship between the age and haemoglobin content of red blood corpuscles. It seemed possible that, towards the end of their life span, the circulating corpuscles might become leaky and have lower refractive indices than normal, or alternatively they might shrink slightly with age and consequently have higher refractive indices.

Two patients with mild iron deficiency anaemia (and consequently readily capable of assimilating iron) were given 10 microcuries of Fe_{59}, which has a half life of 45 days, by intravenous injection of the trichloride. This very rapidly passes from the circulating blood into the bone marrow without becoming attached to the existing red cells, and subsequently reappears after being incorporated in the haemoglobin molecules of the newly formed corpuscles (Wetherley-Mein et al., 1956).

Ten days later, when the utilization of the injected Fe_{59} was expected to be at a maximum, samples of their blood were withdrawn and examined by phase contrast microscopy when suspended in a range of isotonic bovine plasma albumin solutions. With both cases it was found that in a solution with a refractive index of 1·381 nearly 50% of dark and bright corpuscles were visible. Blood from each patient was then centrifuged at a fairly slow speed for 20 minutes in an excess of this protein solution, and a partial separation of the denser and less dense corpuscles was effected (Plate 3.5–3.7). Re-examination of specimens after centrifuging showed that in both cases samples from the bottom of the centrifuged suspension now had approximately 30% more of the denser cells (appearing dark under phase contrast) than the top fraction (Plate 3.3, 3.4). In the second case cell counts were also made which indicated that the total number of red corpuscles remained evenly distributed.

Similar samples of blood after centrifuging were used to determine the numbers of Fe_{59}-labelled corpuscles in upper and lower fractions. Measurements were made with 10 ml samples in annular plastic cups fitting around a sodium iodide scintillation counter. These measurements showed that within the limits of experimental error and statistical variation the radioactivities of upper and lower fractions were not significantly different.

These results, which are summarized in Table 5, indicate that, in the two cases investigated, the newly formed corpuscles included those of both high and low density and that therefore the haemoglobin content of the corpuscles did not appear to alter significantly with age. A very brief note of this conclusion was published at the time (Ross, Morris, Hall & Monks, 1958).

TABLE 5

Summary of the experimental results obtained by Ross, Morris, Hall & Monks (1958) in 1957 in a centrifuging experiment of labelled red blood corpuscles to determine if their refractive indices varied with their age

	Case 1	Case 2	
Date of administering 10 micro-curies of Fe_{59} by intravenous injection	2.8.57	24.9.57	
Date of withdrawal and examination of blood samples	12.8.57	4.10.57	

Percentage of dark cells visible in the populations suspended in isotonic bovine plasma albumin of refractive index 1·381 when examined by ordinary +ve phase contrast microscopy (from cell counts)

In sample before centrifuging	50%	63%	
After centrifuging—			
Sample from upper fraction	37%	51%	} approx. 30%
Sample from lower fraction	66%	79%	separation

Recorded radiation in 10 ml samples from the upper and lower centrifuge fractions (counts per second)

Sample from upper fraction	8·9	9·7	} not
Sample from lower fraction	8·2	9·6	significantly different

No. of red blood corpuscles per ml of suspension in the upper and lower centrifuge fractions

Sample from upper fraction	(not counted)	170,000	} not
Sample from lower fraction	(not counted)	170,000	significantly different

4.10 The recognition of reticulocytes in fresh blood samples

It has already been mentioned (p. 75) that Galavazi and the present writer found that it was possible to recognize a definite reticular pattern in some red blood corpuscles from mice with phase contrast microscopy when they were mounted in near-matching saline/protein media. Morphologically, the reticular pattern was not exactly like the pattern which can be seen in fixed preparations stained, for example with Azure II in fixed material, and the proportion of living corpuscles exhibiting this visible reticular pattern was slightly lower (see Fig. 19). The latter all had refractive indices lower than 1·381, which is appreciably lower than the refractive indices of most normal mature mouse red blood corpuscles (see Fig. 20). Fig. 19 shows the proportion of these recognizable

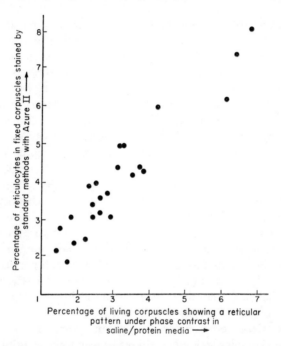

Fig. 19 Graph showing the close correlation obtained by Galavazi (1963) between the percentage of reticulocytes in blood samples, fixed and stained with Azure II, and the percentage of cells which exhibited a recognizable reticular pattern, in blood from the same samples examined alive by phase contrast microscopy after they had been mounted in a saline/protein medium with a refractive index a little higher than that of the haemoglobin that they contained.

cells with a reticular pattern (abscissa) plotted against the proportion of reticulocytes recognizable after fixing and staining with Azure II in the 24 different samples of mouse blood which Galavazi investigated. It is clear that a linear relationship exists, although a slightly greater proportion of cells with a reticular pattern can be recognized in the fixed and stained material than in the saline/protein immersion media. There seems little doubt, however, that the corpuscles exhibiting a reticular pattern in the saline/protein were reticulocytes and that therefore reticulocytes do (at least in mice) have lower corpuscular haemoglobin concentrations than normal.

4.11   The effects of high altitude and/or 'stress' on corpuscular haemoglobin concentration

In 1960 and 1961 the present writer, A. J. van der Eb and G. Galavazi made a series of investigations with the intention of determining the effects of high altitudes on the pattern of corpuscular haemoglobin concentrations in the blood of both mice and human subjects; in this they were greatly assisted by Dr. W. H. Weihe, who at that time was at the Department of Physiology at the University of Berne, Switzerland. It was established by Hurstado, Merino & Delgardo as far back as 1945 that prolonged stays at high altitudes result in a polycythaemia, i.e. a rise in the number of red blood corpuscles per unit volume, to well above the values given by normal red cell counts in subjects at low altitudes. The effect of this is to increase the carrying capacity of the blood so as to compensate for the low oxygen tensions at these high altitudes. These authors, together with Verzár (1945) and Verzár & Vögtli (1945), also recorded a small but significant rise in the mean corpuscular haemoglobin concentration, as well as an increase in cell numbers in subjects arriving at high altitudes. They suggested that such populations might contain a proportion of cells with higher corpuscular refractive indices than normal and that these might conceivably increase the oxygen carrying capacity of the blood still further.

Investigations were therefore carried out by immersion refractometry on the blood of mice and humans at sea level in Leiden, altitude o metres, and after stays of varying length at a relatively low altitude, in Berne, altitude 540 metres, and at a very high altitude in the Jungfraujoch High Altitude Research Laboratory, altitude 3454 metres.

As a basis for comparison van der Eb in 1960 first measured the distribution of corpuscular refractive indices in blood from 8 different genetic strains of mice (obtained from the Antoni van Leeuwenhoek Huis, Cancer Research Institute in Amsterdam) at sea level; these are shown in Fig. 20. This appeared to define the normal range of corpuscular haemoglobin concentrations at low altitude nearly completely, although Galavazi in 1961 found a small proportion of corpuscles in blood from mice from yet another strain (strain N.M.R.I., see Fig. 21) living in Berne, which had refractive indices as low as 1·372. Thus the range, 1·372–1·394 may reasonably be taken as indicating the lower and upper limits of the refractive indices of mouse corpuscles measured with these media at low altitudes.

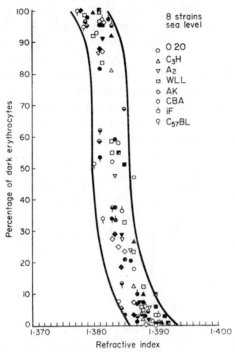

Fig. 20 Corpuscular refractive indices found in the blood of 20 different mice from 8 separate genetic strains at sea level. With one exception all the values obtained lie within the two parallel curved boundary lines, which are taken to indicate the upper and lower limits of the distribution of corpuscular refractive indices found in mice at sea level. (From van der Eb, 1961)

Mice from Leiden and from Berne were then taken up the mountain to the Jungfraujoch High Altitude Research Laboratory for periods of up to just over 100 days and samples of the blood from some of these individuals were examined by immersion refractometry every day during the initial ten days of their stay and at approximately fortnightly intervals thereafter. The immediate and most striking difference about the blood of these mice (as illustrated in Fig. 21) was the extremely rapid appearance of a small proportion of 'hyperchromic' cells with higher refractive indices than found in any individuals before they were transported up the mountain. These had refractive indices as high as

1·407, and began to make their appearance in the circulation within two days of the mice arriving at the Jungfraujoch Laboratory, and attained a maximum of about 8% of the red population after about a week, after which the proportion seemed to stay constant for the duration of the life span of the corpuscles. These hyperchromic cells were not permeable dead cells, since under prolonged observation they were not seen to darken, and they were not reticulocytes, for although the reticulocyte count also increased these were separately recognizable and found to have lower refractive indices. Some investigations were also carried out on a limited number of human subjects, and a similar proportion of hyperchromic cells was found in individuals that had recently arrived at the Jungfraujoch High Altitude Laboratory, but not in any individuals that had been resident there for many months.

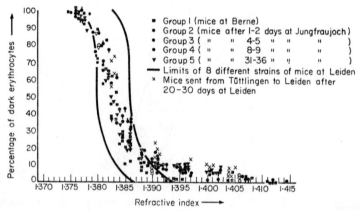

Fig. 21   Corpuscular refractive indices (and haemoglobin concentrations) found in the blood of mice at Berne, altitude 540 metres, and after stays of various length at the Jungfraujoch high altitude research laboratory, altitude 3454 metres. Also shown are the corpuscular refractive indices of one batch of mice sent by train from Tüttlingen, altitude 650 metres, to Leiden, altitude 0 metres. (From Galavazi, 1963)

All these findings, initially made by Ross and van der Eb in 1960, were fully confirmed by Ross & Galavazi in 1961, and it really looked as if the effect recorded was due to the high altitude. Then Galavazi most fortunately extended the investigation to more individuals at low altitudes and found exactly the same hyperchromatism in one batch of mice of the strain N.M.R.I. which was sent by rail from Tüttlingen, West Germany, altitude 650 metres, to Leiden, altitude 0 metres, although other similar mice sent by rail on journeys through a comparable range of quite low altitudes exhibited no hyperchromatism.

From this it was obvious that the hyperchromatism found at the Jungfraujoch was *not* solely due to the high altitude but can be induced by other factors. The most probable explanation is that it may be an effect of 'stress'. It is well known that sudden transportation to a very high altitude can give rise to considerable discomfort and nausea in humans (the present author and his colleagues certainly experienced these during the first 48 hours after their arrival at the Jungfraujoch Laboratory) and one can imagine that the experience is equally uncomfortable for mice. If the crate containing the mice sent from Tüttlingen to Leiden had been subjected to more than usual rough handling, these mice might also have felt 'stress'. The whole matter clearly needs to be much more fully investigated and some insight gained into the nature and origin of these hyperchromic cells; if it were ever established as a consistent effect of certain kinds of 'stress', it might not be altogether fanciful to see it having some relevance in forensic medicine, or even in providing evidence of cruelty to animals. Anyhow, it is not, as we at one time thought, induced exclusively by anoxia.

4.12 Refractometric studies on leucocytes

Hitherto, the whole of this chapter has been concerned with the use of immersion refractometry for studies on erythrocytes but the technique can be even more easily applied to the study of leucocytes, since their lower refractive indices mean that less concentrated immersion media need to be used, and the potentialities of the technique may be almost as promising as in the study of red blood corpuscles. The present writer in 1952, with Dr. E. B. Howie, obtained a few isolated values for the cytoplasmic refractive indices of normal human polymorphs (1·363–1·367) and lymphocytes (1·356–1·362) but the only extensive investigation in the field so far has been the extremely interesting one carried out by Keohane & Metcalf (1959) on the changes in the solid content of mouse lymphocytes during active immunization. These workers found that during the period of 8 days after inoculation of the mice with T.A.B. (dead typhoid bacillus) to produce an immunity reaction, the refractive indices of these lymphocytes rose from around 1·355 ($\approx 12\%$ solids) to 1·358 ($\approx 13·5\%$ solids) and then in the next two days fell drastically to around 1·353 ($\approx 10·5\%$ solids) and subsequently rose again. They suggested that these changes might be indicative of the synthesis of an antibody protein or a protein associated with RNA and its extrusion from the cells after a certain period of time.

4.13   The evaluation of refractometry as a research technique in haematological studies

Can refractive index measurement by immersion refractometry provide a powerful and effective new research tool in the field of haematology? The results which have been collected together here suggest that it might be but this can only really be determined by haematologists themselves. The first thing that needs to be done is to use a truly isotonic mounting medium by applying some test similar to that devised by Galavazi (p. 64), so that all refractive index measurements can be immediately translated into corpuscular haemoglobin concentration or, in the case of leucocytes, corpuscular solid concentrations. After that time alone will see if these techniques prove to be useful.

5

Qualitative Interference Microscopy in Cytology and the Measurement of Phase Change

5.1   The historical development of interference microscopy

The application of the principles of interferometry to microscopy is no new development. The first practical interference microscope appears to have been constructed on the principle of the Jamin interferometer as far back as 1893 by Sirks who was, like Zernike who pioneered the phase contrast microscope 40 years later, a Dutchman. He called his instrument, which from its design could only use low-power objectives and which as far as is known was never used for examining biological material, an *interferentiemikroskoop* (Sirks, 1893).

In the ensuing 50 years, several other interference microscopes were invented, described or developed, notably by Sagnac (1911), Linnik (1933 and 1938) and by Frederickse (1935a). It was Frederickse (1935b) (also a Dutchman) who appears to have been the first person to have used an interference microscope to obtain measurements on cells. It was not until the late 1940s, however, that the important potentialities and possible applications of interference microscopy began to be widely appreciated. The successful exploitation of the phase contrast microscope at that time probably contributed more to stimulating this interest than any other factor. The result was a positive spate of invention and over 20 different instruments of great ingenuity and varying efficacy were designed, constructed and described by different authors between 1947 and 1957. Not all of these designs left the drawing board and only relatively few of the instruments constructed were suitable for cytological investigations; of these a mere three only were manufactured commercially and became generally available for biologists to use. For those interested, the developments of this period have been admirably reviewed by Rienitz in the book *Beitrage zur Interferenz-mikroscopie* by

Krug, Rienitz & Schultz (1961). In the English translation of this book (*Contributions to Interference Microscopy*, 1964) he has included some new material and continued his survey into the early 1960s. His is the first account in which an attempt has been made to obtain an objective assessment of individual contributions in this field and apportion the credit where it is rightly due. This was needed, because there has undoubtedly been some element of chance in the factors that have determined the commercial adoption and exploitation of particular designs of instrument, and some of the inventions of other instruments which might have been equally suitable (notably perhaps those of Philpot, 1948, 1952) have received less recognition than they have deserved. It appears that only one privately designed and specially constructed interference microscope has so far been used in any really notable cytological investigations: this is the high power shearing interference microscope employing two Wollaston prisms invented by A. F. Huxley in 1952 and 1954 and subsequently used for his remarkable studies with Niedergerke of the changes in the widths of the A-band and I-band regions in single isolated frog muscle fibres (Huxley & Niedergerke, 1954) which led to the discovery of the interdigitating ultrastructure of the actin and myosin rodlets. Apart from this, this book is exclusively concerned with investigations which have been carried out with commercially available interference microscopes or their prototypes, since almost all the published cytological studies to date have been with these instruments.

5.2   The basic operative principles of an interference microscope

Like phase contrast microscopes, interference microscopes render transparent phase objects, such as living cells, visible by converting the phase changes in the light passing through them into changes of wave amplitude; but, unlike the phase contrast microscope, this is not achieved by causing a single beam of directly transmitted light and the light diffracted by the object itself to produce a destructive or additive interference. Instead it is produced from the interference between light passing through the object, a separate beam of direct light passing through a different region altogether and the light diffracted by the object. The details of the ways in which this can be achieved are far too numerous to discuss here, and are to be found in Barer (1955b), Hale (1958), Smith (1955), as well as in Rienitz (1964) who provides the most comprehensive account of all. Usually it involves the splitting and subsequent recombination of one or more beams of light (although other means can be employed). This is usually done in two main ways: either by making the light take two different paths through the instrument by reflection from a number of reflecting and semi-reflecting surfaces (as in the Dyson microscope and the Horn microscope) or (as in the Smith microscope, the Françon–Johansson microscope and the Normarski-type microscopes) by splitting the light into two component beams and recombining them by means of birefringent crystals. In both systems, the optics of the microscope are so arranged that one part of the split beam passes through an object, such as a cell, and is often called the 'object beam', and the other part passes through a clear area of field and is called the 'reference beam'.

It is unnecessary to give full accounts here of the optics and detailed method of operation of each of these commercially marketed interference microscopes, because, unlike nearly all commercial phase contrast microscopes, they are each provided with operational manuals which discuss their optics and contain enough detailed information about their operation to enable the user of each to form some evaluation of the quality of the images obtained with them. A few observations on their relative merits for certain types of cytological investigations are given below (pp. 108–116). The remarks about interference microscope images which now follow apply (except when otherwise stated) to all the interference microscopes suitable for biological use which are now, or have been, commercially available.

5.3 The appearance of the microscope field and the nature of interference colours

In all these systems now in common use, the image can be made to appear in two different forms: the 'fringe field' appearance or the 'even field' appearance. In most microscopes a change over from one appearance to the other can be achieved by an instrumental adjustment to the microscope itself, but in some cases an accessory is needed, such as the fringe field eyepiece, used with Smith microscopes, to effect the change. If a white light source is used the 'fringe field' viewed under the microscope appears traversed by a series of parallel coloured fringes which lie across both the background and the images of cells, but in the region of the cell images these fringes are displaced by amounts which depend on the phase changes in the light passing through each different region of each cell, so that the line of a fringe passing through a cell with typically heterogeneous refractile properties will appear kinked and bent, as it crosses the image of the cell (see Figs. 32 and 33 in Chapter 8). If white light is used with the 'even field', the whole of the background field appears in one uniform colour (actually formed by greatly widening part of a single fringe in the 'fringe field' condition), and the different regions of each cell will show up in different colours related to the phase changes in the light passing through each individual region. In both types of image, 'fringe field' and 'even field', the colours visible are Newtonian interference colours. These are subtraction colours, and each of them can be regarded as being derived from white light with one principal wavelength eliminated by interference; thus if the spectral green light is eliminated by the trough and crest of this wavelength coinciding, spectral blue and spectral red will predominate, forming a colour which appears bluish-red, and so on. These colours form a well-known series of successive orders and each order represents a phase change of a whole wavelength between two beams of interfering white light. The shift in colour which any region of an object exhibits up or down this Newtonian series is directly proportional to the phase change in the light passing through that particular region.

For critical quantitative and qualitative interference microscopy, however, monochromatic or nearly monochromatic light is normally used in preference to white light, and the differences in colour observable with white light usually show up as differences in relative brightness or intensity. Thus a 'fringe field' is traversed by alternating regularly spaced dark and bright bands which are displaced in the images of cells or other phase objects; in an 'even field' the background appears at a uniform intensity and the contrasting intensities of cellular details depend upon the phase changes in the light passing through them. It is this 'even field' instrumental adjustment which is now most often used by interference microscopists in studying cells both qualitatively and quantitatively. This is because the cell image is more closely comparable to the typical phase contrast image and the image of a cell in a fixed and stained preparation viewed by ordinary light microscopy; and also because quantitative phase change measurements can be made visually to a much higher degree of accuracy than with the 'fringe field', without the need to use costly accessory equipment such as a microdensitometer (Chapter 8, pp. 197–204). A 'fringe field' may often be preferable if phase change measurements of more than a wavelength have to be made, but these only occur in some kinds of cytological material and the phase changes that need to be measured can nearly always be substantially reduced by compression or immersion techniques (pp. 128–135 and pp. 150–158).

5.4   The reduction of optical artefacts and the relationship between image intensity and phase change

For qualitative studies on cells, the kind of image which one gets with an 'even field' under an interference microscope is a truer representation than a phase contrast image in two important respects: firstly, the 'halo', 'shading off' and 'defocused annulus' optical artefacts are normally absent, and, secondly, the relationship between intensity and phase change is linear over a greater range than in most phase contrast microscopes. The result of the elimination of the 'halo' and 'shading off' artefacts is that the image of an object of uniform thickness and re-fractive index, such as that shown in side view in Fig. 7A (p. 21) will look more like Fig. 7B and not like Fig. 7C, its phase contrast image. The exceptions to this are the images produced by the 'double focus' objectives which are alternatively available with the Smith interference microscope. These cause a slight 'halo' and 'shading off' effect because the 'reference' and 'object' beams here are incompletely separated (pp. 104–107).

It has already been mentioned (p. 24), that one of the disadvantages of phase contrast microscopy for cytological studies lies in the fact that cells and their inclusions can and often do act as lenses which defocus the image of the annulus and produce serious deterioration in the phase contrast images of the cellular structures inside such lens-shaped regions. This defect is absent in nearly all interference microscope images because it is not usual for interference microscopes to derive their illumination through an aperture with a special shape which can be imaged in the optical system (although the slit illumination in the Françon–Johansson microscope and in two of the Normarski-type microscopes (pp. 114–116) are exceptions in this respect).

It seems quite probable that this may be the main reason why the internal morphological details of some special kinds of cells that contain a complex assembly of varied structures are undeniably more easily seen under an interference microscope than under a phase contrast micro-scope. An example of this is provided by the studies of David, Mallion & Brown (1960) of the Golgi network in the neurons of the spinal cord of a cat before the classic Golgi silvering technique was applied, and of the network observed and photographed under interference microscopy by David (1963) in similar living neurons. These networks, were clearly demonstrated under interference microscopy; under phase contrast microscopy they cannot be seen so satisfactorily or unambiguously.

9

The increased linearity in the relationship between intensity and phase change is also an advantage in evaluating the quality of a cell image because it means that the relative brightness of cellular details in the interference microscope image compared to the background are often more truly indicative of the phase changes which they produce than would be the case with a phase contrast image. It can be appreciated by referring to Fig. 5 (p. 18) that with phase contrast microscopy, even when a 90° +ve phase plate with as low an absorption as 25% is employed, the relationship between phase change in an object and the relative darkness of its image is only linear over a range of about 25° or one fifteenth of a wavelength; but under an interference microscope employing a maximally bright 'even field' in monochromatic or nearly monochromatic light, it can be seen by referring to Fig. 22 (p. 100) that this relationship remains nearly linear over a range of rather more than 90° or a quarter of a wavelength.

This means that when living cells, mounted in aqueous media of low refractive index such as isotonic saline, are examined by interference microscopy under these conditions, not only their outer extremities (which give low phase changes) will appear darker than the background, but also many internal regions including large parts of the cytoplasm (which give rather greater phase changes) will often appear still darker; only their thickest or most highly refractile regions such as lipid droplets will appear with diminished contrast or even bright ('reversed'). In the equivalent phase contrast image of the cells far more of its regions will appear in this reverse contrast. However, these interference microscope images, although they are in some degree truer representations of a cell, nevertheless have certain disadvantages when compared to phase contrast images for morphological studies. Because small phase changes are not overemphasized by the 'halo' effect, the thinner extremities of certain types of cell and tenuous pseudopodia are not nearly so conspicuous as under phase contrast, nor are the boundaries around the images of those internal features in cells which give only small phase changes between them and their immediate surroundings. The result is that the overall impression which one gets of an 'even field' interference microscope image of a cell shows undeniably less contrast than the phase contrast image. These disadvantages, however, are more than offset by the advantages enumerated above, and in particular by the absence of obscuring halos around objects giving large phase changes in the internal regions of the cell. The proper appreciation of the interference microscope image of a cell is largely a matter of getting familiar with it.

5.5 'Ghost' images and image overlap

One disadvantage inherent in the design of several of the commercially marketed interference microscopes is the presence of a secondary or 'ghost image' of every object alongside its principal image, which is of a different colour or contrast. This particular artefact is absent in the Dyson and Horn microscopes (and in the Smith microscope employing 'double focus' objectives) but is present in all Smith microscopes which use a 'shearing' system of optics, in the Françon–Johannson microscope and in the Normarski-type microscopes when they are adjusted to give image doubling. In the Smith microscope this secondary image is an astigmatic image which can never be brought into sharp focus,* but in the Françon–Johansson system and the Normarski microscopes both images are equally sharp and neither can be regarded as primary or secondary. The presence of this second image can frequently result in there being an overlap in the two adjacent images of a cell or a group of cells, particularly when high power objectives are used (p. 111). The morphological interpretation of detail in the region of image overlap is difficult and measurement of phase changes in these regions is virtually impossible. The use of a rotating stage on these microscopes, by which the 'ghost images' and the principal images can be made to move around each other, usually enables the entire area of a single isolated cell to be scrutinized without overlap. With interference microscopes employing this 'shearing' system, however, it is only possible to examine a portion of the borders of larger aggregations of cells or of continuous sections because however the specimen is orientated, all the central regions of such areas will be overlapped with secondary images. (See colour plates II, I-K (facing p. 154) and III (facing p. 186)).

5.5.1 Study of cell morphology by 'differential' interference microscopy

The foregoing remarks in this chapter outlining some of the advantages of interference microscopes over phase contrast microscopes for the study of cell morphology apply only to the transmitted light interference microscopes that have been in common use prior to 1966, and it could be argued that, in some respects, these advantages are somewhat marginal. Very recently, however, several instruments capable of employing the system of 'differential' interference microscopy devised and

---

* In the Smith interference microscopes, the 'ghost images' are in fact invisible for objects (such as bacteria) which are too small to be resolved by the highly astigmatic extraordinary beam.

described by Normarski (1955) have been developed; this system undoubtedly appears to have certain very striking advantages over all others for certain types of morphological studies.

The 'differential' image can be obtained in certain types of double-refracting instrument employing a 'shearing' system if the actual amount of 'shear' is made extremely small. Ideally, this 'shear' should be half that of the resolution limit of any given objective. This means that, instead of getting the familiar image doubling and 'ghost' images typical of shearing systems, one sees, in white light, a single image of a 'flat tint' (Normarski, 1955) with all boundaries representing detectable phase gradients sharply outlined in contrasting colours. A cell will thus appear to have much the same overall colour as the background, but its left-hand and right-hand edges, and the corresponding edges of all its internal structures that are of differing refractive indices, will show up in the contrasting interference colours typical of those exhibited in the principle and 'ghost' images in the more familiar kind of 'shearing' systems, where the images are doubled. The best microscope adjustment for the examination of morphological details with this 'differential' system appears to be when the background colour is dark grey in the zero order of the Newtonian series. The images of phase boundaries in the object then show up as contrasting bright lines, and the whole picture bears some resemblances to those seen with dark ground illumination, but without the latter's inherent optical artefacts. With background fields of other colours, the appearances of these phase boundaries resemble more closely those given by oblique illumination (but without their artefacts) or to those given in electron micrographs of shadow-cast material.

Allen, David & Hirsh (1966a) have demonstrated, on both theoretical and practical grounds, that, in contrast to the normal 'shearing' system that produces image-doubling, 'differential' interference microscopy gives optimum contrast at the highest resolution and with the largest condenser numerical apertures, and that the effect of out-of-focus images in diminishing this contrast is negligible. Furthermore, the depth of the field in focus with such high resolution objectives is only about one Airy disc, which enables cellular material, and even whole transparent organisms, to be 'optically dissected', by successively focusing the different cells and organelles at different planes. A remarkable demonstration of this was embodied in a cine-film showing details of the cellular structure and ciliary activity in the region of the wheel apparatus in a living specimen of a rotifer, shown at the centenary meeting of the Royal Microscopical Society in London in 1966, and reported by

David, Allen, Hirsh & Watters* (1966). An equally remarkable set of photomicrographs showing details of the spindle structure in living endosperm cells from the plant *Haemanthus* was obtained and published by Bajer & Allen (1966). Spindle fibres in living dividing cells cannot normally be seen at all under phase contrast microscopy or with the interference microscopes previously developed; this was thought to be because the refractive indices of the spindle fibres were extremely close to that of the material in their immediate environment. Allen, however, considered the alternative possibility that they were normally invisible because such fibres occurred in sizeable bundles, and that, in phase contrast and ordinary interference systems, the fibres out of focus contributed phase disturbances that degraded the images of those that were in focus. The clear images obtained with the 'differential' system confirm this view, since with this system the contrast of all out-of-focus material is minimal.

There can be little doubt that there are other morphological details within cells which are normally rendered similarly invisible through the presence of adjacent structures, and it is reasonable to expect that this system may shortly become an extremely valuable means of displaying morphological features in living cells that have hitherto been difficult or nearly impossible to demonstrate, especially in such cells as neurons or liver cells with cytoplasm crowded with refractile inclusions. It is, therefore, encouraging that at least four different microscope firms are now about to market instruments capable of employing this 'differential' system (p. 115). Its use for quantitative interference microscopy is, however, very limited, and, for this, the more familiar 'shearing' system employing complete image doubling is almost always better (Allen, David & Hirsh, 1966).

5.6 The use of special mounting media to improve interference microscope images

It has already been said that some cells are so thick or so refractile that when they are mounted in a medium of low refractive index, such as isotonic saline, they produce phase changes of more than a wavelength in their central regions, and when they are viewed under an interference microscope with an 'even field' these cells will exhibit one or more complete fringes as one passes from their edges inwards and their internal structures may be difficult to interpret. In these cases, just as with

* An extremely valuable series of papers by these authors, on the optical properties of polarising interference microscopes, will shortly appear in the Journ. Roy. Micro. Soc.

phase contrast, morphological examinations are often greatly facilitated if such cells are mounted in isotonic saline protein with higher refractive indices than isotonic saline, and for morphological examinations a saline/protein solution with a refractive index rather greater than that of the cytoplasm, but less than that of many of the cell inclusions, is often found to be the most satisfactory (Plate IIB (facing p. 154)).

5.7 Distinguishing phase-retarding and phase-advancing objects

With cells mounted in water or saline, it is almost always valid to assume that every region of each cell will be to a greater or lesser degree phase retarding; but with cells mounted in saline/protein solutions, it is necessary to be able to distinguish between phase-retarding and phase-advancing regions; and this is not always as immediately obvious as it is under a phase contrast microscope. When white light is used with an interference microscope employing an 'even' field, objects giving phase retardations or phase advances of less than a wavelength will exhibit shifts in colour in opposite directions up or down the Newtonian series from the colour of the background; it is only necessary to determine which direction signifies a phase retardation or a phase advance at the particular setting of the microscope in question. The easiest way to do this is to compare the appearance of the specimen with an object known to give phase retardations, e.g. a human oral epithelium cell mounted in water. If, for example, the microscope is set up so that the background is second order red in the Newtonian series and an oral epithelium cell so mounted exhibits a purple cytoplasm and bluer nuclei, one would be correct in assuming that, at this particular instrumental setting, a phase retardation is indicated by a shift up the Newtonian series from the second order red towards second order blue. Then if, without read-justing anything but the fine focusing of the instrument, the specimen of oral epithelial cell is replaced with a specimen containing cells mounted in isotonic saline/protein and the cytoplasm of these cells appears yellow and their inclusions red, purple or blue against a background colour of second order red, one could justifiably conclude that the cytoplasm which now exhibits a colour shift down the Newtonian series is phase advancing and that the inclusions enveloped by the cytoplasm are phase retarding. This is a better way of distinguishing phase-retarding from phase-advancing objects than by the movement of the Becke line upon defocusing (p. 32), which is a method which has been advocated in some instruction manuals, because Becke lines are only prominent at boundaries where marked differences in phase change occur, and they can sometimes be confused with interference fringes. This method, however, is based on the assumption that there is no shift in the order of the Newtonian interference colours when the specimen is changed. In practice this assumption is almost always justified when ordinary thin preparations of cells, suspended in aqueous media, are examined. See colour Plate I (facing p. 138).

Another way of distinguishing these two kinds of objects can be used when monochromatic or nearly monochromatic light is employed. All commercial interference microscopes are equipped with some means of measuring phase changes, and, with this, the relative darkness or brightness of an 'even field' background and cellular details can be altered at will (pp. 99–101). The knob controlling this mechanism needs to be turned in opposite directions for measuring phase retardation and phase advances respectively. If, when starting from a maximally dark background, one turns such a control in the direction appropriate for measuring a phase retardation, the object in question begins to become darker, this indicates that it is phase retarding, while if it becomes brighter it is phase advancing. These arguments, however, only apply if the phase changes in the object are less than half a wavelength. Relatively small advancing or retarding phase changes of this kind are the ones most often encountered when studying cells immersed in saline/protein media. Objects giving greater phase changes than half a wavelength have recognizable dark and bright fringes at their edges in monochromatic or nearly monochromatic light. If such an object is phase retarding, a succession of the fringes will move from the edges towards its centre if the phase change measuring control of the microscope is moved in the direction appropriate for measuring a phase retardation. If, on the other hand, this sort of object is phase advancing, a similar movement of the controls will cause these fringes to move outwards. These movements of fringes can equally well be appreciated if white light is used and this method is extremely useful when dealing with objects giving phase changes of several wavelengths.

5.8   The measurement of phase change by interference microscopy

5.8.1   Approximate measurements in white light

The greatest single advantage of interference microscopes over phase contrast microscopes in cytology lies not in their undoubted superiority for qualitative investigations discussed above, but in the fact that with interference microscopes the actual phase changes themselves can be measured to a high degree of accuracy. This enables a very great deal of quantitative cytological data to be obtained which cannot possibly be obtained with a phase contrast microscope and the implications of this capability are discussed in subsequent chapters. Phase changes can be measured in the 'fringe field' from the displacement of the fringes caused by different parts of a phase object such as a cell, but to do this at all accurately requires densitometry of photomicrographs of the fringes across the field and the object (see Chapter 8); although this method is indeed accurate, it is also troublesome and laborious, and it is not now often employed. Nearly the same accuracy can be obtained with an 'even field', because every commercially available interference microscope is equipped with some means by which the greatly widened fringes which cause this even field are made to progress successively across it, so that, if white light is used, the nearly uniform colour of the background field can be made to change through a regular succession of interference colours progressing either up or down the Newtonian series. Each region of an object, such as a cell, in this 'even field' will appear in a different colour to the background, and will exhibit a shift up or down the Newtonian series with respect to the background colours according to the amount and sign of the phase change occurring at that particular region; these colours too will change through a regular succession of interference colours when the background colour is changed.

Thus it is apparent that one way of actually measuring a phase change of less than a wavelength is to set the instrument so that the background field is some recognizable colour—second order red is perhaps the most critical and easily recognized—and then turn the appropriate microscope control in the appropriate direction to change the colour of the object and the background until the object under scrutiny becomes the same colour as was the background. This approach is clearly illustrated in the sequence of cinemicrographs at the bottom of Colour Plate III (facing p. 186). In G the background is of second order red, in K this colour is transferred to the cytoplasm of the myoblasts shown in the photographs, in M it is transferred to the nucleoli and in O to some of the lipid droplets. If this is done correctly, the phase change in the light passing through the object, relative to that passing through the background medium alone, is related to the amount by which it was necessary to turn the control. Thus this colour-shifting control is also a phase change measuring control. In some instruments, such as the English and American versions of the Smith interference microscope, the phase changes can be deduced directly from the calibration of this control, but in others (such as the Dyson microscope) the distance the control is turned to measure any given phase change has to be compared with the distance it needs to be turned to measure a whole wavelength before an absolute value for the phase change measured can be arrived at, and this is slightly more troublesome.

5.8.2   The 'extinction transfer' method of measurement in monochromatic light

The transfer of colour from the background to the object is not, however, a very accurate way of measuring small phase changes, even though in the experienced hands of people possessing full colour vision it is possible to measure in this way accurately to about one thirtieth of a wave-length. A far better way, advocated as a standard procedure by all interference microscopists and manufacturers of interference microscopes, is to use monochromatic light or nearly monochromatic light, and first adjust the phase change measuring control so that the background field appears maximally dark, and then turn it in the appropriate direction for measuring a phase-retarding or phase-advancing object until the object appears maximally dark. It is certainly easier for most observers to recognize the instrumental settings which give a maximally dark background and a maximally dark appearance to the object than for them to attempt to compare from memory the colour of an object to the colour that a microscope field had been, and it is often possible to obtain an accuracy of one fiftieth of wavelength in measuring the phase changes through many objects by this means. This standard procedure is commonly called the 'extinction point' or 'extinction transfer' method (Richards, 1963), a rather misleading name since even when every effort is made to obtain as nearly monochromatic light as possible (e.g. with the use of a mercury arc lamp and appropriate green filters) the extinction of the light is never absolute. (Actually, it is the author's experience that rigorously monochromatic light is seldom really necessary for measurement, and that a tungsten lamp with an Ilford 807 mercury green filter, for example, will give enough 'extinction' to enable phase changes to be measured within the permissible limits of accuracy imposed by other factors (pp. 101–8, 161–3). Disadvantages of using the 'extinction point' method to measure phase changes through very small microscopic objects are discussed in Chapter 8, p. 184.

5.8.3   The 'minimum visibility' method of measurement in monochromatic light

An alternative method is to start with the instrumental setting at which the background field appears maximally dark, and turn the phase change measuring control only half the distance required to produce extinction. At this setting the object in question will show up with exactly the same brightness or intensity as the background; and this 'match point' may often be easier to recognize than the instrumental setting at which the object or region being measured appears maximally dark. The instrumental accuracy in making a phase change measurement by this matching or 'minimum visibility' method is halved, but sometimes this is more than offset by the increased visual accuracy with which the exact instrumental setting can be determined; and for measuring small objects such as bacteria the author finds it superior (Chapter 8, p. 190). Fig. 22 shows the relationship between the intensity of the

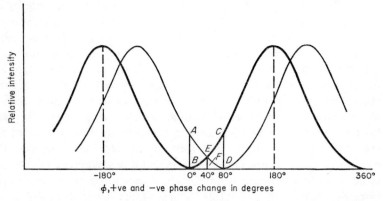

Fig. 22   Graph (based on those of Davies, 1958) showing the relationship between phase change and background intensity (thick line) and the intensity of an object giving a phase retardation of 80° (thin line); it shows two methods of measuring this phase change: the 'extinction transfer' method (by the horizontal distance between *AB* and *CD*) and the 'minimum visibility' method (by the horizontal distance between *AB* and *EF*).

appearance of the background and a microscopic object giving a phase retardation of 80° plotted against the instrument settings equivalent to phase changes of −180° to +360°. The point at which the background is maximally dark is taken as being 0°, at which setting the distance *A–B* indicates the brightness of the object being measured. When the phase change measuring control has been turned by an amount equivalent to a measurement of +80°, the object is maximally dark and the background is as bright as the object originally was (indicated by *C–D*). This is the second instrumental setting for the 'extinction point' method. If, however, the phase change measuring control had only been turned half this distance, equivalent to a phase change of +40°, it can be appreciated that the object will then appear to have exactly the same brightness as the background (indicated by $E-F$); and thus this represents the instrumental setting for the 'matching' or 'minimum visibility' method of measuring phase change. However, the curves illustrated in Fig. 22 are to some extent idealized and they are somewhat modified in practice by systematic errors in phase change measurements which can be introduced by a number of factors which will now be discussed.

5.9   Systematic errors in phase change measurement

5.9.1   Errors resulting from diffraction due to the inhomogeneity of the object

Davies (1958) has shown that the curve depicting the changes in the intensity of the image a phase object with phase change depicted by a thick line in Fig. 22 will be reduced appreciably in amplitude if the object exhibits marked variations in its refractile properties as most cells do to some extent; he indicates a way in which this particular error can be eliminated by averaging two phase change measurements made on either side of the point of maximum background brightness. This, however, is seldom necessary to apply in practice because usually the error is small (around one-thirtieth of a wavelength) and within the limits of variability of most biological material. A rather similar reduction in amplitude may be caused by pigmented cells such as red blood corpuscles due to light absorption and, ideally perhaps, red light should be used for measurement on corpuscles, but again the absolute error is small and in all comparative results it can be disregarded.

5.9.2   Errors arising from the obliquity of the incident light

Another systematic error in phase change measurement is the 'obliquity error' due to the fact that the lateral rays from the microscope condenser usually have to pass through a greater thickness of material than rays lying nearer to or on the optical axis of the microscope. This is discussed both by Davies & Deeley (1956) and Davies (1958), and by Richards (1963); they all conclude that this error can be reduced to about 5% by closing the condenser aperture down to a numerical aperture of around 0·5. This error is, of course, only fully manifest in the case of objects which are wider in the directions at right angles to the microscope's optical axis than they are thick in the direction parallel to this optical axis, such as microscope sections, flattened cells and cell aggregates. It will not apply to free floating spherical cells or spherical bacterial cocci and may be expected to be less pronounced with cylindrical cells such as bacilli. Here again, this error is not usually important if comparative measurements are needed rather than absolute measurement of phase change.

5.9.3   Errors in measurements made near phase boundaries, and on small microscopic objects

An important source of error can, however, arise from the diffraction effects at the boundaries of small microscopic objects. This not only puts a limitation on the accuracy with which it is possible to make direct linear measurements in visible light (see Chapter 8), but it also puts a lower limit on the size of the object which is sufficiently well resolved to enable accurate phase change measurements to be made on it. On theoretical grounds, Casperson (1936, 1950) considered a related problem—the justifiability of measuring ultraviolet absorptions near the edges of absorbing objects—and concluded that, with an objective with a numerical aperture of about 1·2, an object would have to have a width of 3–4 times a wavelength of light for measurement through its centre to be free from this error; but Wilkins (1950) concluded that under certain conditions measurements on rather smaller objects than this would be valid. On these grounds Davies (1958) suggested that, with high resolution interference objectives, measurements of phase change through the centres of bodies with widths below 3–4 times the wavelengths of the light used should be treated with caution.

Around that time, however, some experimental evidence was obtained which gave an indication as to how close to a phase boundary one could justifiably make phase change measurements by interference microscopy and this experimental evidence is, of course, more valuable than any purely theoretical approach. Huxley & Hanson (1957) in the course of their studies of the solid content of mammalian myofibrils by interference microscopy, encountered difficulties in measuring the phase changes through the individual cross-striations owing to the very small intervals between them and they had to determine the minimum distance from these phase boundaries which allowed a valid phase change measurement to be made. To do this they had to obtain a phase object with an absolutely square edge so that there was no phase gradient at this boundary, and then make a densitometer trace of the intensity gradient across the image of this boundary when viewed by interference microscopy. The objects they selected for this were protein crystals, especially myoglobin crystals about 0·8 μ thick and 5 μ across, which had been prepared in a very pure state by Dr. J. C. Kendrew. These were photographed in an 'even field' with mercury green light under a Dyson interference microscope, using a 2 mm objective, adjusted so that the crystal appeared appreciably darker than the background. Densitometer traces across the boundaries of the images of these crystals showed a steep intensity gradient 0·6 μ wide. Thus it is safe to conclude that phase change measurements made with similar interference microscope objectives, which had a numerical aperture of 1·3, cannot be made within 0·3 μ of the middle of a phase boundary, but are probably valid if made beyond this limit. It is of course possible that the permissible limit is even narrower than this,* since the edges of these crystals used as test objects may not have in fact been quite square; however, these results certainly suggest that it may be justifiable to measure phase changes through the centre of objects only a little over 0·6 μ wide in green light (with a wavelength of around 0·55 μ) and that, in general, objects need be no wider than about 1·3 wavelengths of light for valid phase change measurements to be made through their centres if the interference objectives of the highest numerical aperture are used.

5.9.4 *Errors due to a non-uniform field and the 'wedge effect'*

Variations in phase change in the light passing through parts of the background field not occupied by a specimen can be caused by at least three factors. One is by using a mounting medium which is not homogeneous in refractive index over the whole preparation. This is particularly liable to occur in immersion refractometry, when aggregates of living cells are taken from saline and immediately mounted in saline/protein solutions of higher refractive index without allowing time to ensure that the small amount of the original saline, which inevitably has to be taken along with the cells when they are placed in the new solutions, equilibrates with the saline/protein of higher refractive index. Concentration gradients in the immediate vicinity of such cells are immediately obvious in white light as zones of changing interference colour. They usually disappear completely if the preparation is allowed to stand for a few minutes, but phase change measurements should never be made unless the background is of uniform colour or intensity. Uneven thicknesses in slides and coverslips or local refractive index differences in the glass with which they are made can naturally also cause phase differences in the background field, but these are seldom noticeable if slides and

---

* The smallest size which can be measured to a stated accuracy must also depend upon the condenser aperture. Increasing the aperture steepens the diffraction gradient at the edge of the image and thus tends to compensate for the necessarily underrated value created by the obliquity error (Smith, 1966a).

coverslips of good quality are used (Ambrose, 1948). A more frequent cause of phase changes in the background field, and one which is extremely difficult to avoid completely in practice, is the 'wedge effect', caused by a more or less uniform gradient in the thickness of a mounting medium when the distance between the slide and the coverslip is slightly different in one place from another. This has caused some concern to interference microscopists, and for a time it was considered it might be especially important in the case of instruments using a shearing system where phase changes are made by comparing the intensities of an object and a clear region of the background laterally displaced from it, because at first sight it would appear to introduce an error. This was investigated by Koester (1958) and his conclusions, which are discussed by Richards (1963), are that in fact no error in phase change measurement is introduced by this factor, because it is not the absolute values of phase change in the object and reference area that are important in making and measuring the phase change due to the object, but the difference between them. When these readings are subtracted, the 'wedge effect' cancels out in the direction of shear.

Smith (1966a) makes the following observations on the 'wedge effect': 'In interference systems where both beams traverse the same slide the only effect of a wedge in the preparation is to demand re-adjustment of the interferometric alignment. After such re-alignment the uniform field should be obtained. What usually happens is that the "wedge" tends to have a lenticular component (a curvature) and it is this component which produces a phase gradient in the object field. The basic assumption of all phase change measurement is that the background reading is taken where the object is located. This is obviously not possible in a rigorous sense, so one must be content with the background in the object's immediate vicinity. It is important to insist that when there is an obvious phase gradient across the field, one should select a region which is in the same iosphase as the object.' This means that the 'reference area' should be at some point as near as possible to the cell but shifted from it in a direction at right angles to the direction of the phase gradient (or parallel to any fringes visible in the field). Such measurements could indeed be made even in a 'fringe field' instrumental setting provided the reference point is rigorously selected.

5.9.5   Errors in phase change measurements made with the 'double focus' objectives in Smith interference microscopes

In the 'double focus' objectives which are sometimes used with Smith interference microscopes, the object and reference beams are incompletely separated. This not only introduces optical artefacts, 'halo' and 'shading off' to some degree, but introduces additional difficulties when they are used for measuring phase changes. Indeed, Richards (1963) states 'the double focus system is *not* recommended for quantitative work' and Hale (1958) says 'the double focus objectives cannot be used for measurement of the optical retardation produced by the object'. The latter statement simply is not true and as it may sometimes happen that a cytologist may find himself in possession of an instrument equipped only with these 'double focus' objectives, it could be of some assistance if their capabilities and limitations in obtaining quantitative measurements are defined as precisely as possible.

They are in fact quite satisfactory for measuring phase changes through objects which have a relatively small area. The numerical aperture of the 'double focus' objective being used determines the size of its reference area and this places a limitation on the maximum size of the object which can be measured. From Fig. 23A it will be seen that, because the foci of the reference and object beams are superimposed, some of the reference beam is always intercepted by the object. This has the effect of giving a low error in phase change measurements of certain values. The maximum amount of this error depends on the relative areas of the object and reference area, and two examples of this are illustrated in Fig. 22B–E for the 2 mm 'double focus' objective, which has a reference area approximately 20 μ in diameter. It can be seen that an object 5 μ in diameter will only intercept 6% of the light of the reference beam, so that at the most phase change measurements on such an object will be 6% low, an amount that can be frequently neglected. A larger object, however, say 14 μ in diameter as illustrated in Fig. 23D, E, will give a maximum low error of 50%. This cannot be disregarded and the remedy here is to use a lower power 'double focus' objective with a larger reference area. These errors, however, are maximum errors that only occur when the phase change due to the object is $\frac{1}{4}$, $\frac{3}{4}$, $1\frac{1}{4}$ wavelengths or multiples of this series. Objects giving phase changes of $\frac{1}{2}$, 1, $1\frac{1}{2}$, etc., wavelengths are correctly measured regardless of the size of the object (Smith, 1959).

This has been confirmed experimentally by the present writer using the 2 mm Smith 'double focus' and 'shearing' objectives to make measurements on identical bacilli of *Lactobacillus bulgaricus*, approximately 1 μ in diameter, and the *nebenkerns* in the spermatids of *Locusta migratoria*, 4·5 μ in diameter. The very small differences found between the measurements with the two kinds of objectives were no greater than the random errors found with similar repetitive measurements made with

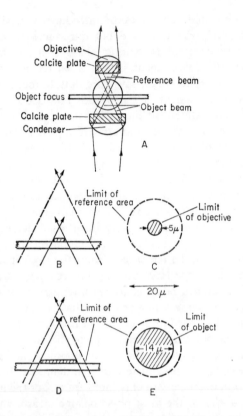

Fig. 23   Showing how the maximum low errors in making phase change measurements with the 'double focus' objectives of the Smith interference microscope are affected by the size of the object relative to that of the reference field.

A—A diagrammatic representation of the paths of the 'reference' and 'object' beams in the 'double focus' condenser and 2 mm objective.

B and M—Enlarged diagrams of the parts of the ray paths surrounded by a circle in A. In B, with a circular object 5 μ in diameter, only 6% of the light of the reference beam is intercepted, and the error introduced can usually be ignored. In D, with a circular object 14 μ in diameter, nearly half the light of the reference area is intercepted which can cause a very considerable error in phase change measurement.

C and E are plan views of B and D respectively in the plane of the objects. The dotted line represents the limit of the reference area, which, with the 2 mm objective, is approximately 20 μ in diameter.

the same objective. A comparison of the measurements of bacterial thickness obtained with the Smith 'double focus' and 'shearing' objectives which were obtained by the half-shade eyepiece matching method described in Chapter 8 (pp. 184–187) are illustrated below in Table 6.

TABLE 6

The mean retardations of light, of wavelength 542 mμ, through living *Lactobacillus bulgaricus* from fourteen different cultures mounted in 0·25% NaCl, and their mean thicknesses calculated from these and the mean refractive index of the culture (which was 1·404 in every case)

Culture no.	Date of culture and subcultures	Date of examination	Mean retardation (φ) from 10 measurements on different bacilli (wavelengths)	Mean thickness (t) (μ)
Measurements with the 2 mm double focus objective of the Smith microscope				
1	11/7	20/7	0·155	1·21
2	11/7, sub. 16/7	21/7	0·154	1·21
3	11/7, sub. 16/7 and 24/7	27/7	0·146	1·14
4	25/7	28/7	0·147	1·14
5	25/7	29/7	0·148	1·15
6	25/7, sub. 27/7	29/7	0·145	1·13
7	25/7, sub. 27/7	29/7	0·149	1·16
8	25/7, sub. 27/7	29/7	0·143	1·13
9	25/7, sub. 27/7	30/7	0·151	1·19
10	25/7, sub. 27/7	30/7	0·148	1·16
Measurements with the 2 mm shearing objective of the Smith microscope				
11	11/7, sub. 16/7	21/7	0·151	1·19
12	11/7, sub. 16/7 and 24/7	27/7	0·158	1·23
13	25/7	28/7	0·146	1·14
14	25/7	29/7	0·151	1·18

5.9.6 The accuracy of determining zero phase changes with interference microscopy

The whole principle of immersion refractometry by phase contrast microscopy described in the first part of this book (Chapters 3–4) depends on measuring phase changes of zero when one obtains a refractive index match; interference microscopes can, of course, be used in exactly the same way to measure the refractive indices of the cytoplasm of cells immersed in special media. If white light is used, it is probable that interference microscopes are not quite as accurate in determining a refractive index match as most phase contrast microscopes are, but it is certainly true to say that the refractive index of the cytoplasm of a cell more than 10 μ thick will lie within 0·002 of that of the mounting medium if the colour is visually indistinguishable from a background

10

colour of second order red. When monochromatic light or nearly mono-chromatic light is used, the accuracy of matching is increased, and it can definitely be said that the accuracy with which it is possible to measure refractive indices by interference microscopy with immersion refracto-metry lies well within the range of variability found in most cellular material.

5.10 Some remarks on interference microscopes suitable for cytological studies which are, or have been, commercially available

As has already been said, detailed descriptions of the optics, mode of operation and capabilities of each of the half-dozen or so commercially available interference microscopes which can be used for cytological studies is inappropriate in a book of this kind, because these are treated at length in the instruction manual which each manufacturer supplies with their instrument. In addition, Hale (1958) and Davies (1958) have compared the Dyson and Smith microscopes in considerable detail, and comparisons of the optics of these and other instruments are also given by these authors and by Barer (1955b), Rienitz (1964) and Françon (1961).

Nevertheless, a few observations, based mostly on the writer's personal experience with these instruments, are not wholly out of place, since new instruments are now being marketed and certain of the more obvious qualities of the older ones appear never to have been discussed.*

5.10.1 The Dyson interference microscope

The Dyson interference microscope, constructed and described by Dyson (1949a, b) was until very recently manufactured by Vickers Instru-ments Ltd. (formerly Cooke, Troughton and Simms Ltd.), York, England. Its manufacture was discontinued in 1963 but many of these instruments are still around in good working order. It was the first commercially manufactured interference microscope to be used exten-sively for cytological investigations, and all the classical work of Davies,

* The recently developed 'Nikon' interference-phase microscope will not be dis-cussed in this survey, since it is not, strictly speaking, an interference microscope, but a variable contrast phase contrast microscope, with the variation in contrast produced by interference. (This needs to be emphasized, because the author knows one reputable cytologist who bought one of these instruments thinking it had all the capabilities of a true interference microscope.)

Wilkins, Chayen & La Cour (1954) was done with this instrument, as was the investigation on mammalian myofibrils by H. E. Huxley & Hanson (1957) in which the amounts of actin and myosin in the different striations were first accurately quantified.

It produces interference by an elaborate arrangement of reflecting and semi-reflecting surfaces by which the light is separated into two components, one of which passes through the objects in the visible field and the other forms an evenly distributed 'comparison beam' which passes in the form of a hollow cone well outside the periphery of this field; subsequently these beams reunite. Thus there are no 'ghost' images in the field (p. 93), and phase changes can be measured by comparing the phase changes produced by the object with those produced in an optically homogeneous region of the adjacent background. Objects in the 'comparison beam' well outside the field of view do not in themselves affect the accuracy with which these phase changes can be measured, but the contrast between the object and the background field or fringes drops appreciably if more than about a third of the comparison area is obstructed in this way. Thus, this microscope cannot be used for making measurements in the middle of continuous preparations, such as microscope sections, although such measurements can usually still be made if nearly half the field is covered with such a preparation.

'Fringe field' and 'even field' can be obtained by a simple instrumental adjustment without appreciably disturbing the specimen, and in the latter setting phase changes are measured by operating a wedge plate with a micrometer screw. One cannot derive phase change measurements directly from the graduations on this micrometer screw, however, and it is necessary to calibrate these readings against the number of turns required to measure a phase change of a full wavelength, and express all the measurements as fractions of this. The resolution of the optics is excellent, but there is a lot of light loss at the various reflecting surfaces and this necessitates a powerful light source.

Its chief disadvantage for cytological work lies in the fact that it is rather difficult to set up and adjust, and part of this needs to be done when each preparation is examined. In particular, the fact that the condenser, the wedge plate and the objective have to be covered with films of an immersion oil each time a specimen is mounted increases the hazard of including air bubbles in the optical system, and precious minutes may be lost in examining a rapidly deteriorating living specimen. Nevertheless, the necessary skill and speed can be acquired with practice, and when this is achieved the high qualities of the instrument can be fully appreciated.

5.10.2   Smith interference microscopes

The original Smith interference microscope constructed and described by Smith (1947) has been manufactured and marketed by Vickers Instruments Ltd., Purley Way, Croydon, England (formerly Charles Baker of Holborn Ltd.) since 1954. For many years it was marketed as the 'Baker' interference microscope. A similar instrument differing only in the design of the stand, and using English objectives and condensers made in the Croydon factory, was manufactured under licence after 1953 by the American Optical Co., Buffalo, N.Y., U.S.A. It was marketed under the name of the 'A.O. Baker' interference microscope but since 1963 its production has been discontinued. There are, however, a large number of these instruments in North America. More recently, since 1961, Messrs. Carl Zeiss of Oberkochen, West Germany have marketed an interference microscope developed by Dr. H. Piller (1962) which, although it differs in design from the instrument just described in certain details (since it is intended as an accessory to certain standard Zeiss polarizing microscopes), is essentially the same as the original Smith microscope in its optical principles, and for the purposes of this review it can be regarded as another variant of the Smith interference microscope.

These microscopes produce interference by splitting a beam of plane polarized light with a birefringent crystal below the object plane so that one part of the divided beam is made to pass through an object while the other part passes through an adjacent area. This is the 'shearing' system of optics. As an alternative, a 'double focus' system of optics can be employed in the English and American 'Baker' Smith interference microscopes in which the beams are separated by a differently arranged birefringent crystal, so that one part of the beam passes through the object and the other part is distributed evenly around it, and forms a rather imperfect image on the same optical axis but in a different plane of focus. In both systems the beams are recombined again by a second suitably orientated birefringent crystal above the object plane, which forms a single component with the objective.

With the 'shearing' optics most commonly used with all these instruments, a second 'ghost' image is formed to one side of the principle image in the direction of shear. The separation of these images are identical in the English and American versions of the 'Baker' Smith microscope since identical optical components are employed, but a distinctly greater variation has been achieved in the 'Zeiss' interference microscope. Table 7 (based on measurements made by Galjaard and the present author in 1962) shows the amounts by which the images are separated in the two microscopes with objectives of different power. The increased 'shear' of the Zeiss instrument is a definite advantage, since it means a greater area of cellular material is accessible for quantitative measurements, it has already been pointed out (p. 93) that phase changes through objects in the region of overlap cannot be measured.

TABLE 7

Image separations in interference microscopes using 'shearing' optics
(from Galjaard & Ross, 1962)

	Baker interference microscope	Zeiss interference microscope
Objective × 10	330 μ	546 μ
Objective × 40	160 μ	175 μ
Objective × 75*	83 μ	—
Objective × 100	27 μ	54 μ

* A very recently developed water immersion objective.

The English and American 'Baker' Smith microscopes normally produce only an 'even field' but both can be made to produce a 'fringe field' by means of a special compensator incorporated in an eyepiece which is sold as an accessory. In the 'Zeiss' microscope the production of an 'even field' or a 'fringe field' depends on which of two compensators are used, and these are normally both supplied with the instrument. In all three instruments, phase change measurements in an even field are directly proportional to the rotation of a graduated analyser and, consequently, unlike the Dyson and Horn microscopes, they can be read off the instrument directly. All three instruments are easy to set up and align with a little experience and no elaborate readjustments are necessary when one biological specimen is exchanged for another. Consequently they are especially well suited for use with living cells.

The original English 'Baker' Smith interference microscope has perhaps been used for more published cytological investigations than any other interference microscope, and it is certainly the instrument which the present writer has used most often. Its prototype was used by Mitchison & Swann (1953) to measure the changes in the cytoplasmic refractive index of compressed fertilized sea urchin eggs during their first division. They found similar, but less marked, falls in refractive index during prophase, as the present author found in 1952, in dividing locust spermatocytes (Ross, 1954b). Its principal disadvantage over the other two is that the standard version is not equipped with a rotating stage, although this will be supplied by Vickers Instruments Ltd., with a small mechanically moved slide holder superimposed on it, if specially requested. This addition should be insisted upon by all users who intend to do serious quantitative work because its use enormously increases the area of cellular material accessible for measurement. The 'Patholux' version of this instrument, which is now available, has a rotating mechanical stage as a standard fitting.

The American Smith 'A.O. Baker' interference microscope is essentially the same as the English version, except that the 'shearing' objectives and condensers are differently orientated in the instrument so that the 'ghost' image lies on the opposite side of the principal image. It has a rotating stage. Its only disadvantage is that one of its accessories, a half-shade eyepiece, tends for reasons discussed on pp. 118–120 to produce erroneous phase change measurements, but when the instrument is used alone it is totally free from these errors.

The West German 'Zeiss' microscope, which was tested by Galjaard and the author in 1962, appeared to give rather purer interference colours than the early model of an English 'Baker' with which they compared it and in monochromatic light the adjustment of maximally dark field was definitely more critical, but this comparison may not be generally applicable. No great differences were detected in the quality of the images seen with each instrument, although they were both perhaps slightly inferior to those obtained with comparable objectives in the Dyson microscope. The only disadvantage of the Zeiss microscope is that it does not have any 'half shade' device for the critical measurement of phase changes but in practice it is seldom really necessary to have one.

5.10.3   The Horn interference microscope

The Horn interference microscope, constructed by Horn (1957, 1958, 1959a, b), developed and manufactured by the firm of Ernst Leitz of Wetzlar, West Germany, is a truly magnificent technical achievement, because until recently it was considered to be almost impossible to construct a practical microscope on these lines (see Barer, 1955b). It produces interference on the principle of the Mach–Zehnder interferometer, by splitting a light beam into the components at a semi-reflecting surface and taking these through two entirely separate parallel-mounted sets of objectives before recombining them below a common set of eyepieces. By this arrangement, the 'comparison beam' passes through an entirely uninterrupted field in which a 'dummy' preparation, in the form of a slide and coverslip enclosing a clear mounting medium free from any object, can be placed.* This not only means that there are no 'ghost' images or risk of image overlap, but the interference pattern in the image of the specimen is unaffected by the reference beam, however extensive this preparation is, and therefore measurements can be made right in the middle of extensive sections. The only snag in this seemingly perfect state of affairs is that one still needs a clear 'reference area' in the microscope field to relate one's measurements to; if one makes measurements too far away from such a clear area, local variations in the thickness of the specimens, or in the refractive index or thickness of the mounting medium or glassware, may become important and introduce errors. Consequently, it is still usually necessary to make measurements near to the edges of a section and it is strongly to be recommended that at least some small clear area should be included in the microscope field as a 'reference area'. The solution of the problem, however, may lie in perforating a continuous section with small holes at regular intervals so that one such small clear area can always be included in the field or in making scratches on the microtome block (p. 147). It ought not to be beyond the scope of human ingenuity to devise some means of introducing such perforations into a specimen while it is still on a microtome block before it is sectioned, and the total cellular material lost need only be a very small proportion of the whole. Anyhow, this is the only interference microscope with which large continuous preparations can be studied both qualitatively and quantitatively.

'Fringe field' and 'even field' can be obtained by a simple instrumental adjustment without disturbing the specimen, and phase changes are measured by means of a wedge plate in the comparison beam which is moved by a micrometer screw. Phase change measurements can be derived directly from the graduations of the screw if the mean wavelength of the light being used is known, since these are the same in each instrument (i.e. one division on the drum = a phase change of $4\cdot16°$ in light of wavelength $0\cdot546$ μ; Walter, 1965). One disadvantage of this instrument is that the high degree of craftsmanship involved in its construction is inevitably reflected in its high cost, for this is comparable to that of a medium-resolution electron microscope.

The only major cytological or histological investigation which has so far been carried out with this instrument has been the very interesting study of total solid and polysaccharide material in the intracellular

---

* In the most recent version of this microscope the dummy slide is replaced by an adjustable rotating glass wedge.

matrix of hyaline cartilage undertaken by Galjaard & Szirmai in Leiden in 1959–61 (Galjaard, 1963; Galjaard & Szirmai, 1965). These authors always had a clear area in their microscope field as a 'reference area' and by taking consecutive photomicrographs of each specimen in 'fringe field' or 'even field', they evolved a very elegant and accurate densitometric method of estimating phase changes (see Chapter 8).

5.10.4   The Françon–Johansson interference microscope

As the present author has never actually seen one of these instruments, his remarks cannot be considered to be as authoritative as in the case of the other instruments and therefore will be kept brief. This microscope was being marketed around about 1958 by the Svenska Ackumulator Aktiebolaget Jugner, Stockholm, Sweden; but it appears that very few instruments were actually made, and it is doubtful if any exist outside Scandinavia. It was derived from an interference eyepiece devised by Françon (1952, 1956) which employs a Savart plate, an arrangement of two identical uniaxial birefringent crystals cut at 45° to their axes and crossed with respect to each other. Johansson & Afzelius (1956) introduced a compensator below this system enabling phase changes to be measured; this consisted of a rotating wedge by which the angle at which the light strikes the Savart plate is altered, and a hole in this wedge provides a reference area (see Johansson, 1957). It is essentially a 'shearing' system, and pairs of equally sharply-focused images are formed alongside each other in opposite contrast (which in white light exhibit opposite colour shifts), so that it is entirely a matter of arbitrary choice which image is regarded as the 'ghost' image. This has one advantage in that phase change measurements can be made by rotating the wedge plate in opposite directions to measure the phase change produced by each image in turn, and the results can be averaged. It is also possible to measure phase changes in white light by matching the colour of the object to that of the clear field viewed through the hole.

The disadvantages of the system would seem to be: firstly, it requires a slit illumination which impairs resolution of the image in the plane at right angles to the slit, and it is possible that lenticular cellular objects may defocus the image of the slit (p. 24); secondly, the accuracy of phase change measurement is dependent on the accuracy with which the rotating wedge can be made. An advantage shared by certain of the Normarski-type interference microscopes described below lies in the fact that, because interference is produced in the vicinity of the eyepiece, it can therefore be used with most standard objectives and condensers.

5.10.5 Normarski interference microscopes

Normarski (1955) described a form of 'shearing' double-refracting interference microscope, in which interference was produced by polarized light being divided and recombined with a Wollaston prism; and, although he was by no means the only originator of systems of this kind (see Huxley (1952, 1954) and Smith (1947, 1955)), he developed an additional system by which a Wollaston prism could be tilted to give varying amounts of 'shear' between the images. This enabled both image doubling and the very useful 'differential' interference microscopy to be obtained in the same instrument; no less than four different microscope firms are now manufacturing or are about to manufacture instruments embodying these principles. These are the P.Z.O. polarizing interference microscope M.P.I.5 developed by Professor M. Pluta and manufactured by the Polski Zaklady Optyczne, Warsaw, Poland; the 'Interphako' microscope developed and described by Dr. H. Beyer (1966) and manufactured by Messrs. Carl Zeiss, Jena, East Germany; an instrument developed by Dr. H. Piller manufactured by Messrs. Zeiss of Oberkochen, West Germany; and an instrument soon to be manufactured by Messrs. Reichert in Vienna, Austria.* No details are available to the present writer about the last instrument (except that it will take the form of accessory equipment to a standard Reichert polarizing microscope), and his experience with the others is of the limited kind gained at exhibition stands which precludes the considered objective judgments which familiarity alone can provide. The Polish and East German instruments resemble the original instrument described by Normarski (1955) in that they employ slit illumination. Consequently, it might be expected that this will inevitably result in some loss of resolution, although in the East German Zeiss instrument this slit can be replaced by diffraction gratings which permit the use of the full condenser numerical aperture with monochromatic light of certain wavelengths. Both are very versatile instruments capable of giving 'fringe fields' and 'even fields' with both the image doubling and 'differential' contrast imparted by the variability of shear. In the West German Zeiss interference microscope a Wollaston prism below the object plane enables the slit illumination to be dispensed with, and the full numerical aperture of the condenser can be employed for 'differential' interference microscopy. It was with the prototype of this instrument that Professor R. D. Allen and his associates in Princeton, U.S.A.

* The author has been informed that the American Optical Co. has just taken over Messrs. Reichert, and that it is now uncertain whether this interference microscope will be marketed or not.

achieved their notable practical and theoretical investigations described on p. 94.

5.11   Optical accessories designed to increase the accuracy of visual phase change measurements

It is usually possible to measure the phase changes through most cellular regions to an accuracy of one-fiftieth of a wavelength by the 'extinction point' or 'extinction transfer' method or by using the 'minimum visibility' method, but both methods are limited by the difficulty which an observer has in estimating the instrumental setting at which the background field or the object appears maximally dark; they tend to give especially big errors when small microscopic objects are measured (Chapter 8, pp. 184, 187). Consequently, for certain purposes accessory equipment designed to increase the accuracy of phase change measurement may be needed. Hale (1958) has found a photometer eyepiece helpful in gauging the instrumental setting which will give a maximally dark field, but this cannot be used to make a similar estimation of the maximally dark intensity of a small object in the field. The best way of doing this visually is by introducing into the field an area of known intensity with which the intensity of the background and the object can be matched in turn. Three such intensity-matching devices have been manufactured for use with three of the commercially available interference microscopes. These are, the Smith half-shade eyepiece manufactured as an accessory for the English Smith ('Baker') interference microscope made by Vicker's Instruments Ltd., Croydon, England; the Koester half-shade eyepiece manufactured as an accessory for the American Smith 'A.O. Baker' interference microscope, made until recently by the American Optical Co., Buffalo, N.Y., U.S.A.; and the Payne photometer-eyepiece manufactured for the Dyson interference microscope which was until lately made by Vicker's Instruments Ltd., York, England.*

* Messrs. Carl Zeiss of Jena, East Germany, are developing a fourth half-shade matching device for their 'Interphako' (Normarski-type) interference microscope. No details of its construction appear to have been published so far, but from the illustration (bild 8) in the instruction manual *Interphako Nf für durlicht* it would seem that the microscope field will be divided into two halves out of phase with each other by a fixed amount in much the same way as in the Koester half-shade eyepiece described on p. 120. If so, it is difficult to see how it can avoid sharing the latter's disadvantages; it would appear as if, for reasons discussed at greater length in Chapter 8, visual measurements made with it on small microscopic objects could be subject to very appreciable systematic errors.

5.11.1 The Smith half-shade eyepiece

The Smith half-shade eyepiece, one of two described by Smith (1954) is still being marketed and merits a detailed description. It is used in place of the ordinary monocular or binocular head on the English Smith interference microscope, and on favourable (non-biological) specimens an accuracy of 1/200 of a wavelength has been claimed for it. Its optical principles are illustrated in Fig. 24A. Light passing up the body tube of the microscope passes into the glass prism illustrated and impinges on the surface aa'. This is a glass/air surface which is placed at such an

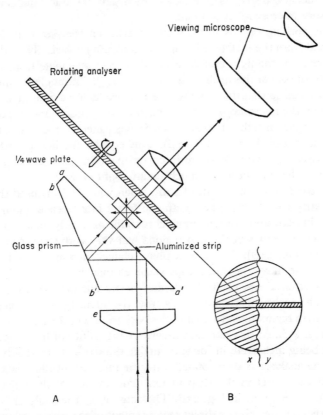

Fig. 24 A—The optical principles of the Smith half-shade eyepiece, an accessory to the Smith interference microscope. Redrawn from a sketch by Mr. F. H. Smith and reproduced with his permission.

B—The appearance of an empty field through the eyepiece in monochromatic light at two typical settings of the analyser: x, with the analyser set to give a dark background field and a bright strip image; y, with the analyser set so as to give a bright background field and a dark strip image.

angle to the incident light that this is all totally internally reflected. Not all the surface of the back of prism aa' is, however, of plain glass. There is a specially treated region in the plane of the primary image, formed by the field lens e below the prism, in the form of a narrow horizontal strip on which metallic aluminium has been deposited. The light is internally reflected from this region also, and then all of it is reflected from the surface bb' and passes out of the prism through a quarter-wave plate and rotating paroloid analyser similar to those in an ordinary Smith interference microscope. The primary image, formed in the plane of the metallized strip, is then viewed by means of the additional inclined accessory microscope illustrated.

The working of this instrument depends on the fact that the light reflected from the metallized strip is (elliptically) polarized in a different manner from the light that is reflected at the same angle from the unmetallized part of the surface aa' (Smith, 1954). The angles of the prism are arranged so that this has the effect of producing a final image of the object on the microscope stage in which there appears superimposed, an image of the metallized strip which is permanently 120° out of phase with the rest of the field, Fig. 24B. This enables the image of the strip to be used as a very sensitive intensity-matching device when monochromatic light or nearly monochromatic light is used.

Because of the phase shift of 120°, when white light is used the half-shade strip will always appear with a different interference colour to that of the background; but in monochromatic or nearly monochromatic light the intensities of the two regions will vary with the setting of the analyser (Fig. 24B). To make a phase change measurement it is first necessary to move the microscope stage, so that the image of the object being measured lies partly inside and partly outside the image of the strip. The analyser is then rotated so that the intensity of the background in the strip region matches that of the background in the rest of the field, as in Fig. 25A. At this setting, the relative intensities of the image of the object being measured, inside and outside the strip, are markedly different. The analyser is then rotated until the intensity of the image of the part of the object in the strip region matches that of the object lying outside the strip, as in Fig. 25B. The rotation of the analyser between these two settings gives a direct measurement of the phase change given by the object; as these two settings can be obtained with great precision, phase change measurements accurate to 1/120th of a wavelength can frequently be obtained if the area of the object being measured is fairly large.

However, with small objects a systematic error is introduced in a rather curious manner, because when the images of such objects are less wide or not very much wider than the strip itself, the very different intensity of the adjacent regions of the strip will mislead the eye in its assessment of the match of the object at the second position of the analyser described above. This effect is fully described and evaluated in

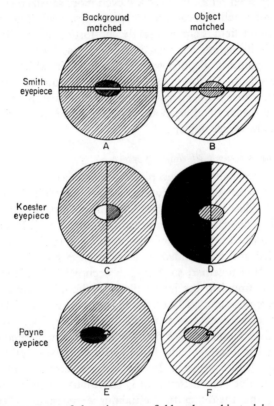

Fig. 25 The appearances of the microscope field and an object giving a uniform phase change in this field when phase change measurements are made with each of the three commercially available eyepieces, employing an intensity-matching device to increase the accuracy of measurement. The matching areas depicted are correctly to scale with the total areas of their respective fields.

Chap. 8 (pp. 180–192). When the half-shade eyepiece is used to measure small cellular details, there is a tendency to turn the analyser too far, so that when the image of the object appears matched inside and outside the strip, the part inside is actually darker. This means that a systematic high error in phase change measurement is being made. The device is therefore not satisfactory for measuring phase changes or small objects as it is at present designed, but the remedy is quite simple. The aluminized surface can be carefully removed at one end so that the image of the strip does not cross the whole field. The end of the strip will then form a much more satisfactory comparison area. If a few small 'islands' of aluminized surface are left behind in a region from which the rest of the strip has been removed these are even more satisfactory as comparison areas for small objects, see Chapter 8 (p. 189). The width of the strip seen in the field is almost exactly one-fortieth of the diameter of the field, and if its length were made the same as its width it would be excellent for almost all purposes. Experiments in which this was done are described in Chapter 8. In general it can be said that this subjective error is reduced by having the comparison area as small as possible, and such small areas are just as good for measuring the phase changes of the larger objects.

5.11.2   The Koester half-shade eyepiece

The Koester half-shade eyepiece designed for use with the Smith interference microscope manufactured in the United States by the American Optical Company (the 'A.O. Baker' interference microscope) has been fully described by its inventor (Koester, 1959). It is a simple and ingenious device in the form of a biquartz plate made of two sections of right-handed and left-handed quartz cut perpendicular to the optical axis and butted together, so that each occupies half of the microscope field, and mounted in the image plane of the microscope between the quarter wave plate and analyser. The plate is of such a thickness that the image in the two halves of the field illustrated in Fig. 25C and D are permanently 20° out of phase with each other. The method of operation is illustrated in Fig. 25C and D with the same two settings as for the Smith half-shade eyepiece. Its great disadvantage will be at once appreciated. The comparison area is enormous, since it consists of half the field, so that the difficulty of obtaining a true match when measuring small objects, just discussed in the case of the Smith half-shade eyepiece, is present to a marked degree. Indeed, even with quite large objects it may be difficult to avoid being misled by the differing intensities of the adjacent background regions. In Fig. 25D the object being measured is actually of the same intensity in both halves of the field; but the half in the left-hand section appears brighter than the half in the right-hand section because of the surrounding dark background field. The remedy is to use an eyepiece diaphragm to reduce the size of the field to less than that of the object when the second analyser setting is being determined, but this is not very practicable for very small objects. The Smith and the Koester eyepieces are only suitable for use with the Smith interference microscopes, but both can be adapted to fit the British or American instruments.

5.11.3 The Payne eyepiece-photometer

The Payne eyepiece-photometer was designed for use with the Dyson interference microscope but could easily be adapted for use with any interference microscope. It is described and discussed more fully by Hale (1958) and by Davies (1958) and in the instruction manual of the Dyson interference microscope. In the image plane there is an inclined glass surface on which is a small semi-circular fully reflecting area which is illuminated separately by a system of mirrors from the light source which can be varied in intensity by means of two polaroids. This is the comparison area, which is set at a suitable fixed intensity for making a measurement, and matched successively to the background and the object as before. This comparison area is the smallest in any of the devices so far described, being only one-fifteenth of the diameter of the field in length and one-thirtieth in width (see Fig. 25E, F), which means that the matching of small objects is much less liable to systematic errors of the kind described above. The variability of its intensity also enables random errors of measurement to be reduced to a minimum. Ten successive measurements on a single specimen of *Lactobacillus bulgaricus* made by the present writer in 1959 showed a maximum variation of one-fortieth of a wavelength, and in nine of these the variation was less than one-fiftieth of a wavelength. This compares favourably with similar successive measurements made on bacilli with the Smith half-shade eyepiece, which showed a maximum variation of one-thirtyfifth of a wavelength (Ross, 1957a and b). For these reasons the present writer regards the Payne eyepiece-photometer as the best of the three devices to increase the accuracy of phase change measurements as they are at present designed, in spite of being rather troublesome to set up and align initially. It could also easily be modified as a colour-matching device by the insertion of a compensator between the two polaroids (Smith, 1959), although in its present form it can only be used with monochromatic or nearly monochromatic light.

5.11.4 Extremely accurate measurement of phase changes by phase modulated light methods

A brief mention should be made here of a method of measuring phase changes with extreme accuracy that does not rely on visual or photometric comparison of image and background intensities (see Chapter 8), which has been developed independently by Professor R. D. Allen and his associates in Princeton, U.S.A. (Allen, Brault & Moore, 1963; Allen, Brault & Zeh, 1966; Allen & David, 1966) and by Professor J. Dyson in Teddington, England (Dyson, 1966). This depends on the fact that the birefringence of certain crystals, notably that of ammonium dihydrogen phosphate, undergoes small fluctuations when placed in an alternating current. If such crystals are used in a double-refracting interference microscope as additional compensators, they can be made to detect, within very fine limits, the instrumental setting (represented by maximum darkness in the background or the specimen) at which the fundamental disappears and only the second harmonic is left. Any departure from this setting can be made to give a detectable signal. By this means it is claimed that phase changes of as little as 1/50,000 of a wavelength can be measured without difficulty.

At present it would seem as if this fantastic accuracy is of little use for most cytological investigations, since not only is the variability in cellular material enormously in excess of this, but the accuracy obtainable in the measurement of thickness in visible light, and not the accuracy of phase change measurements, is nearly always the limiting factor in determining the accuracy of values obtained from phase change and thickness measurements (pp. 161–3). It might, however, be profitably applied to the determination of the measurement of the thickness of objects of known refractive index along the lines described in Chapter 8, pp. 180–197. No doubt other possible applications of this extremely elegant, albeit most costly and elaborate, method will become apparent in due course.

6

Quantitative Interference Microscopy in Cytology

1: Measurements on whole living cells or portions of living cells, and on cells in histological sections

6.1 The scope of interference microscopy in cytological studies

The fact that phase changes are capable of being measured with interference microscopes makes them extremely effective and versatile instruments in obtaining a great deal of varied quantitative information about cells. This can be obtained by a great variety of different approaches, some relatively simple and direct, some distinctly more lengthy and some rather tortuous and cumbersome.

Broadly speaking, the cellular data obtainable fall into three categories. Firstly, as with phase contrast microscopy when immersion refractometry is employed, refractive indices and hence cellular solid concentrations can be measured; however, in addition to the cytoplasm being measurable as with phase contrast, with interference microscopy the refractive indices of cell inclusions can also be measured. The implications of this capability are many and varied (Chapter 7). Secondly, values for the dry mass of cells mounted in water and of some of their constituents can be obtained directly (see p. 124) and values for the dry mass of cellular inclusions can be derived from the refractive indices and volumes (Chapter 7, p. 170). Finally, it enables thicknesses to be measured in a manner which overcomes some of the difficulties inherent in the direct linear measurement of objects in a microscope field (Chapter 8). To obtain these data a great number of different methods have been employed, and even more have been suggested, by various

II

authorities. It often happens that a number of different approaches can in fact be used to achieve the same end, but, in the opinon of the writer, some are definitely better than others. Therefore, since one of the main aims of the book is to present these techniques in as straightforward a way as possible to those unfamiliar with this field, and to dispel some of the esoteric aura which has grown around the subject (and which has un-doubtedly deterred many biologists from using those instruments at all), some selection seems necessary. Consequently, particular emphasis will be placed on the more simple and direct approaches which have been tried by this author and others and have proved their worth practically; only a limited number of the very numerous methods and formulae which have been proposed by various authors from time to time for working out the required values will be discussed here. A wealth of alternative methods, many of which are excellent, are to be found in the works of Barer (1956b), Barer & Dick (1957), Davies (1958) and Hale (1958). With the methods and approaches which are discussed in detail below all the necessary data about the dry mass, refractive index and thickness of cells and their constituents can be obtained by methods which are practically efficacious and not too involved.

6.2   The direct measurement of dry mass from single phase change measurements

The most striking way in which phase change measurements can be used to obtain quantitative cytological data is derived from the fact that the phase changes through an object mounted in water is directly pro-portional to its dry mass per unit area. Thus, if a cell is mounted in water (or a medium such as isotonic saline which has a refractive index which is, for this purpose, negligibly greater than that of water) a value for this cell's dry mass, m, in grams, can be calculated from the equation:

$$m = \frac{\phi w \times A \times \lambda}{100\alpha} \tag{6}$$

where ϕw is the mean phase change given by the cell in water in fractions of a wavelength, A is the area of the cell in sq cm, λ is the wavelength of light used, expressed in cm, and α is the mean specific refraction incre-ment of the cell's contents which, in living cells, can in nearly every case be assumed as being equivalent to 0·0018 (see Chapter 1). In this and nearly all the subsequent equations given in the book the phase change ϕ is expressed in wavelengths or fractions of a wavelength and these values can either be +ve in the case of phase retardations or −ve in the case of phase advances (see eqn. 11, p. 135). It is, however, often more convenient to express phase changes in degrees since the Smith interference microscopes, for example, measure these directly. In this case $\phi/360$ must be substituted for ϕ in this and the subsequent equations (eqns. 7–14, 16 and 17).

The implications of the fundamental fact that phase changes measured in water are proportional to dry mass multiplied by area are far reaching. It means that the phase retardations measured through any region of a cell mounted in water are directly related to the actual amount of material other than water in that particular region. Thus, simply measuring the phase changes in the light passing through different regions of the cell will provide an indication of the distribution of the dry masses of the materials lying within it. In 1952–3 Davies & La Cour, for example, by taking a succession of interference photomicrographs at different instrumental settings of a staminal hair of *Tradescantia* and subjecting them to densitometric analysis, were able to make a linear plot along the axis of the hair recording the variations in dry mass across the two terminal cells. The regions of the cellulose walls gave quite large phase retardations and therefore had a fairly high dry mass. The vacuoles gave low phase retardations which indicated a low dry mass in the regions. The chromosomes in the dividing nuclei gave the highest retardation of all and the spindle gave an intermediate value (Davies, Wilkins, Chayen & La Cour, 1954).

This direct approach, measuring dry mass per unit area directly from phase change measurements, was the one employed by almost all the earlier users of interference microscopes in investigations of cytological problems. Davies, Wilkins, Chayen & La Cour employed it in the wide variety of problems which they tackled when they first established the potentialities of interference microscopy for such work, which they reported in their classical paper in 1954 (see above). Davies used it again in his collaboration with Engström & Lindström when they established, by their concurrent measurements on preselected regions of a variety of different mammalian cells, that there was a close correspondence between the values for the dry mass of the material in each region obtained by interference microscopy and by the absorption of x-rays (Davies, Engström & Lindström, 1953). H. E. Huxley & Hanson (1957) used the same approach in evaluating the dry mass of actin and myosin in mammalian myofibrils before and after myosin extraction, and Davies, Barter & Danielli (1954) used it to evaluate alkaline phosphatase activity in the brush borders of cells of mammalian kidney and duodenum by measuring the dry mass of a transparent end-product (calcium phosphate) after various time intervals. These are only a few of the most notable of the cytological investigations that were carried out by quantitative interference microscopy employing this particular approach and a number of others in which values for the dry mass of cells of cellular constituents were also derived directly from phase change measurements made on them in water, are reviewed by Davies (1958).

However, in spite of its directness and theoretical elegance, this approach has some serious disadvantages, and is not by any means always the most fruitful one in yielding quantitative cytological data of interest to the biologist. Its main disadvantages are apparent when this approach is used for measurements on living cells and these are twofold. Firstly, because such cells are by their nature normally very heterogeneous in structure and usually contain a large number of inclusions with varying refractile properties, it is often difficult to obtain values for the dry mass of a whole cell by this method even though its whole area may be determined quite easily. All the individual phase changes caused by each of these different regions and all their individual areas need to be measured, and their individual dry masses worked out and summated, before the dry mass of the whole cell can be arrived at. This may be very laborious. It is true that this can be achieved much more quickly by special integrating devices (p. xviii) but these are extremely complex and costly to construct and the designs at present published are not entirely satisfactory.* Secondly, although at first sight it would seem as if the dry masses of individual optically homogeneous cell regions such as living cell inclusions could be measured in this way, this is seldom possible in practice since the phase changes measured through such an inclusion are not of phase changes caused by the inclusion alone but by the overlying and underlying cytoplasm as well (Fig. 26A, p. 150), and the exact thickness and refractive index of these layers are often very difficult to determine and allow for. The direct approach is, however, more satisfactory in obtaining measurements of the dry mass of such individual inclusions and other recognizable cellular constituents in fixed sections since, if these are thin, one can often justifiably assume that each recognizable cellular region occupies the whole thickness of the section. But even here care needs to be taken to ensure that the dry mass of the material in the particular region being measured is unaffected by fixation and also that it is insoluble in water and does not diffuse away (see Danielli, 1958).

---

* Except for those of Smith (1966b, 1967) and Lomakka (1965); see Introduction, p. xviii.

The directness and seeming ease with which values for the dry mass of cellular material can be arrived at by phase change measurement with the interference microscope has had one rather unfortunate effect in that it has, to some extent, led to the neglect of the capabilities of the interference microscope in measuring other quantities of equal biological interest. The refractive index of a cell or part of a cell, for instance, is just as interesting to a cytologist but can often be even more informative, since it not only indicates the degree of hydration of different parts of its contents but can provide a clue to many other of its properties as well (see Chapter 7) and the refractive indices of regular-shaped cellular objects can be derived from phase change measurements almost as easily as values for dry mass.

6.3 Measurement of the refractive index and thickness of living cells in non-matching media, from single phase change measurements

Since the phase change in the light passing through an object is proportional to the product of the refractive index of the object relative to that of its surrounding medium and its thickness, this means that, if its thickness is known, the refractive index of an object surrounded by a medium of a different refractive index can be measured. This is given by the equation

$$n_o = \phi \times \frac{\lambda}{t} + n_m \qquad (7)$$

where n_o = the refractive index of the object, n_m = the refractive index of the mounting medium, ϕ = the phase change (+ve or −ve) in the light passing through the object, expressed as a fraction of a wavelength, λ = the wavelength of light used (most conveniently expressed in μ), and t = the thickness of the object in the direction of the optical axis of the microscope (in μ).

This means that objects with refractive indices too high for them to be measured easily by immersion refractometry, e.g. living cells with refractive indices higher than the most concentrated protein solution obtainable, and also objects that cannot be surrounded by a medium with the same refractive indices as they have, such as cytoplasmic inclusions in living cells, can be measured by these means. Similarly, the thickness t, of an object of known refractive index can be measured by applying the equation:

$$t = \phi \times \frac{\lambda}{n_o - n_m} \tag{8}$$

the symbols being the same as in eqn. 7.

The refractive index values measured by this approach are not as accurate as those which can be measured by immersion refractometry in matching media, because this accuracy is limited by the accuracy with which it is possible to measure t, the thickness of the cell or part of a cell in the direction of the optical axis of the microscope. The accuracy with which such thicknesses can be measured is discussed in some detail in Chapter 7 (pp. 162, 163) and in Chapter 8 (pp. 193–197). Because of this, this approach cannot normally be recommended for measuring refractive indices of cellular materials that are accessible for measurement by immersion refractometry. It has one advantage, however, in that any errors that may arise from the incorrect adjustment of the tonicity of saline/protein immersion media are absent.

6.4   Barer's 'double immersion' method of measuring the refractive index and thickness of living cells

If an object is capable of being immersed successively in two media of different refractive indices and neither its thickness nor its refractive index is known, both can be obtained by an ingenious 'double immersion' method devised by Professor Barer and used by him for measuring the refractive indices and thicknesses of human mouth epithelial cells in 1953. The object is immersed successively in two media of known refractive index, and the phase change in the light passing through it is measured in each. The refractive index of the object n_o can then be calculated from the equation:

$$n_o = \frac{\phi_1 n_{m2} - \phi_2 n_{m1}}{\phi_1 - \phi_2} \tag{9}$$

where n_{m1} = the refractive index of the mounting medium with the lower refractive index; n_{m2} = the refractive index of the mounting medium with the higher refractive index; ϕ_1 = the phase change (e.g. in wavelengths) given by the object mounted in the medium of lower refractive index (n_{m1}) and ϕ_2 = the phase change (e.g. in wavelengths) given by the object mounted in the medium of higher refractive index (n_{m2}).

The thickness of the object, t, in μ, is given by the equation

$$t = \frac{\phi_1 - \phi_2}{n_{m2} - n_{m1}} \times \lambda \tag{10}$$

where λ = the wavelength of light used, in μ, and the other symbols are as in eqn. 9. (In Barer's original paper (Barer, 1953b) the function $\times \lambda$ was omitted from eqn. 10 but this was evidently simply a slip which in no way invalidates the method. It is, however, worth drawing attention to since the same unaltered equation is given by Goldstein (1965). Eqn. 10, given here, is the correct one.)

In practice, it is often extremely difficult to observe the same cell successively in two different mounting media, as it is usually washed out of the field when the medium is being replaced. Even cells such as amoebocytes, that can adhere to glass surfaces, often undergo local changes in thickness while this is happening so that the method is usually impracticable for single cells unless they are slightly compressed to a constant thickness in a cell compressor. This was certainly the experience of Barer & Dick (1957) who made successive measurements, in saline and a 5% isotonic solution of acacia gum, at selected points in the cytoplasm of chick fibroblasts which had been grown in tissue culture and which were extended and adhering to a glass surface. Although every possible precaution was taken, and the cells were irrigated with the new medium in an irrigation chamber which had been specially designed by Dick (1955) so that the cells should be disturbed as little as possible while the medium was being replaced, the difficulties of avoiding all disturbance to these cells proved very formidable and in many cases the irrigation itself was thought to have produced local variations in the thickness of the regions under observation which induced errors in the results. The mean of the refractive index measurements obtained with the method corresponded quite closely with the cytoplasmic refractive indices measured by matching immersion refractometry, but individually they showed departures from it of up to ± 0.008 or 4.5% of solids. Barer & Dick concluded that matching immersion refractometry was considerably more accurate for measuring the refractive indices of these regions. If local variations in thickness account for all the errors, it would certainly appear as if these difficulties could be circumvented if cells are first compressed to a constant thickness in a cell compressor and then irrigated with the second immersion medium; but equally satisfactory measurements of refractive index and thickness can be obtained from measurements of such compressed cells mounted in a single immersion medium by using Ambrose's and Klug & Walker's 'bubble' method (p. 134) and so there is no point in doing this.

Even though it may be rather inaccurate for measurements on single living cells, however, Barer's 'double immersion' method is the only satisfactory way of measuring the thicknesses of individual uncompressed living cells in vitro, and the values for the thicknesses of different parts of the cytoplasm of living chick fibroblasts published by Barer & Dick (1957), which ranged from rather less than $0.5\,\mu$ in the thinnest pseudopodia to nearly $2.5\,\mu$ in the immediate vicinity of their nuclei, provide a valuable indication of the miminum and maximum vatical depth of the material in these well-extended adhering cells grown in tissue culture. These data can be of great value in assessing whether every region of such cells are likely to lie within the depth of focus of a particular microscope objective, and this in its turn can be of considerable importance in evaluating the densitometry of photomicrographs of similarly extended cells (see Ross & Jans, in preparation). This method of measuring cell depth is more reliable than any method which relies on focusing the upper and lower surfaces of an object successively by turning and measuring the movement of the fine adjustment of the microscope, for although this focusing method is in extremely common use, Galbraith (1955), in a paper which is less well known than it deserves to be, was able to demonstrate that it was open to so many objections and difficulties that it is to all practical intents and purposes valueless (see also Richards, 1959).

Although the double immersion method is subject to inaccuracies when applied to single cells, it can, however, more satisfactorily be applied to cell populations when the cells themselves are sufficiently optically homogeneous, e.g. many bacteria and bacterial spores, by measuring the phase changes in a selected number of different cells in each medium and obtaining values for mean phase change in each case. Provided that the individual variations of cell thickness and refractive index are not very great, and that there is no marked correlation between the two, the values for the mean thickness and mean refractive index of the population obtained in this way can be both accurate and meaningful. This was the approach used by Ross & Billing (1957) when they established the high solid content of resting bacterial spores. This work deserves to be discussed in some detail since it provides a good illustration of the use of this method on cell populations and the conditions (outlined above) that are necessary for its use.

Some small cells and organisms, notably the spores of many fungi and bacteria, have refractive indices too high to be measured by direct matching immersion refractometry with the immersion media usually employed. Bovine plasma albumin, for example, will not dissolve to form solutions of a higher concentration than about 55% w/v with a refractive index of 1.433; concentrations as high as this are made only with difficulty (Barer & Joseph, 1955a). Consequently spores of this kind always give retardations in phase when placed in any available concentration of the mounting medium, and the only way in which it is possible to find their refractive indices is by Barer's 'double immersion' method.

Table 8 shows the mean of the phase change measurements obtained on 10 different spores of each of the three species of bacteria in water and in concentrated protein solutions, and the values for their mean refractive indices derived from their data from eqn. 9 (p. 128).

TABLE 8

The mean phase retardations (in degrees) of light of wavelength 542 mμ passing through bacterial spores of three different species in water and in concentrated protein solutions and their mean thickness and refractive indices calculated from these values

Organism	B. cereus		B. cereus var. mycoides		B. megaterium	
	Expt. 1	Expt. 2	Expt. 1	Expt. 2	Expt. 1	Expt. 2
Refractive index of protein medium (n_{m2})	1·3926	1·3960	1·3925	1·4000	1·3925	1·3880
Mean retardation in water (degrees) (ϕ_1) from 10 measurements on different spores	126·8	132·8	123·6	124·6	134·0	130·2
Mean retardation in protein (degrees) (ϕ_2) from 10 measurements on different spores	84·8	87·4	86·4	79·4	95·0	96·0
Mean thickness in μ (t)	1·08	1·11	0·96	1·02	1·00	0·93
Mean refractive index (n_o)	1·512	1·513	1·528	1·519	1·537	1·545

Before any firm conclusions could be drawn from these results regarding the water and solid content of the spores, however, it was first necessary to establish that conclusions about the refractive indices of the spores based on mean phase change measurements obtained in this way were, in fact, justified. This might not be so if a spore population showed great variability in thickness or refractive index or if, for example, the refractive index and thickness of the spores were in some way correlated; for if this was so, and if (as was likely) the two samples selected had included different proportions of spores of each size-range, a false value for the mean refractive index of the sample could result. This was done in the case of *Bacillus cereus* by measuring the phase changes in light passing through 10 individual spores mounted in water and at the same time estimating their widths as closely as possible by linear measurement with an eyepiece micrometer scale. Values for their refractive indices were obtained from these measurements by eqn. 7 on p. 127. This method was not very accurate, since its accuracy is in fact limited by the accuracy with which it is possible to measure thicknesses by direct linear measurement (see Chapter 7, pp. 162–3) and for reasons discussed in Chapter 8 (pp. 180–197) it is generally considered that such linear measurements made in visible light are unlikely to be more accurate than to ± 0·2 μ. Consequently this error in thickness measurement was used to calculate values for the upper and lower limits of the refractive index of each spore also.

TABLE 9

Individual measurements of the maximum width and retardation in degrees of light of wavelength 542 mμ passing through 10 individual spores of *B. cereus* mounted in water, and the refractive indices of the spores calculated therefrom

Spore no.	Width (to the nearest 0·2 μ.) measured by micrometer eyepiece	Retardation through spore in water (degrees)	Refractive index of spore	Range of refractive index of spore assuming a maximum error in width (t) measurement of ± 0·2 μ
	(t)	(ϕ_1)	(n_s)	
I	0·9 μ	96	1·495	1·466–1·542
2	0·9 μ	114	1·524	1·490–1·579
3	0·9 μ	112	1·521	1·488–1·576
4	1·1 μ	128	1·509	1·482–1·549
5	1·1 μ	120	1·490	1·474–1·534
6	1·1 μ	124	1·504	1·478–1·541
7	1·1 μ	126	1·507	1·480–1·544
8	1·1 μ	134	1·519	1·490–1·558
9	1·3 μ	150	1·510	1·485–1·539
10	1·5 μ	176	1·511	1·490–1·538

(Range of refractive index of vegetative cells of *B. cereus*   1·384–1·388)

From these results, shown in Table 9, two clear conclusions could be drawn in spite of the relative inaccuracy of the method. Firstly, the individual refractive indices of both the larger and smaller spores (whose diameter varied from 0·9–1·5 μ) were very similar; secondly, the two values for the mean refractive indices and thicknesses of *B. cereus* obtained by the 'double immersion' method lay well within the range of refractive indices and the measured thicknesses obtained for the individual spores. Therefore, this appeared to confirm that the mean refractive index values obtained by Barer's double immersion method were valid and could be taken as providing a reliable indication of the degree of hydration of the spores.

Table 10 shows the results of measuring the mean refractive indices of the spores of *Bacillus cereus*, *B. cereus*, var. *mycoides* and *B. megaterium*, compared to the refractive indices of the vegetative cells of the same organisms obtained by direct immersion refractometry; also their respective solid contents and water contents derived from eqns. 2 and 3 (pp. 35 and 36), assuming that they consist predominantly of proteins with a refraction increment of 0·0018, and with a specific volume of 0·75 ml/g (p. 36). It is immediately clear that the water content of the spores is very much less than that of the vegetative cells, and is comparable to that found in seemingly dried protein products such as leather, wool and dried casein. This is of particular interest in the light of Davies' confirmation (1958) that the refraction increment of highly concentrated crystalline proteins is the same as dilute solutions, 0·0018, for it probably means that both the spores and the dried protein products tabulated here must contain appreciable amounts of 'bound water'.*

TABLE 10

The water and solid content of bacterial vegetative cells and spores derived from refractive index measurements (assuming $\alpha = 0·0018$)

Material		Mean refractive index	Mean solid content (in g/100 ml)	Mean water content (in g/100 ml)
Vegetative cells				
B. cereus		1·386	29·0	78·0
B. cereus var. mycoides		1·400	36·5	72·5
B. megaterium		1·388	30·0	77·5
Spores				
B. cereus	Experiment 1	1·512	99·0	26·0
	Experiment 2	1·513	99·5	25·5
B. cereus var. mycoides	Experiment 1	1·528	108·0	18·0
	Experiment 2	1·519	102·5	23·0
B. megaterium	Experiment 1	1·527	113·0	15·0
	Experiment 2	1·540	114·5	14·0
Leather		1·530[a]	109·0	18·0
Wool		1·540[a]	114·5	14·0
Dried casein		1·540[a]	114·5	14·0

[a] Chamot & Mason (1938)

* But see the footnote on p. 7.

It may seem strange that it required interference microscopy to establish that bacterial spores had far less water in them than the corresponding bacterial vegetative cells. This could have been inferred by any microscopist who compared these images under a phase contrast microscope, since, if an ordinary $90°$ +ve phase contrast objective is used, most bacterial vegetative cells appear more or less uniformly dark, whereas the spores derived from them usually have appreciably smaller diameters than the vegetative cells, and their middle regions appear bright. This indicates that they have a much higher refractive index (see Chapter 2, p. 16).

One further observation needs to be made when discussing the application of Barer's 'double immersion' method for measuring small microscopic objects such as bacteria: this is that the accuracy of the results obtainable with it obviously depends on both sets of phase change measurements, those in the medium of low refractive index, ϕ_1, and those in the medium of higher refractive index, ϕ_2, being strictly comparable. This may not always be true when visual methods are used to measure rather small phase changes through small objects and if a systematic error occurs which is different in each of the two media, the results will, of course, be invalidated. An instance in which this probably happened, when an unmodified Smith half-shade eyepiece was used to measure the very small phase changes caused by bacterial vegetative cells mounted in water and in protein media, is discussed in Chapter 8 (p. 187). In the case of the bacterial spores cited above the phase changes in both instances were probably large enough for the systematic errors, if they occurred, to have been nearly the same in both mounting media. In conclusion, it is probably justifiable to say that the double immersion method can be very valuable, but it is desirable to have some independent means of checking its validity in any particular instance. In addition to its use in studying living cells, Goldstein (1965) has employed it extremely profitably for measuring cellular materials in fixed sections (p. 147).

6.5   Ambrose's and Klug & Walker's 'bubble' method for measuring the refractive index and thickness of living cells

Finally, both the refractive indices and thicknesses of compressed cells can be arrived at by an elegant method first used independently by Ambrose and by Klug & Walker in 1957, when an air bubble, large enough to be in contact with both slide and coverslip, is introduced in the preparation adjacent to the cells being measured. The phase changes, +ve and −ve, through the compressed part of the cells and the air bubble (with a refractive index of 1) are measured, and their thicknesses, t, which are assumed to be equal, are given by the equation:

$$t = \phi_a \times \frac{\lambda}{1 - n_m} \qquad (11)$$

where ϕ_a = the phase change measured through the air bubble (a negative value), n_m = the refractive index of the mounting medium and λ = the wavelength of light used. The refractive index of the compressed part of a cell adjacent to the bubble, n_c, can be calculated from the equation:

$$n_c = \frac{n_m(\phi_a - \phi_c) + \phi_c}{\phi_a} \qquad (12)$$

where ϕ_c is the phase change measured in the compressed region of the cell and the other symbols are as in eqn. 11.

This, of course, can only be done on compressed regions of a cell that happen to be optically homogeneous, and care must be taken to see that the air bubble is not actually in contact with the cell, as this can have very deleterious effects indeed on living cells (Dick, 1954). A perfusion chamber is unnecessary since the mounting medium is not replaced and this medium can be of any convenient refractive index. This method was used by Davies (1959) for measuring the refractive indices of crystalline proteins in his important work in determining their specific refraction increment (p. 6, Chapter 1).

The method is in some respects improved if, instead of an air bubble, a drop of liquid paraffin is used, and this modification of the method is fully discussed in connection with the measurement of living cell inclusion in the next chapter (p. 158).

6.6 Problems especially relevant to the interference microscopy of living striated muscle fibres

Living striated muscle fibres are one of the most difficult cytological materials to study quantitatively by interference microscopy, but the problems involved in their study need to be discussed since many of them become relevant in the study of other cytological material as well.

There are three main problems to contend with in studying living striated muscle fibres and some of these are more intractable than others. Firstly, there is the problem of whether it is possible to ensure that the region of a fibre being studied is intact and undamaged. Secondly, there is the problem of distinguishing the very weakly birefringent I-band regions from the rather more refractile and more strongly birefringent A-band regions and of measuring the two refractive indices of the latter with interference microscopes. Finally, there are the problems arising from the diffraction effects at the very closely spaced phase boundaries within the interval of a single sarcomere which occur both between the I-bands and A-bands and between them and the still narrower Z-bands and H-bands associated with each of these regions; the errors that may result if the bands are not exactly aligned with the optical axis of the microscope; and of the possible effect of the 'obliquity error' (p. 101) on phase change measurements made on these regions.

6.6.1   The viability of preparations of living muscle fibres and of other very extensive cells

Because of their great length, living muscle fibres (and nerve cells) are nearly impossible to dissect out intact over their entire length. It is true that some very remarkable preparations of frog muscle fibres were made for study by interference microscopy by A. F. Huxley & Niedergerke (1954) and A. F. Huxley & Taylor (1955) in which single fibres were dissected out over the greater part of their length, and the origins and insertions of their fibres kept intact, but these dissections frequently took several hours to prepare and attempts by even these superlatively skilled workers to make similar preparations of the much thinner mammalian muscle fibres were unsuccessful, although a few successful preparations of reptilian muscle fibres, which are of intermediate thickness, were made by Niedergerke (A. F. Huxley, 1958). Almost all interference and phase contrast microscope studies of mammalian muscle have in fact been made either on fairly long pieces of freshly dissected fibres or, as in the case of the studies of H. E. Huxley & Hanson (1957), on isolated myofibrils. The question which has to be considered is whether those fragments resemble individual intact fibres sufficiently closely for valid inferences to be drawn from measurements made on them. Short lengths of cut muscle fibres can certainly, in one sense, be regarded as living cells since, provided such fragments contain enough nuclei, they are capable of undergoing regeneration and reforming themselves into fully functional muscle fibres. Some of the details of the process by which the regeneration takes place are not yet fully understood, but the studies by Lewis & Lewis (1917), Wilde (1958), Capers (1959), Murray (1960) and others on the regeneration of muscle fragments in tissue culture have effectively disproved the one-time widely held view that nuclei multiply by amitosis; it now seems most probable that, when a muscle fibre is cut or otherwise injured, the undamaged nuclei and sarcoplasm near the site of the injury form themselves into discrete uninucleate myoblasts, and these subsequently fuse with each other again to form a multinucleate syncytium (a 'muscle strap') which differentiates once more to become a fully contractile cross-striated fibre. Not only muscle fibres but nerve cells also possess the potentiality for regeneration, and here again it is the part that still possesses an undamaged nucleus (the cell-body at the proximal part of the axon) which retains this regenerative capacity.

Even though a cut muscle fibre can regenerate, it is undeniable that its full physiological function is impaired for some time after transection or injury, and inevitably there must be some leakage of its contents and entry of external fluids in the immediate region of its cut ends. The big question, which is at present not clearly resolved, is whether the interchange of material affects the more central regions of such a cut fibre four or five millimetres away from the cut ends, and, if it does, how long does it take to do this. These regions give the *appearance* of remaining intact and unaffected for at least 20 minutes after the fibres have been cut from a freshly killed animal and mounted under a microscope, and often for longer; but A. F. Huxley (1958) has expressed the opinion that, when a fibre is cut, some of the water from the mounting medium rapidly enters every part of it. The fact that the values for the water content of mammalian muscle (of around 80%) that have been obtained by weighing pieces of the whole tissue before and after drying, are nearly 10% lower than the mean values for the water content of the cut mammalian fibres obtained by Ross & Casselman (1960) lends some support to this view. On the other hand, water and solid estimations based on bulk weighing of tissues are often far from reliable, and the refractive index measurements obtained by Ross & Casselman showed extremely little individual variation between one cut fibre and another. Moreoever, their refractive indices remained constant from the time the material was first examined, which was within five minutes of the death of the animal from which they were removed, until at least 20 minutes later. This suggests that if any changes in concentration occurred in those centre regions of the fibres molecular diffusion must have taken place very rapidly through nearly half a centimetre of fibre for it to reach equilibrium within five minutes, and this equilibrium must have been achieved at almost exactly the same level of concentration in every individual fibre examined.

Plate I   Colour photomicrographs of segments of living muscle-fibres under a Smith interference microscope with a tungsten light source without a filter. All the photomicrographs were taken with a 2 mm shearing objective and are to the same scale, indicated at the bottom of the page. The reference area in every case is on the left of the photograph and the fibres are all orientated with their long axes in the north–south direction in the field.

A—A fibre mounted in a saline/protein solution with a refractive index of 1·360, with the analyser set to give a yellow background. The I-bands near the edge of the fibre show the same colour as the background.

B—The same preparation as in A, with the analyser set to give a red background. The I-bands again match the background colour.

C—A similar preparation to that in A and B, mounted in a saline/protein solution with a refractive index of 1·360. The analyser is set to give a blue background and the I-bands at the edge of the fibre match this colour. The unmatched A-bands show up in yellow-green which indicates a shift up the Newtonian series.

D—The same preparation as in C with the analyser set so that the background and matched I-bands show up in red. The unmatched A-bands are now blue, which indicates a similar colour shift.

E—A preparation of a fibre mounted in a saline/protein solution with a refractive index of 1·365. The fringe adjustment of the microscope condenser was the same as in C and D. The analyser was set to give a blue background and the A-bands match this colour. The unmatched I-bands show up in indigo, which indicates a shift down the Newtonian series, and a phase shift in the opposite direction of that of the unmatched bands in C.

F—The same fibre as in E, with the analyser set so that the background and matched A-bands show up in purple-red. The unmatched I-bands are orange-yellow, which indicates a phase shift in the same direction as in E.

G—A fibre mounted in a saline/protein solution with a refractive index of 1·360. The muscle-bands are exactly aligned with the optical axis of the microscope, so that the I-bands match the red background colour in the centre as well as at the edge of the fibre.

H—A much-stretched fibre, mounted in a saline/protein solution with a refractive index of 1·360. In the regions of greater stretch the I-bands do not match the red background colour but are yellow, which indicates that they have a lower refractive index than the mounting medium.

See pp. 96, 139 and 141.

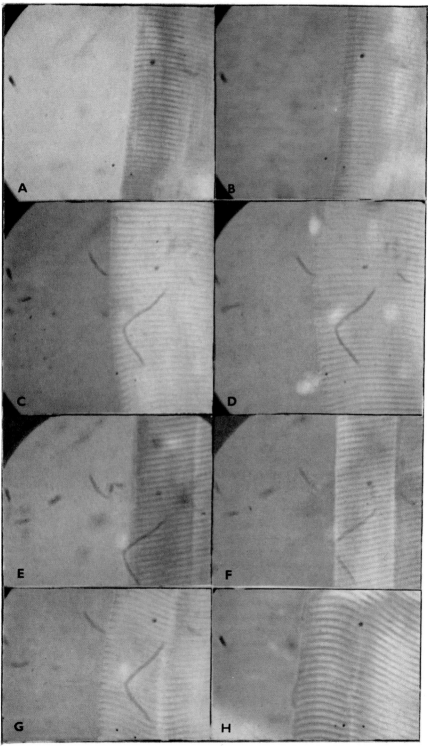

20μ

6.6.2   *Distinguishing A-bands from I-bands in muscle fibres*

In normal 'resting' (i.e. unstretched and uncontracted) mammalian muscle fibres, the A-band regions and I-band regions are nearly equally wide and they cannot therefore be distinguished from each other by their widths. Two different approaches can, however, be used to distinguish them; they can be recognized by the marked birefringence of their A-band regions or from the fact, now established beyond all dispute by the studies by electron microscopy of H. E. Huxley (1953, 1957) and by interference microscopy of H. E. Huxley & Hanson (1957), that these A-band regions contain more solid material than the I-band regions and therefore have higher refractive indices.

By changing the objectives and condensers it is possible to convert the Smith interference microscopes quite rapidly into plane-polarizing microscopes which show up the birefringent A-bands very adequately. The disadvantage of this approach is that it is not always easy to find a band which is clearly recognizable under both optical systems (an adjacent piece of dirt may sometimes, however, provide the required clue) and the inevitable delay in changing the optical systems of the microscope increases the risk of the specimen deteriorating.

As with much other cellular material, the structure of living muscle fibres is much more readily distinguishable under an interference microscope if they are mounted in isotonic saline/protein media with refractive indices close to that of their own material. If one or other set of bands appears to match the background in such a solution it is possible, when white light is used, to determine whether the other set has a higher or lower refractive index than the matched set from their colour in the manner already described in detail in Chapter 5 (p. 96). The colour photomicrographs shown in Plate I provide an illustration of this. Plate I, C and D are of a fibre with matched I-bands, and, to obtain the shift in background colour from blue of C to the purple-red of D, the phase change measuring control on the microscope was turned in a direction appropriate for measuring a retardation, and the unmatched bands changed from yellowish-green to blue. In Plate I, E and F the mounting medium had a slightly higher refractive index, and it was the A-bands which were matched. When the instrument was adjusted to give a blue background, as in Plate I, C, the unmatched phase-advancing I-bands exhibited a colour shift in the opposite direction to that of the A-bands in C, and, similarly, with a purple-red background this shift, shown in F, was opposite to that shown by the unmatched bands in D.

12

6.6.3   The refractometry of birefringent objects

Interference microscopes can be used for measuring both the refractive indices of birefringent objects if the planes of vibration (or electric vectors) of the ordinary and extraordinary rays in the object being measured are known. With the Dyson or Horn microscopes, which do not use a polarizing system to produce interference, this can be done quite simply by using a rotating polaroid below the condenser illuminating the object field which can be turned so as to occlude each set of rays in turn. The phase change due to each set of rays can then be successively measured or suitable immersion media can be used to produce zero phase changes for each set of rays. The Smith microscopes rely on a polarizing system to produce interference, but their objectives and condensers are so oriented that, for all objectives other than the 2 mm 'double focus' objective, the plane of vibration (electric vector) of the 'ordinary' object beam is in the 'north–south' direction in the microscope field as viewed by an observer in the normal position behind the instrument (Smith, 1956). Consequently, it is necessary to orientate the object in the field so that the plane of vibration of its ordinary ray is also in this direction for the refractive index due to this to be measured and at right angles to this to determine its other refractive index. (The reverse is true for the 2 mm 'double focus' objective where the plane of vibrations of the 'ordinary' object beam is east–west in the field.) Since nearly all objects of biological origin are positively birefringent, the refractive index due to the ordinary ray will be the lower of the two in almost all cases.

In practice it is seldom necessary to take into account the birefringence of parts of living cells when estimating their solid content from refractive index measurements, since this birefringence is usually rather weak, and the difference between the two refractive indices is less than the experimental error of the technique. The birefringence of the A-band regions of living muscle fibres, however, is approximately $0 \cdot 004$, so that their w/v solid content will be about 1% higher than that found with the ordinary ray and 1% lower than that found with the extraordinary ray. The birefringent inclusions in living cells, such as chromosomes and certain phospholipid droplets, all have lower birefringences than $0 \cdot 004$, and their refractive indices can seldom be estimated to this accuracy. With the shearing objectives on the Smith microscope, an elongated object such as a muscle fibre can, of course, only be orientated with its long axis in the 'north–south' direction in the field because when it is orientated 'east–west' two images will overlap.

6.6.4 Problems arising from the close spacing of the bands

The most formidable difficulty in applying immersion refractometry to portions of living mammalian muscle fibres undoubtedly lies in the close spacing of the bands which comprise the I-band, A-band, H-band and Z-band regions so that there are no less than six phase boundaries within a single sarcomere interval: in mammalian resting fibres this interval is never more than $2 \cdot 5$ μ wide. Indeed, in these resting fibres no single homogeneous band region is sufficiently wide for it to be possible to make measurements as much as $0 \cdot 3$ μ away from a boundary even under objectives of the highest numerical aperture, and so all the measurements on every band will be subject to errors due to diffraction (pp. 102-3). Therefore, when any region of such a fibre is mounted in a medium in which it appears to match the background, this does *not* mean that it has the same refractive index as the mounting medium, because the colour or relative brightness of the band in question will be actually changed by the immediately adjacent bands of different refractive index. The effect of this is to give measurements of the more highly refractile A-bands which are lower than their true value, and of the less refractile I-bands which are too high, since both are affected by the presence of the other. It is thus only possible to arrive at *minimum* refractive index values for the A-bands and *maximum* values for the I-bands in fibres in their resting state. Fortunately, by stretching the fibres, it is possible to obtain longer lengths of I-band and of H-band regions on which true phase change measurements can be made. H. E. Huxley & Hanson (1957) were able to use these values to obtain measurements of the total solids in the isolated myofibrils of rabbit in the I-bands, H-bands and in the narrower A-bands (where the material of the I-bands and H-bands overlap). Ross & Casselman (1960), however, were only able to obtain minimum and maximum values for the solid concentrations in the A-bands and I-bands when they used immersion refractometry with interference microscopy on portions of whole fibres of mouse. The fact that the I-bands, which in the resting state matched the background colour, changed colour in a direction characteristic of a phase advance when they were stretched (Colour Plate I, H) showed that the adjacent phase boundaries did indeed affect the measurements and that values for the I-band regions at least could have been obtained by mounting such stretched fibres in media of rather lower refractive index. This, however, was not done by Ross & Casselman (1960).

It need hardly be said that, in order to make measurements on structures of this kind, all the bands must be aligned exactly along the optical axis of the microscope and it is often quite difficult to find regions that fulfil this condition. They are, however, readily recognizable and since the thickness of a fibre is normally considerably greater than the interval between any of the bands, a region showing clear cut boundaries must have been orientated nearly perfectly. But measurements of such regions may be still expected to be affected by the 'obliquity errors' (p. 101) since the more peripheral rays illuminating such an object will not lie on the optical axis. However, in practice, it is doubtful if the obliquity error is of great importance when zero phase changes (as indicated by matching backgrounds) are being measured: some support for this is provided by the fact that Ross & Casselman (1960) obtained exactly the same refractive index match in 10 μ sections of fixed unstained fibres mounted in methyl salicylate refractive index 1·536 as they obtained with 30 μ sections of these fibres mounted in the same medium, even though, in the latter case, the more lateral rays had more unmatched material to pass through.

Exactly the same problems arise in studying other structures exhibiting closely spaced banded structures by interference microscopy. With the gene-bearing and non-gene-bearing regions (bands and interbands) of polytene chromosomes, for instance, it is only possible to obtain minimum and maximum values respectively for their solid content (see Chapter 7). Phase contrast with immersion refractometry cannot be used on structures of this kind since the halo effect at all the phase boundaries is so marked that it completely obscures the immediate adjacent region and makes even erroneous matching virtually impossible. Some striated muscle fibres, notably those of insects and other invertebrates, have a much greater sarcomere interval than mammalian fibres, and in these cases many of these difficulties caused by adjacent phase boundaries do not arise.

6.7   The quantitative interference microscopy of cellular structures and cell products in histological sections

There can be no doubt that the potentialities of the interference microscope for making biologically important quantitative investigations on cell structures in histological sections are almost as great as those for investigations by interference microscopy on isolated living cells. At present this potentiality cannot be said to have been as fully explored and, although quite a number of investigations along these lines have been reported, e.g. by Hale (1956), Hallen (1962) and Strenram (1958), but many of the particular difficulties involved in this approach have only recently begun to be properly evaluated.

6.7.1   Studies of enzyme activity from the accumulation of a reaction product

These difficulties become particularly apparent when attempts are made to make measurements on the cell structures themselves, and these will be discussed below. It is also possible, however, to use an interference microscope to estimate enzyme activity in the different regions of a section by determining the changes in the dry mass of artificially produced transparent and non-diffusing end-products, and this is in some respects a more straightforward procedure. This approach was pioneered by Davies, Barter & Danielli in 1954, whose technique for measuring alkaline phosphatase activity by interference microscopy in the brush borders of rat kidney tubule epithelial cells and of duodenal epithelium can be regarded as a classic achievement which has not really been much improved upon since. A qualitative test to indicate the activity of alkaline phosphatase in a section had been developed independently by Gomori (1939) and Takamatsu (1939). This involved incubating the section at an alkaline pH with a substrate consisting of an excess of phosphate and calcium ions which resulted in a transparent precipitate of calcium phosphate being formed in those parts of the sections where alkaline phosphatase was present. Since, however, the precipitate is transparent and therefore invisible, it was then converted into a black precipitate of colbalt sulphide by treating it first with cobalt chloride and then with hydrogen sulphide. By changing the initial substrate this technique has subsequently been modified to form a test for quite a wide variety of enzymes. It remains a qualitative test rather than a quantitative one because the amounts of cobalt sulphide formed are not necessarily related to the amounts of the calcium salt deposited initially, and furthermore the optical densities in the section are not always simply related to those amounts of cobalt sulphide either. However, phase contrast observations by Danielli (1954) indicated that in the case of alkaline phosphatase activity the calcium phosphate deposited by the first reaction from the substrate might very well be quantitatively indicative of the enzyme's activity since this was then visible and seemed to accumulate with the time of the reaction. Actual measurements of the dry mass per unit area of this precipitate by Davies, Barter & Danielli (1954) with an interference microscope showed that this was so and those workers obtained a very elegant demonstration of this enzyme's activity by the following technique.

The sections were incubated with the substrate over a certain period of time and the progressive increases in the phase changes through the calcium phosphate precipitate at the sites of the enzyme's activity were measured at various time intervals. The precipitated calcium phosphate was then dissolved out by perfusing the section with an excess of phosphate buffer followed by washing with distilled water and the section was once again reincubated with an excess of the substrate and the rate of redisposition of the calcium phosphate measured by interference microscopy. Almost exactly the same increases in phase change (proportional to the increases in dry mass per unit area) were found to occur at the previously active sites after the same time intervals, and however many times this was repeated the rate of redisposition seemed to remain the same. This indicated that this enzyme remained in situ in these sections and retained its activity. In their final detailed paper, these authors also investigated the effects of varying the pH, the concentration of the substrate and the temperature upon the rate of deposition of the precipitate (Barter, Danielli & Davies, 1955), and in his review article Danielli (1958) gives a full statement of the necessary conditions for investigating enzyme activity in this way. In particular it is necessary to ensure that the enzyme is not destroyed during the reaction and that neither the enzyme nor the end-product diffuse away from the primary sites of activity, that the substrate is present always in adequate quantities, and also that the reaction is stoichiometric. If the actual dry mass of the end-product is to be determined, it is of course necessary to know its specific refraction increment (p. 6). This, in the case of the calcium phosphate here which contained some water of crystallization, was as a result of some determinations by Davies, taken as being 0·0011.

6.7.2 Studies of cell structures and naturally occurring cell products and of the penetration of mounting media

The use of interference microscopy for making quantitative measurements on cell structures and naturally occurring cell products in cells in histological sections was pioneered by Hale (1956) in his study of the colloid in the cells of the thyroid gland of guinea pigs and by Stenram (1957) in his studies of the nucleolar RNA in the liver cells of protein-fed and protein-deprived rats. These studies have been added to by various workers, but it is probably fair to say that it is only in the more recent work of Galjaard (1962), Galjaard & Szirmai (1965) and perhaps even more in that of Goldstein (1965) that the difficulties and possible sources of error inherent in this approach have been fully appreciated, and the basis laid for very profitable future studies by this method.

All these difficulties really stem from one origin and lie in the fact that, whereas the internal structure of an intact living cell is not normally penetrated by the molecules of the medium in which it is immersed except in a highly selective manner dependent on that cell's normal physiological activities, once such a cell is fixed and sectioned, molecules from an external medium can pass freely through its substance, provided that the spaces in the interstices of the fixed material of which it is comprised are large enough to accommodate them.

The effects resulting from this are twofold. Firstly, in general, mounting media with large sized molecules will tend to be excluded from the finer meshes of fixed cell structures, while smaller molecules from other mounting media may be readily admitted. This may result in entirely anomalous refractive index measurements if immersion refractometry is tried. It has already been mentioned (Chapter 3, p. 54) that Barer & Joseph observed that the chromosomes in certain fixed cells permitted the penetration of xylene but excluded the much larger globular protein molecules in bovine plasma albumin solutions. Galjaard & Szirmai (1965) concluded that 5 μ sections of unfixed cartilage would permit the free entry of ethyl alcohol, glycerol and xylene, but partially impeded the entry of the larger molecules of sucrose and liquid paraffin, since they found that the phase changes which they measured through the sections of cartilage mounted in these latter two media were less than would have been predicted if total penetration had occurred.

Secondly, just as they can impede the entry of larger molecules, the meshwork enclosing the intracellular spaces in fixed cells in sections can also impede the exit of molecules, and thus can be of great relevance to the problem of effectively dewaxing a section of cellular material which has been embedded in paraffin-wax. It is obviously of great importance that, before any measurements of dry mass are made on sectioned cellular materials in water, the sections are fully and completely 'cleared' of paraffin wax or other embedding media. Although the obstinate retention of paraffin wax in certain cell regions was reported by Nedzel as early as 1951, the method which was developed by that author for its virtually complete removal does not seem to have been carried out by any interference microscopist before Goldstein (1965). The method consists of bringing the sections down through xylene and the alcohols to water in the normal way, and then back up through the alcohols to xylene before once again bringing the sections to water. Neither Nedzel nor Goldstein can suggest why this should be so much more effective than leaving the sections in xylene, but it does appear to remove any paraffin-wax almost completely.

It is just possible that the incomplete removal of paraffin-wax may have accounted for the unexpectedly low figures, of around 14%, which Stenram (1957) obtained for the percentages of RNA in the nucleoli in the liver cells of rats. In every other way Stenram's experimental approach seems to have been thoroughly sound, but it depended on first finding the refractive indices of the nucleoli before and after digestion with RNAse; the actual refractive index measurements which he obtained on these bodies, 1·557 before and 1·550 after digestion, are significantly higher than the commonly accepted values of 1·53–1·54 for pure dried protein products such as leather, wool and dried casein (p. 133) and much higher than the values of 1·454–1·477 which Davies (1959) found for the refractive index of β-lactoglobulin. The high refractive index values which Stenram found for the nucleoli could, however, be accounted for if all the paraffin-wax in their internal spaces had not been entirely removed, and the situation might have been further complicated if the liquid paraffin, which he appears to have used as one of his immersion media, had penetrated the nucleoli incompletely.

The above example is mentioned only to illustrate the difficulties arising from the penetration into the internal spaces of cell substances by foreign molecules and these difficulties have been especially studied by Goldstein (1965). He has stressed their relevance to all histological staining processes, since the penetration of dyes into tissues will partly depend on the size of the dye molecules and the sizes of the spaces left in the cell substances after fixation. Using a very similar technique to that developed independently by Galjaard & Szirmai (1965), Goldstein made a more exhaustive study of this phenomenon. He found that several different cell substances would permit the complete entry of the molecules of some mounting media and partially impede the entry of others. The maximum size of the molecules which can enter completely gives some indication of the size of the spaces of the interstices of the cell substance in question. For example, glycerol penetrated completely into goblet cell mucin, but was to some extent excluded from entering collagen, and nitrobenzene was impeded from entering both substances but entered goblet cell mucin much more readily than it entered collagen. Thus one can justifiably conclude that the spaces within the fixed collagen were, on the average, smaller than those in the fixed goblet cell mucin. The fact that many mounting media with small molecules will penetrate the cell substances in a section completely, however, has led to the concept of the 'effective thickness' of a section or of different regions of a section, a term originally employed in interference microscopy by Hale in 1956. The real thickness of a section is assumed to be the thickness at which it was cut by the microtome, but its 'effective thickness' can be defined as the ratio of the volume of the solid material in a particular region to the volume of mounting medium in its interstices. This provides a measure of the thickness that a particular region of a section would occupy if it was entirely comprised of its solid material so closely packed together as to exclude all the mounting medium in its internal spaces; this in its turn gives an indication of the total volume of the spaces enclosed by the matrix of the cell substances. It does, of course, give no indication of the sizes of the spaces themselves which are of equal importance in the study of dye penetration, but it has already been mentioned that some indication of this case may be gained by finding out which sort of media are capable of completely penetrating and which are not. Goldstein also found that fixed tissues tended to swell in water and that very aqueous mounting media were consequently unsuitable if Barer's 'double immersion' method is used to measure the refractive indices and 'effective thickness' of cell structures; for this reason he was critical of this aspect of Hale's investigation of the thyroid collagen in guinea pigs (p. 144). He himself obtained refractive index measurements on a variety of cellular materials in sections by double immersion in benzene, nitrobenzene, mixtures of xylene and nitrobenzene, carbon tetrachloride, xylene and a mixture of xylene and methyl salicylate. The results he obtained corresponded closely to those which he also obtained by matching immersion refractometry with phase contrast on the same materials with a variety of other media including anilene, methyl salicylate, methyl benzoate and mixtures of the last two.

There can be little doubt that studies along these lines have a very promising future and that much valuable information may eventually be derived on the sizes of the spaces in different cellular regions and substances after various fixation procedures and that these may be found to be correlated with their stainability. Even in the study of living cells, problems of intrastructural penetration can be very illuminating. An example of this, described more fully in Chapter 7 (pp. 167–170), is provided by the fact that the polytene chromosomes of *Chironomus* appear to permit the entry of the globular protein molecules of bovine plasma albumin when they are extruded from the living nuclei, but exclude much of the solid material of similar concentrations in the nuclear sap. Here it looks as if molecular shape is at least as important as molecular size in determining what will enter and what will not, and it is suggested that the larger molecules of the nuclear sap consist mostly of rather long-chain molecules of polypeptide or RNA whose entry might tend to be impeded.

The examination of a section by interference microscopy necessitates having a structure-free reference area in the field (pp. 104, 113). Galjaard &

Szirmai achieved this by confining these examinations to the edges of the sections, but Goldstein scratched the sections at close intervals while they were in the blocks to provide tissue-free reference areas. This is a more straightforward procedure than that suggested in Chapter 5 (p. 113).

Quantitative Interference Microscopy in
Cytology
2: Measurements on living cell inclusions

7.1 Methods of measuring the refractive indices of cell inclusions

The phase change, or optical path difference, that can be measured to
a high degree of accuracy with an interference microscope, in the light
passing through an object relative to that passing through the adjacent
background field is directly proportional to the product of the difference
between that object's refractive index and that of the medium which
surrounds it, and its thickness. Consequently, if the thickness of an
isolated homogeneous object, in the direction of propagation of the light
passing through it, is known, its refractive index can be calculated from
the phase change that it produces. Unfortunately, this simple principle
cannot be directly applied to measuring the refractive indices of cell
inclusions in situ since, lying as they do within the cell, they are surrounded by media that will themselves affect and alter the phase changes
measured. It is therefore necessary either to isolate the inclusion from
the cell or else to devise some means by which the phase changes contributed by the intracellular media that surround the inclusions are
either eliminated or accurately evaluated. Although a number of elegant
techniques exist for isolating inclusions in physiological media (e.g. by
microdissection and centrifuging), however carefully this is done, and
however intact they may appear, such inclusions, torn from their context, are almost certainly always modified to some extent and refractive
index measurements made on them do not necessarily provide an accurate
indication of their refractive indices when they were still in their proper
position within an intact cell. Such measurements, therefore, cannot be
relied on, and only occasionally help to provide valuable information
(p. 169).

Fortunately, with many kinds of cell material it is possible to use the interference microscope to measure the refractive indices of inclusions as they lie within undamaged living cells, and some of the techniques for doing this will now be described.

7.1.1 Measurement of the refractive indices of cytoplasmic inclusions by the immersion of the cells in special media

Living cells are most commonly examined mounted in (isotonic) physiological saline media with refractive indices only a very little higher than that of water, and all the cells contents, including the cytoplasm and nuclear sap, usually have refractive indices higher than this. Consequently, the phase changes that occur in the light passing through all regions of such cells relative to that passing through the mounting medium alone are phase retardations. Fig. 26A shows a simple diagram

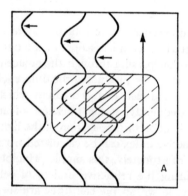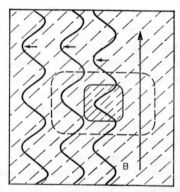

Fig. 26   A—Diagrammatic representation of a living cell, containing an inclusion with a higher refractive index than its cytoplasm, mounted in a medium with a lower refractive index than its cytoplasm, such as saline. Light passing up through the cell is retarded in phase by amounts proportional to the refractive indices and thicknesses of the structures it traverses.

B—Diagrammatic representation of the same cell as in A, mounted in a medium with the same refractive index as the cytoplasm. Only the light passing through the inclusion is retarded in phase. The light traversing the cytoplasm is unchanged in phase.

of a cell of this kind containing an inclusion with a higher refractive index than its cytoplasm mounted in a saline medium of relatively low refractive index. The light passing through the cytolasm alone is indicated as having been retarded a quarter of a wavelength (90°) compared to that passing through the surrounding mounting medium. The phase change in the light passing through the inclusion and the overlying and underlying cytoplasm is represented as being a half a wavelength (180°), but it is impossible to estimate just how much of this is due to the inclusion itself and how much to the cytoplasm unless both the refractive index and intervening thickness of the cytoplasm is known; in all ordinary preparations of living cells the latter is usually impossible to estimate at all accurately.

This phase change caused by the cytoplasm can, however, be completely eliminated if the living cells, instead of being mounted in saline, are mounted instead in a saline/protein medium with the same refractive index as the cytoplasm. Fig. 26B shows a diagram of the same cell as that depicted in Fig. 26A mounted in such a medium. Because the mounting medium is isotonic, the cell is unchanged in volume and, because it has the same refractive index as the cytoplasm, no phase change at all occurs in the light traversing it. Consequently, the only phase change that occurs is in the light passing through the inclusion, and this phase change is due to the product of the refractive index and thickness of the inclusion alone. Under an interference microscope, the cytoplasm of such a cell will appear to exactly match the colour or intensity of the background field, and will therefore be almost invisible, while the inclusion alone will stand out with a contrasting colour or intensity indicative of a phase retardation, as in the cells shown in Colour Plate II C and in Plate 4. The technique has therefore been likened to a form of 'optical dissection' of the living cell.

If the thickness of the inclusion in the direction of the propagation of the light passing through it is accurately known, its refractive index, n_i, can be calculated by using exactly the same formula as that used for measuring the refractive index of an isolated particle, i.e.:

$$n_i = \left(\phi \times \frac{\lambda}{t}\right) + n_m \qquad (13)$$

where ϕ is the phase change measured through the inclusion expressed as a fraction of a wavelength, λ is the mean wavelength (in μ) of the light used and n_m is the refractive index of the mounting medium and of the cytoplasm in which the inclusion lies. To obtain a medium with exactly the same refractive index as the cytoplasm, it is necessary to make up a range of isotonic protein solutions of different concentrations until one is found in which the cytoplasm, under the interference microscope, appears to be neither phase advancing nor phase retarding. As interference microscopes, even when used with white light, are very sensitive in detecting small phase differences, such matching media will normally have refractive indices within 0·001 of that of the cytoplasm (p. 107).

Plate II, A and B shows living spermatids from the testis of *Locusta migratoria* mounted respectively in media with refractive indices just lower and just higher than that of their cytoplasm; such media are better than saline for the morphological study of living cell material. The background in each case is red of the second order of the Newtonian series, and the microscope has been adjusted so that a shift in colour up this series towards the blue indicates a phase retardation and a shift down the series towards the yellow indicates a phase advance. The spermatids can be seen to contain a (very heterogeneous) nucleus lying in clear homogeneous cytoplasm, which contains one other quite big inclusion, a *nebenkern* formed from an aggregation of all the mitochondria in the cell which, at this particular stage of spermatogenesis, is homogeneous and spherical. In Plate II, A, the (slightly phase retarding) cytoplasm appears reddish blue and the *nebenkern* more fully blue. In Plate II, B (which is of a collection of spermatids without any spermatocytes) their cytoplasm, which is phase advancing, appears yellow; but the centres of the *nebenkerns* appear nearly exactly the same red colour as the background. This means that, although they themselves are phase retarding, the acceleration in phase of the light passing through the cytoplasm has been equal to this retardation. In neither of these cases can any conclusions be drawn about the refractive index of the *nebenkern* itself, except for the obvious one that it is higher than the cytoplasm.

Plate 4.5, 4.6, on the other hand, illustrates similar spermatids of *Locusta migratoria* mounted in a medium with exactly the same refractive index as the cytoplasm. Only the nuclei and *nebenkerns* are visible in Plate 4.5 and 4.6 which shows the cells at the two microscope settings necessary to measure the phase retardation in the light passing through the centres of the *nebenkerns* by the extinction-point method; in Plate 4.5 the background is maximally dark and in Plate 4.6 the centres of some of the *nebenkerns* are maximally dark. Because the *nebenkerns* were almost perfectly spherical, it was possible to measure their diameters at right angles to the optical axis of the microscope with an eyepiece-micrometer; it was assumed that the diameters were equal to their dimensions at right angles to this axis in the direction of the propagated light.

The results of measuring the mean retardations and thicknesses of *nebenkerns* in 20 different cells, mounted in a matching saline/protein medium with a refractive index of 1·354, are shown in Table 11A. Values for their refractive indices were calculated from formula above, and are also shown. From these, their approximate total solid content could also be calculated because the mitochondria of which they are comprised consist almost entirely of protein and lipoprotein with mean refraction increments (α) of 0·0018. These are shown in the final column.

Two interesting conclusions can be drawn even from a study of these simple measurements, which were originally made by the writer simply to demonstrate the validity of the technique, Ross (1954a). Firstly, there is clearly an inverse relationship between the diameter of the *nebenkerns* (here measured only to the nearest 0·5 μ) and their density as expressed by their percentage of solid content. This, however, is what one might expect, because the *nebenkern* is formed by the coming together of all the mitochondria in the cell; as they come closer together, the body formed by their aggregation will become smaller in diameter, and at the same time denser. Secondly, the highest refractive index recorded (1·3814) can be taken as an indication of the lowest possible value for the refractive index of an individual mitochondrion, assuming that, in this case, the mitochondria in the *nebenkern* had no water left between them at all. This, of course, is extremely unlikely but, in view of the difficulty of making accurate measurements of the refractive indices of individual mitochondria in living cells owing to their extremely small thickness (p. 102) an extreme lower limit of this kind is quite valuable. Actually, some approximate measurements made in 1961 by Veeraart and the writer on the (relatively large) mitochondria visible in mammalian pancreas cells after pilocarpine treatment indicate that they probably have very much higher refractive indices than this: values ranging from 1·44 to 1·49 were recorded, indicating that these mitochondria most probably contained between 50% and 90% of solid matter (w/v) (Veeraart, 1962).

7.1.2 Measurement of the refractive indices of cytoplasmic inclusions by the compression of the cells

Many living cells mounted in physiological media can be compressed without any apparent detriment to them between a slide and coverslip until they are as little as one-third of their original thickness, and have a considerable area of their surface membranes in contact with the glass surfaces. If a compact group of similar cells with clear cytoplasm are mounted and slightly compressed in this manner, it is not necessary for the mounting medium to be of the same refractive index as the cytoplasm to make it possible to use the interference microscope for measuring the phase changes caused by the cytoplasmic inclusions, because the cytoplasm itself, which will then fill all or most of the background field, can be used as a reference area for the measurements. This is made clear in Plate 4.2, which is a diagram of a group of contiguous compressed

Plate II   Colour photomicrographs of a variety of cell material under a Smith interference microscope with a tungsten light source without a filter. (Scales: for A and B as indicated in B, for D and E as indicated in D, for F, G and H as indicated in H, and I, J and K as indicated in I.)

A—A group of spermatocytes and dividing and differentiating spermatids of *Locusta migratoria* mounted in saline/protein with a refractive index a little lower than the cytoplasm of the cells. The spherical *nebenkerns*, in the spermatids, *n*, are markedly blue, indicating that they are phase retarding.

B—A group of similar spermatids to those in A, mounted in saline/protein with a higher refractive index than the cytoplasm. Because of the phase acceleration in the cytoplasm, the *nebenkerns*, although really phase retarding, appear the same colour as the background field (see p. 96).

C—A group of Erlich ascites tumour cells from a mouse, mounted in a saline/protein medium of the same refractive index as their cytoplasm and their nuclear sap. In the cells indicated, nucleoli (*nl*) can be seen surrounded by nuclear sap of the same colour as the cytoplasm and background field. Lipid droplets are also visible in the cytoplasm (see p. 159).

D—A salivary gland cell of *Chironomus* mounted in saline and compressed so that none of the cytoplasm, *c*, or the salivary vesicle, *s*, lies above or below the nucleus. Some of the (non-gene-bearing) interbands of the chromosomes, *i*, match the colour of the nuclear sap, indicating that they both have nearly the same refractive index.

E—A similar cell to the one in D, mounted and compressed in a saline/protein solution with the same refractive index as the nuclear sap, which is the same second order red colour as the background field (see pp. 167–168).

F—A part of a similar cell to that in E, nuclear sap second order red.

G—The same field as in F, with the analyser turned so that the interbands are mostly second order red.

H—The same field again as in F and G, with the analyser turned further, so that the (gene-bearing) bands are mostly second order red (see p. 169).

I—An isolated chromosome from a salivary gland cell of *Chironomus* mounted in saline. Background second order red.

J—The same chromosome with the analyser of the microscope rotated so that some of the interbands are second order red.

K—The same chromosome again, with the analyser rotated still further so that some of the bands, e.g. *b*, are second order red. (Photomicrograph I has been accidentally printed the wrong way round with respect to J and K, but the same band, *b*, is indicated in all three pictures.) Note the laterally displaced 'ghost' images (see p. 93).

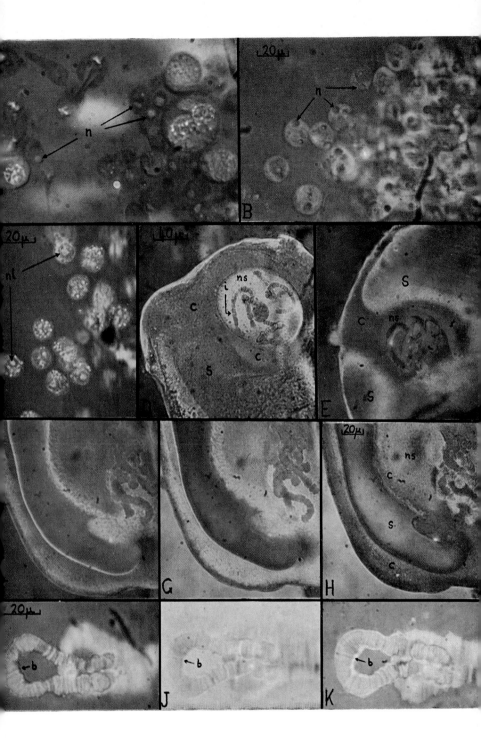

TABLE 11A

The phase retardation of light, of wavelength 542 mμ, passing through the centres of the spherical *nebenkerns* in 20 developing spermatids of *Locusta migratoria* mounted in an isotonic protein medium with a refractive index equal to that of their cytoplasm; the measured diameters of these bodies, and their refractive index and solid content calculated from these measurements

Diameter of nebenkern (in μ)	Phase change retardation (in wavelengths)	Refractive index	Approx. % solid assuming α = 0·0018)
t	φ	n_t	
4·2	0·184	1·3771	24·0
4·2	0·216	1·3814	26·0
4·2	0·210	1·3807	26·0
4·2	0·167	1·3750	22·5
4·2	0·189	1·3778	24·0
4·7	0·189	1·3751	22·5
4·7	0·200	1·3764	23·5
4·7	0·200	1·3764	23·5
4·7	0·205	1·3770	24·0
4·7	0·184	1·3745	22·0
4·7	0·216	1·3783	24·5
4·7	0·210	1·3777	24·0
4·7	0·161	1·3720	21·0
4·7	0·178	1·3739	22·0
5·3	0·189	1·3730	21·5
5·3	0·194	1·3736	22·0
5·3	0·210	1·3753	23·0
5·3	0·194	1·3736	22·0
5·3	0·178	1·3719	21·0
5·3	0·200	1·3742	22·0

TABLE 11B

The phase-retardation of light, of wavelength 542 mμ, passing through the centres of spherical *nebenkerns* in five developing spermatids of *Locusta migratoria*, mounted in saline, that were closely packed together and slightly compressed; the measured diameters of these bodies, and their refractive indices and solid content calculated from these measurements, assuming the refractive index of the cytoplasm to be 1·354

Diameter of nebenkern (in μ)	Phase change retardation (in wavelengths)	Refractive index	Approx. % solid assuming α = 0·0018
t	φ	n_t	
4·2	0·147	1·3783	22·0
4·2	0·178	1·3781	24·5
4·7	0·139	1·3703	20·0
4·7	0·158	1·3728	21·0
4·7	0·200	1·3780	24·5

13

spermatids mounted in saline. Because of this compression practically all the mounting medium has been squeezed out of the preparation in the vicinity of the cells and the space between the slide and the coverslip is almost entirely filled with the cell material. It can be seen at once that, in these circumstances, the phase changes measured through the *nebenkerns* will be exactly the same as that measured in the immersed cell in Plate 4.1.

This is experimentally demonstrated in Plate 4.7, 4.8, which are photomicrographs of spermatids of *Locusta migratoria*, containing *nebenkerns*, compressed and mounted in saline, under an interference microscope adjusted to exactly the same settings as those of the photomicrographs of the separated immersed cells illustrated in Plate 4.5, 4.6. As in these, the first figure shows the background of the preparation (in this case formed of the cytoplasm) as maximally dark, and in the second figure the centres of many of the *nebenkerns* are maximally dark.

In order for the phase changes due to the inclusions so measured to be used for calculating their refractive indices, the refractive index of the cytoplasm in which they lie must also be known. One way of obtaining this is from the technique of immersion refractometry carried out on similar cells mounted in another preparation, and Table 11B shows the values for the refractive indices and percentage solid content of five *nebenkerns* measured in a compressed preparation of spermatids mounted in saline, assuming that the refractive index of their cytoplasm was the same as that on the cells in the preparations in which it was measured by immersion refractometry (1·354). It will be seen that the values obtained are closely comparable with those in Table 11A.

If, however, the thickness of the preparation is known, the refractive index of the cytoplasm of compressed cells can easily be calculated from the difference in phase change between the light passing through the cytoplasm and the light passing through an adjacent region of the background field filled with the same thickness of mounting medium. A simple and ingenious way of measuring the thickness of a microscope preparation containing living cells with an interference microscope was discovered, independently, by Ambrose and by Klug & Walker in 1957 (both mentioned by Davies, 1959). This is the 'bubble method', already briefly described on p. 134. A preparation is made in which an air bubble is deliberately included near the cells whose thickness is required to be measured, and the number of interference fringes at the edge of the air bubble (each of which represents a phase advance of one wavelength) are counted, and any additional fraction of a wavelength is estimated as accurately as possible. Such a bubble must of course be large enough

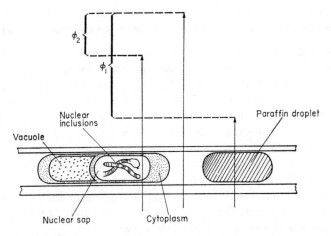

Fig. 27 A cell mounted in saline and compressed until there is almost no cytoplasm immediately above and below the nucleus. A 'bubble' of liquid paraffin is also enclosed in the preparation near the cell. The thickness of the preparation can be calculated from the phase change ϕ_1, and the refractive indices of the saline and the paraffin; the refractive index of the nuclear sap can be calculated from this thickness and ϕ_2. The phase change through nuclear inclusions relative to the nuclear sap can then be measured, and from this their refractive indices can be calculated if their thickness also is measured.

to establish contact with both slide and coverslip (see Fig. 27). The thickness of the preparation between the slide and coverslip at that point, t, can then be calculated from the equation:

$$t = \phi \times \frac{\lambda}{n_b - n_m} \qquad (14)$$

where ϕ is the phase change, in wavelengths and fractions of a wavelength, of the light passing through the bubble relative to that passing through the mounting medium (in this case a $-$ve value); λ is the wavelength (in μ) of the light used; n_b is the refractive index of the substance of the bubble (in this case, with air, $= 1$); and n_m is the refractive index of the mounting medium (which, if it is saline, can be taken as being equal to $1 \cdot 334$ at usual room temperatures).

Once the thickness of the preparation (t) is known, the refractive index of the cytoplasm in a region nearby can be calculated from eqn. 13 (p. 151) where n_t is now the refractive index of the cytoplasm, ϕ is the phase change measured through a clear region of the cytoplasm relative to an adjacent region of the background filled with mounting medium, and t is the thickness of the preparation.

This technique of using an air bubble for measuring the thickness of a preparation is a good one, but it is subject to two minor difficulties:

1. Great care must be taken to see that the air bubble does not actually come in contact with the cell material, since this almost always damages living cells irreparably (Dick, 1955): and yet it must not be too far removed from them in case the coverslip and slide are not quite parallel, and the thickness measured in the region of the bubble is appreciably different from that measured in the region of the cells.

2. In a preparation mounted in a dilute aqueous medium thick enough to contain undamaged cells, the phase change through an included air bubble is large, and the number of fringes at its edge are so numerous and closely spaced that they are quite difficult to count. There is also some danger of their becoming confused with the Becke lines that also occur at phase boundaries.

Consequently, the present writer recommends using a 'bubble' of liquid paraffin rather than of air. This is equally immiscible with the aqueous mounting media of the cells and has no appreciable deleterious effect on them if it accidentally comes in contact with the cells. Furthermore, its refractive index (usually c. 1·475) is much nearer to that of the mounting medium than air is, so that there are considerably fewer fringes at its edge in a preparation of the same thickness, and these are easier to count. The thickness of the preparation is calculated by the same equation as for an air bubble, (eqn. 14, p. 157) except that, being of a higher refractive index than the mounting medium, the phase change measured through it is a +ve instead of a −ve value. An example of this method using a paraffin 'bubble' is illustrated and described below.

7.1.3   Measurement of the refractive indices of nuclear inclusions

In an intact cell, nuclear inclusions are considerably less accessible for measurement than cytoplasmic inclusions, but their refractive indices can nevertheless quite often be measured. Lying, as they do, within the nuclear sap which is itself surrounded by cytoplasm, they form inclusions within inclusions; even when the cell is mounted in a medium with the same refractive index as the cytoplasm, it is very common for the phase changes through the overlying and underlying nuclear sap to introduce modifications in the phase changes observed through the nuclear inclusions in exactly the same way as in the case of cytoplasmic inclusions in the cells mounted in saline or in other non-matching media (p. 150). In many cells the refractive index of the nuclear sap is slightly lower than that of the cytoplasm so that, when the cytoplasm has been matched by a suitable mounting medium, a phase advance occurs in the light traversing the nuclear sap and the values for the refractive index of any inclusion measured within it will be too low. Rather surprisingly, the converse situation seems rarely if ever to occur. The writer has not yet found any cells with the nuclear sap having an appreciably higher refractive index than the cytoplasm.

Quite often, however, cells can be found in which the nuclear sap has the same refractive index as the cytoplasm; in these cases, the phase changes due to the nuclear inclusions alone can be measured. For an example of cells in which this occurs see Plate II, C (p. 154), which is a photomicrograph of living Erlich mouse ascites tumour cells mounted in a saline/protein medium with a refractive index of 1·356. In the cells indicated, it can clearly be seen that the background, cytoplasm and nuclear sap are all of the same second order red colour, and the phase changes due to the (green) nucleoli alone can be measured. The results of measuring the refractive indices of eight such nucleoli in several different strains of ascites tumour cells are shown in Table 12. The figures in the final column for their percentage solid content are subject to the assumption that their thicknesses in the direction of the optical axis of the microscope were the same as that measured at right angles to it, and, as these bodies are considerably less regular in shape than the *nebenkerns* discussed above, this may not have always been quite true. Nevertheless, the results do indicate that the nucleoli in these particular cells contain approximately 50% of solid matter.

If any cell inclusion exhibits more than a small amount of irregularity in shape it is, of course, not possible to obtain any accurate indication of its refractive index from phase change measurements made in the direction of the optical axis of the microscope, and thickness measurements which have to be made at right angles to this: but if a sufficiently large number of measurements of this kind are made on similar bodies, *average* refractive index values may be obtained which can be of considerable biological interest. Examples of such measurements on irregular-shaped nucleoli are discussed on pp. 172, 179.

If the refractive index of the nuclear sap is different to that of the cytoplasm, it is sometimes possible to compress a cell so that both the cytoplasm and the nucleus are compressed and a considerable area of the nuclear membrane comes in close contact with the overlying and underlying cell membrane with only extremely thin layers of cytoplasm in between. This is illustrated diagrammatically in Fig. 27. The cell itself can then be mounted in a medium with the same refractive index as that of the nuclear sap, as illustrated in Colour Plate II, E, F, G, H, which

TABLE 12

The refractive indices of the nucleoli in ascites cells of six different strains measured
in cells where the refractive index of the nuclear sap was the same as that of the
cytoplasm, and their equivalent per cent solid content. (The values are based on the
assumption that the dimensions of the nucleoli measured at right angles to the optical
axis of the microscope were the same as those along this axis, and this may not
always have been quite true)

Strain of ascites	Refractive index of nuclear sap and cytoplasm	Measured width of nucleolus region	Refractive index of nucleolus region	Equivalent % total solids in nucleolus region
		(μ)		% w/v
Erlich	1·357	2·4	1·413	44·0
,,	1·355	1·8	1·453	66·0
Landschutz	1·360	2·4	1·419	47·0
Krebs	1·358	1·8	1·430	53·5
Sarcoma 1	1·360	3·0	1·405	39·5
Crocker	1·359	2·4	1·424	50·0
,,	1·359	1·7	1·425	50·5
EL4	1·361	1·6	1·418	46·5

will then appear of the same colour or intensity as the background field.
Alternatively, if the compressed area of the nucleus is large enough, the
nuclear sap itself can be used as a reference area for measuring the phase
changes due to the nuclear inclusions. In the latter case (illustrated in
Colour Plate II, D) it is not necessary to mount the cell in a matching
medium in order to measure the refractive indices of the nuclear inclusions, but it is necessary to measure the thickness of the squashed
nucleus and its phase change relative to the mounting medium in order
to know the refractive index of the nuclear sap. This is best done by
the paraffin 'bubble' method already described, and illustrated, with
Chironomus chromosomes as an example, in Fig. 27.

Both these methods were used to measure the refractive indices of the
bands and interbands of the polytene chromosomes of *Chironomus*
described on p. 167. Stenram (1957) obtained measurements of the solid
concentration in the nucleoli of the liver cells of rats but first isolating
the nuclei from these cells and then measuring the phase changes
through the nuclear sap adjacent to the nucleoli and the phase changes
through the nucleoli themselves and the overlying and underlying
nuclear sap. From the diameters of the nuclei and the nucleoli he was
able to find out what proportion of the latter phase changes were due to
the nucleoli alone, and hence he could calculate their refractive indices.

In theory this method could be used to measure the refractive indices of cytoplasmic inclusions in intact living cells also, but, as it will only give valid results if the cell and the inclusions are both approximately spherical or regular so that these thicknesses in the direction of the optical axis of the microscope can be deduced, it is not a method which can generally be recommended.

7.2   The limitations and accuracy of the techniques for measuring the refractive indices of living cell inclusions

These methods for measuring the refractive indices of cell inclusions can be applied to a wide variety of cell material, but the cytoplasm or nuclear sap must be sufficiently clear and homogeneous at optical levels of resolution for the inclusions to stand out clearly and for its own refractive index to be measurable. The inclusions must not lie on top of one another. Consequently, in very granular cells, such as mammalian liver cells or many nerve cells, the refractive indices of both the inclusions and the cytoplasm are very difficult indeed to measure by any means. Nevertheless it is sometimes possible, even with quite granular cells, if they can be sufficiently squashed and spread out without actually damaging them.

Refractometric techniques are also very difficult to apply to botanical material, both because the presence of a cellulose wall makes plant cells difficult to separate from one another and often modifies the phase change measurements made on the cell contents, and because of the centrally placed watery vacuole that occurs in so many of these cells. These difficulties do not occur, however, in the case of unspecialized meristematic cells, and Ambrose, working in collaboration with Bajer (1960), has obtained some very interesting measurements on them.

The accuracy of the values that can be obtained for the refractive indices of inclusions in living cells depends on three things:

1. The accuracy with which it is possible to measure the refractive indices of the surrounding cytoplasm or nuclear sap by immersion refractometry.
2. The accuracy with which phase changes due to the inclusion can be measured.
3. The accuracy with which it is possible to measure the thicknesses of the inclusions in the direction of the optical axis of the microscope.

Interference microscopes are quite sensitive instruments when they are used for immersion refractometry. Even when a white light source is used, they show up as distinct colour differences phase changes of as little as one-fiftieth of a wavelength, and, when they are used with monochromatic light their sensitivity is still greater. This means that if an object is only 10 μ thick they are capable of showing up differences in its refractive index of only 0·001. As most of the cells in the preparations examined are rather more than 10 μ thick, it is correct to assume that the refractive indices of the cytoplasm or nuclear sap can be measured to the nearest ±0·001, which is approximately equivalent to the nearest ±0·5% of solid matter.

Phase changes can be measured with an interference microscope accurately to the nearest one-sixtieth of a wavelength, or more accurately if certain of the intensity-matching devices now available are used (p. 116), provided that the object being measured is not extremely small. H. E. Huxley & Hanson (1957) have produced convincing evidence, from a densitometric trace of interference microscope measurements across the edge of a myoglobin crystal with an accurately square edge orientated parallel to the optical axis of the microscope, that, with high resolution objectives, measurements made within 0·3 μ of a phase boundary were affected by diffraction, but measurements made further away from such boundaries were probably accurate. This indicates that phase change measurements made on the centres of homogeneous objects more than 0·6 μ in diameter are probably accurate, and those made on smaller objects will probably be too low. (This is discussed in rather greater detail on p. 102.) It is probably true to say that phase changes measured on homogeneous objects more than 1 μ in diameter are accurate to the nearest one-sixtieth of a wavelength, and it is seldom worth while to make measurements on objects smaller than this.

It is the third factor which provides the real limitation of the technique as a whole: the accuracy with which it is possible to measure thicknesses. All methods of measuring the depths of microscopical objects by focusing with the fine adjustment of a microscope are open to so many objections and difficulties that they are to all practical intents and purposes valueless (see Galbraith, 1955 and Richards, 1959). Consequently, the only practicable method of estimating the thickness of a cell inclusion is by measuring its width at right angles to the optical axis of the microscope and assuming that this is equal to its depth. Fortunately, many cell inclusions are nearly perfect spheres or cylinders, so that this assumption is often justified. But the accuracy with which width can be measured under a light microscope is itself subject to severe limitation. For reasons discussed in greater detail in Chapter 8, no microscopical object can be expected to be measurable more accurately than to the nearest $0.4\ \mu$ because of the diffraction effects at the edges of the image (which are dependent on the numerical aperture of the optical system and the wavelength of light used).

This means that all thickness measurements are subject to an error of $\pm 0.2\ \mu$; it is essential in defining the upper and lower limits of accuracy of all the refractive index measurements made on cell inclusions also to calculate what their refractive indices would have been if their thicknesses had been respectively $0.2\ \mu$ less and $0.2\ \mu$ more than they were measured to be. This has been done in Tables 13 and 14. It is, of course, true that the upper and lower limits so calculated do not represent quite the maximum possible errors in the values for the refractive index measurements because they do not take into account the effects of the smaller errors in the measurement of phase change and of the refractive index of the surrounding medium. But the statistical probability of all three of the factors operating in the same direction to their maximum extent is so low that it is sufficient for all practical purposes to define the accuracy of the techniques as a whole solely in terms of the accuracy with which thicknesses can be measured.

In certain special circumstances the widths of cell inclusions can be measured more accurately than to the nearest $0.4\ \mu$. This is when similarly sized inclusions occur in aggregates and appear to be in contact with one another. It is then possible to measure the width of the aggregate and divide this by the number of individual inclusions that occur within this width. This will give a much more accurate value for the maximum possible width of an individual inclusion than is possible by measuring one alone, but not for its mimimum width, because, if the inclusions appear to touch each other, they must either really be doing so or else be slightly apart from one another with apparently contiguous diffraction gradients at their edges. Consequently, while it is justifiable to apply an error of $-0.2\ \mu$ to get their minimum possible width, the error in their maximum width will be very much less than $+0.2\ \mu$.

An example of this is provided by the small triglyceride droplets that occur in the axons and axon hillocks of the neurons of *Helix aspersa*. These are illustrated in Plate 5.1. A row of 5 globules can be seen in an axon, apparently touching each other and similar in size. The length of the row is $6\ \mu$. These individual globules, therefore, cannot be appreciably more than $1.1\ \mu$ in diameter and may be as little as $0.9\ \mu$. This is taken into account in calculating the upper and lower limits of their refractive indices in the final column of Table 13.

7.3   Special interpretations of refractive index measurements on living cell inclusions

Although refractive index measurements are usually made on the different regions of living cells in order to provide an indication of their water and solid content, it has already been mentioned (p. 127) that in certain circumstances they can provide valuable additional information; some examples of this will now be discussed.

7.3.1   Refractometry as an indication of the submicroscopic morphology of cell inclusions

When refractive index measurements are combined with specific histochemical tests, they can sometimes provide a valuable indication of the submicroscopic arrangement of the chemical substances demonstrated. A striking example of this is provided by a study of the cytoplasmic lipid droplets in the neurons of the snail *Helix aspersa* initiated by Dr. J. R. Baker, in which Dr. J. T. Y. Chou, the present writer and Dr. G. A. Meek participated.

Chou in 1956 showed that there were two kinds of lipid droplets in the cytoplasm of these cells that apparently consisted of pure lipid: small, highly refractile, colourless globules that appeared histochemically to consist of pure triglyceride (T in Plate 5.1, 5.2), that occurred for the most part in aggregates and rows in the axon hillock and the axon itself, and less refractile, larger globules, capable of being stained intravitally with Nile Blue (P in Plate 5.1, 5.2) that were more evenly distributed in the cell body and contained only phospholipid. The results of refractive index measurements made on both of these droplets in the living neurons by Ross & Chou (1957) with the immersion technique are shown in Table 13. It can be seen that, even when the maximum and minimum errors in the diameters of these droplets is allowed for, the refractive indices of the phospholipid globules are considerably lower than those of the triglyceride droplets. The triglyceride globules have refractive indices comparable with those of many pure lipids in vitro (*e.g.* those quoted by the *Handbook of Chemistry and Physics*, 1945) and are quite compatible with their consisting of pure triglyceride. The phospholipid globules, on the other hand, had lower refractive indices that any pure lipid substance, including pure phospholipid.

The only conclusion that one could draw was that the phospholipid-containing droplets must also contain water in intimate association. Now, the phosphoric acid-choline radicle of a phospholipid molecule is hydrophilic, and the molecules tend to orientate themselves with this

TABLE 13

The mean retardation of light of wavelength 542 mμ passing through the centres of lipid droplets in neurons from the dorsal ganglia of *Helix aspersa* mounted in isotonic saline/protein media with refractive indices equal to those of the cytoplasm, the diameters of the lipid droplets and their refractive indices calculated from these values

Measured phase retardation through globule (wavelengths)	Diameter of globule to the nearest 0·2 μ (measured by eyepiece micrometer)	Refractive index of globule from ϕ to t	Range of refractive index of globule; assuming a maximum error in diameter measurement
ϕ	t	n_1	
Triglyceride globules in the axon in a matching medium of n 1·3585			
0·306	1·2	1·496	1·496–1·526
0·277	1·2	1·484	1·484–1·510
0·234	1·0	1·485	1·485–1·517
0·272	1·0	1·506	1·506–1·544
0·228	1·0	1·482	1·482–1·514
Mean refractive index of trigylceride globules, 1·491			
Phospholipid globules in the cell body in a matching medium of n 1·3615			
0·139	1·4	1·415	1·408–1·424
0·111	1·2	1·411	1·405–1·424
0·095	1·0	1·413	1·404–1·426
0·122	1·2	1·416	1·408–1·428
0·182	1·6	1·423	1·416–1·433
Mean refractive index of phospholipid globules, 1·416			

part towards an aqueous phase, so that they form bimolecular lamellae (as, for instance, in V, Plate 5.2): Schmidt (1939), in his discussion of the stable configurations of such molecules, suggested that the submicroscopic structure of a phospholipid droplet in cytoplasm might consist of a series of concentric shells of bimolecular phospholipid laminae alternating with shells of water molecules, as illustrated by P in Plate 4.2. For triglyceride, on the other hand, he suggested the unhydrated and mostly disorientated form shown by T in the same plate.

The writer and Chou (1957) pointed out that their refractive index measurements were certainly compatible with Schmidt's suggestion but additional proof was fortunately soon forthcoming. Chou & Meek (1958) undertook a careful investigation of the same material with the electron microscope using an improved fixation technique, and they took a great deal of trouble to identify the two kinds of globule with certainty.* They

* Subsequent electron microscope studies by McGee Russell (1963) of the neurons of the closely related *H. pommatia* revealed 2 additional kinds of morphologically recognizable lipid droplets in these cells but it is extremely unlikely that Chou and Meek identified the phospholipid droplets in the neurons of *H. aspersa* wrongly.

found that the triglyceride globules had the amorphous form shown in Plate 5.3 and the phospholipid globules did indeed have the concentric laminar structure postulated by Schmidt (Plate 5.4).

7.3.2   *Refractometry as an aid to this histochemistry of cell inclusions*

Having established beyond reasonable doubt that those classes of lipid substances that are capable of forming intimate associations with water can, as a result, occur in the form of droplets with refractive indices lower than that of pure lipid, one can conclude that, when lipid droplets with markedly low refractive indices are found in living cells, they must contain considerable amounts of hydrophilic material. There are only two main classes of lipids that are known to have hydrophilic properties of this kind—phospholipids and cholesterol and the substances related to them—so that, in some cases, low refractive indices can give valuable additional confirmation of the presence of one or other of these groups.

An example of this was provided in the course of an investigation by the writer (Ross, 1961a) of the chemical and physical nature of the cytoplasm and cell inclusions of ascites tumour cells of mice. In all the seven different strains of tumour investigated, the larger cytoplasmic lipid droplets were found by histochemical tests almost always to be composite bodies consisting of a neutral lipid internal part surrounded by a shell of phospholipid which was characteristically thicker in the cells of some strains (notably the Krebs and Crocker strains) than in the others. With Baker's acid-haematein test (Baker, 1946) this region showed up as a black ring enclosing a central region which could be stained in a contrasting colour by Sudan IV. In the living cells, the refractive indices of these droplets could be measured quite easily when they were mounted in media with the same refractive index as the cytoplasm, as can be seen in Plate II, C. Table 14 shows the results of making such measurements. It will be seen from this table that, although by far the majority of the droplets had high refractive indices compatible with their containing mostly non-hydrophilic lipid material, 4 droplets (from the Krebs and Crocker strains) out of the 20 measured had lower refractive indices than any pure lipid substance, even when the maximum and minimum errors in their size measurement had been allowed for. This indicated that these droplets contained appreciable amounts of hydrophilic lipid related either to cholesterol or phospholipids. As they gave a negative reaction to Schultz (1924) and Schultz & Lorh's (1925) (admittedly not very critical) test for cholesterol, this strongly suggested that they did in fact contain quite large amounts of phospholipid. An

TABLE 14

Phase changes, measured through twenty-one large lipid droplets in six different strains of ascites cells, together with their thickness and the values for refractive indices calculated from these data. The final column gives the upper and lower limits of the refractive indices of these droplets, assuming an error of $\pm 0.2\,\mu$ in the measurement of their thickness.

Strain of ascites	Refractive index of cytoplasm	Measured phase change (degrees)	Measured thickness (μ)	Refractive index of droplet	Upper and lower limits of refractive index, assuming an error of $\pm 0.2\,\mu$ in thickness measure
Ehrlich	1·361	188	1·6	1·539	1·518–1·563
,,	1·357	218	2·4	1·494	1·483–1·507
Landschütz	1·356	104	1·2	1·492	1·472–1·537
,,	1·360	144	1·5	1·505	1·488–1·528
,,	1·360	128	1·2	1·522	1·487–1·538
,,	1·360	126	1·2	1·519	1·492–1·550
,,	1·360	132	1·4	1·502	1·485–1·522
,,	1·360	200	1·8	1·519	1·510–1·548
Krebs	1·356	200	1·8	1·523	1·506–1·543
,,	1·356	80	1·8	1·423	1·416–1·443*
,,	1·358	200	3·2	1·451	1·447–1·459*
,,	1·358	140	1·6	1·490	1·475–1·509
,,	1·359	150	1·6	1·499	1·484–1·521
,,	1·358	150	1·8	1·484	1·471–1·500
,,	1·358	188	2·0	1·499	1·488–1·515
,,	1·358	180	1·8	1·508	1·494–1·527
Sarcoma 1	1·360	170	1·5	1·520	1·510–1·558
,,	1·361	120	1·2	1·536	1·489–1·585
Crocker	1·359	80	1·6	1·434	1·426–1·445*
,,	1·359	52	1·3	1·420	1·411–1·430*
EL4	1·361	84	0·8	1·510	1·488–1·571

* These droplets have refractive indices lower than any pure lipid substance, even allowing for maximum error in measurement.

approach of this kind might also be used to indicate the presence of other intracellular hydrophilic substances as well as lipids.

7.3.3 The probable elongated shape of many of the molecules in nuclear sap, as illustrated by a refractometric study of the gene-bearing and non-gene bearing regions (bands and interbands) of polytene chromosomes in Diptera

A quantitative study undertaken by the author and Mr. H. Berendes, more fully reported by Berendes & Ross (1963), of the different regions of the polytene ('giant') chromosomes of *Chironomus* has proved particularly illuminating with respect to the interpretations that can be put on the measurements made.

As inclusions, the polytene chromosomes in the salivary glands of *Diptera* are not usually at all easily accessible for measurement, because they are nuclear inclusions enclosed within a granular cytoplasm (*c* in Colour Plate II, D, E, H) which is closely associated with, and often nearly completely surrounded by, the glandular product which is itself rather granular (indicated by *s* in the same photomicrographs in Colour Plate II). In many species, e.g. *Drosophila*, the chromosomes themselves are so long and coiled that it is usually quite impossible to find any part of them that is not obscured by other regions lying over and under them at different planes of focus. The salivary gland cells of *Chironomus* species, however, have very large nuclei containing quite short uncoiled chromosomes lying in clear homogeneous nuclear sap; when these cells were compressed, the surrounding cytoplasm and salivary vesicules could be almost entirely squeezed out from immediately above and below the nuclei in the manner shown in Fig. 27 (p. 157). The phase changes due to the bands and interbands relative to the nuclear sap could then be measured in all the regions of the chromosomes that happened to have these bands and interbands orientated in the direction of the optical axis of the microscope (see p. 141). Phase change measurements were confined, also, to those regions of the chromosomes where the interval between the individual bands and interbands was 1μ or more, because such measurements were less likely to be affected by diffraction effects from the phase boundaries at the band–interband junctions, or to errors resulting from these bands and interbands not being orientated exactly along the optical axis of the microscope. The chromosomes were assumed to be perfect cylinders and the widths of the regions on which the phase change measurements were made were measured by an eyepiece micrometer. The refractive index of the nuclear sap was measured both by the immersion of the compressed cells in a medium in which it matched the nuclear sap and from the difference in phase change given by the nuclear sap and a saline mounting medium in a preparation compressed to a known thickness as illustrated in Fig. 27. The values obtained for this by each of these methods (1·350–1·356 by the first way and 1·349 by the second way) were very similar, and indicated that the nuclear sap contained between 8·5% and 12% of solids.

From these measurements, the refractive indices of the bands (i.e. the gene-bearing regions, rich in DNA) and the interbands (the non-gene-bearing regions, without DNA) of the chromosomes could be worked out, and values for the percentage of total solids in each of these regions could be obtained. The results of measurements made in this way on the chromosomes of intact cells are shown in Table 15. From this it can be seen that, while the percentage of solid matter in the non-gene-bearing regions of the chromosomes is usually only very little higher than that of the nuclear sap and may be equal to it (as indicated by i in Colour Plate II D), the total of solids in the gene-bearing regions is in every case about 10% higher than that in the non-gene-bearing regions. It must be pointed out, however, that it is quite likely that the real differences in solid content between the two regions may be rather greater than these measurements indicate, because the spacing of the bands and interbands in these chromosomes is very irregular, and it is very possible that some of the apparently homogeneous regions of the bands that were measured included some very narrow unresolved interbands and, conversely, some of the interbands contained similar unresolved bands. If these were present, and a morphological study of polytene chromosomes indicates that this was quite likely, they would have tended to lower the apparent refractive indices of the bands and raised those of the interbands, but the errors introduced are unlikely to have been very big. Another possible source of error lies in the fact that there is some evidence (obtained by Berendes, 1960, 1961) to suggest that these chromosomes, although they are almost always circular in cross-section, are not always in the form of solid homogeneous cylinders, but are sometimes thick-walled tubes with a small central lumen containing a fluid with approximately the same refractive index as the nuclear sap down their centres. If this is true, it is not likely to affect the measurements of the non-gene-bearing interband regions very much, but will again tend to make the values for the total solid matter in the gene-bearing band regions lower than they really are. Consequently, it is probably safe to consider the values given for the refractive indices and solid content of the gene-bearing regions in the first part of Table 15 to be rather too low, and the values for the non-gene-bearing regions may be a little too high.

It was also possible to remove the chromosomes from the cells in an apparently intact condition by compressing the cells until their membranes were disrupted, and washing away the other cell debris. Similar measurements were made on the bands and interbands of these both when they were mounted in saline (as illustrated in Colour Plate II, I, J. K) and when mounted in an isotonic saline/protein solution with a refractive index close to that of the nuclear sap. The results of some of these measurements are shown in the second half of Table 15.

It will be seen that the values for the refractive indices of both the bands and the interbands of the isolated chromosomes mounted in saline are very nearly the same as those measured in the intact cells, but they are mostly just significantly lower. Much bigger differences, however, occurred in the measurements made on the isolated chromosomes mounted in the protein solutions and, from Table 15, the striking thing that appears is that, when the chromosomes were mounted in a solution of approximately 10% of protein, all the values obtained for the percentage total solids in the bands and interbands were almost 10% higher than those in the chromosomes in the intact cells. The rather lower and much higher refractive index values obtained respectively on the isolated chromosomes mounted in saline and in saline/protein compared to those obtained on the chromosomes in the intact cells probably indicates that these chromosomes, unlike intact cells, are permeable to quite large molecules, such as protein. In the case of those mounted in saline/protein, it seems likely that the protein of the mounting medium has freely entered the chromosomes and added its concentration to that of the chromatic material. In the case of the chromosomes mounted in saline, it is possible that some of the solid material in both regions (perhaps the matrix) has seeped out into the saline solution. In these preparations it is important to note that, although they were usually examined within a few minutes of the disruption of the cell and nuclear membranes, no alteration in phase change was ever seen that indicated that anything was entering or leaving the chromosomes, so that such changes as occurred must have been very rapid. This suggests that, unlike cell membranes, these chromosomes are porous to large molecules such as those of protein, It is not unreasonable that they should have this property because otherwise it is difficult to see how the genes, which are themselves large molecules, could otherwise exert their effect on the macromolecular structures of the cytoplasm (see Ross & Jans, in preparation): in support of this, it may be noted that no electron micrographs so far published have ever demonstrated any recognizable membrane around a chromosome.

If, however, all protein molecules were capable of entering the substance of these chromosomes equally readily, one would expect the chromosomes in the intact cells to be completely permeated by the solids in the nuclear sap, with the result that the refractive indices of their bands and interbands would be as high as those isolated and mounted in the saline/protein, which they are not. Some explanation of this discrepancy must be sought. The most likely one would seem to be that there is probably a difference in quality between the protein used for the mounting medium and the protein that most commonly occurs in the nuclear sap.

The bovine plasma albumin used to surround the isolated chromo-

readily capable of entering strands, but there is some material dispersed in the g chains of polypeptide or ted to enter less readily.

7.4   The measurement of the dry mass of inclusions in living cells

7.4.1   The product of concentration and volume

Because they are surrounded by cytoplasm or other material with refractive indices different to that of water, it is not possible to measure the dry mass of living cell inclusions by the direct method of measuring their area and the phase changes in the light passing through them in the simple manner described at the beginning of Chapter 6. It is possible nevertheless to use almost as simple and straightforward an approach to obtain values for their dry mass. This method consists of finding the weight/volume concentration of the substances comprising the inclusion in g/100 ml by measuring its refractive index, and then obtaining a value for its volume from its measurable dimensions and multiplying the two together. The product of the weight-per-unit-volume concentration and the volume of such an object gives a measure of its dry mass, since weight/volume concentrations of solids in solution are defined as being the weight of *dry* solid in 100 ml of the solution. This point needs emphasizing because both Hale (1958) and Walter (1964) state that the product of volume and concentration gives values for 'wet mass' and this is certainly not true if weight/volume concentrations are used. (The total 'wet mass' of a cell or part of a cell, i.e. the total mass of its dry substance plus that of the water associated with it, has been derived by Barer & Dick (1957) as being equal to $100 + 0.25C$ g/ml, where C is

TABLE 15

Measurements of the phase retardations, ϕ through bands and adjacent interbands in regions of measured thickness of the polytene chromosomes of *Chironomus*, with the values for the refractive indices and percentage solid content of the bands (gene-bearing regions) and interbands (non-gene-bearing regions) calculated from them

Thickness of the region of chromosome measured (μ)	ϕ measured through interbands (degrees)	ϕ measured through bands (degrees)	Refractive index and percentage of solids in interbands	Refractive index and percentage of solids in bands
MEASUREMENTS ON CHROMOSOMES IN INTACT, COMPRESSED, LIVING CELLS				
Mounted in saline/protein with a refractive index of 1·356				
10·0	30	108	1·361 ≃ 15·0%	1·372 ≃ 21·0%
6·5	0 (match)	64	1·356 ≃ 12·0%	1·371 ≃ 20·5%
8·0	0 (match)	128	1·356 ≃ 12·0%	1·380 ≃ 25·5%
Mounted in saline/protein with a refractive index of 1·353				
8·0	58	162	1·364 ≃ 16·5%	1·383 ≃ 27·0%
8·0	58	122	1·364 ≃ 16·5%	1·376 ≃ 23·5%
8·4	66	142	1·365 ≃ 17·0%	1·380 ≃ 25·5%
8·0	64	170	1·365 ≃ 17·0%	1·385 ≃ 28·5%
8·0	36	124	1·360 ≃ 14·5%	1·373 ≃ 21·5%
8·0	42	143	1·361 ≃ 15·0%	1·381 ≃ 26·0%
7·6	40	114	1·361 ≃ 15·0%	1·376 ≃ 23·5%
6·0	42	134	1·364 ≃ 16·5%	1·387 ≃ 29·5%
MEASUREMENTS ON ISOLATED CHROMOSOMES, DISSECTED OUT OF THE CELLS				
Mounted in 0·9% saline				
7·6	92	186	1·352 ≃ 10·0%	1·371 ≃ 20·5%
8·0	144	242	1·361 ≃ 15·0%	1·379 ≃ 25·0%
7·2	102	194	1·355 ≃ 11·7%	1·375 ≃ 22·5%
8·8	106	204	1·352 ≃ 10·0%	1·369 ≃ 19·5%
8·0	100	198	1·353 ≃ 10·5%	1·353 ≃ 20·6%
Mounted in saline/protein with a refractive index of 1·356				
8·4	106	200	1·375 ≃ 22·5%	1·392 ≃ 32·5%
7·3	100	206	1·377 ≃ 24·0%	1·398 ≃ 35·5%
6·0	132	204	1·389 ≃ 30·5%	1·407 ≃ 40·5%
7·8	92	198	1·374 ≃ 22·5%	1·394 ≃ 33·5%
7·0	72	174	1·371 ≃ 20·5%	1·393 ≃ 33·0%

equal to the weight/volume concentration of the solid material of its substance, but this parameter is usually of less interest to the cytologist than the dry mass.) The units of dry mass arrived at by multiplying the values for percentage solid concentrations by volumes in cubic microns are excessively small, for they are units of 10^{-13} g or tenths of a picogram: it is a measure of the extreme precision of interference micro-scopy in investigations of this kind that it is possible to obtain biologically significant differences in the dry mass of cell substances to the almost incredibly fine limits of around a fifth of a million millionth of a gram (see Figs. 28–30).

7.4.2   Measurement of the distributions of dry mass in the nucleoli of myoblasts

At the present time it seems as if the only cytological investigation involving the measurement of the dry mass of living cell inclusions using this approach are the studies by the present writer on the changes in dry mass of the nucleoli of living myoblasts during the normal differentiation of muscle straps (Ross, 1964) and in comparing nucleoli in uninucleate myoblasts from normal and dystrophic strains of mice (Ross, 1965). These are worth describing since they provide an illustration of both the difficulties which may be encountered and of the sort of accuracy one can expect to find in the final values.

In these studies the two special difficulties which were encountered stemmed from the fact that the nucleoli are nuclear inclusions, and from the fact that these nucleoli were considerably more irregular in shape than those of the mouse ascites tumour cells described on p. 159. The first difficulty was not so formidable, however, since, as with the ascites tumour cells recorded in Table 12 (p. 160), it was found that if these myoblasts (which had been grown in tissue culture and were thinly extended on glass surfaces) were mounted in saline/protein media with refractive indices between 1·358 and 1·360, both their cytoplasm and the nuclear sap of the majority of the cells appeared under the interference microscope to be of the same colour, and of the same intensity in mono-chromatic light as the background field. This meant that the refractive indices of both the cytoplasm and the nuclear sap in those cells were, to all practical intents and purposes, the same, and equal to that of the isotonic saline/protein mounting media. These refractive indices (1·358–1·360) indicate both the nuclear sap and the cytoplasm of those myoblasts contained around 14–15% w/v of total solid material (see Chapter 5, p. 107).

The difficulty arising from the irregularities in the shapes of the nucleoli, which usually took the form of short but somewhat irregular ellipsoids, was rather more serious, since it meant that it was virtually impossible to obtain accurate values for the refractive indices and volumes of individual nucleoli. This was because, although two of their dimensions could be measured accurately to $\pm 0·2$ μ with an eyepiece micrometer, their third dimension, that in the direction of the optical axis of the microscope, could not be measured at all. Thus, although all the phase changes in the light passing through the nucleoli were measured in the direction of the optical axis of the microscope, it was not possible to determine the exact thickness of nucleolar material through which the light has passed. It was therefore necessary to make an assumption about the third, immeasurable dimension of each nucleolus, and the assumption which was made was that this dimension was equal to the mean of the other two, measurable dimensions at right angles to it. Statistically speaking, this seemed the most sensible assumption to make (although in fact almost identical comparative values for nucleolar dry mass were, in the first instance, obtained by assuming instead that this unknown dimension was equal to the smaller of the two measurable dimensions). However, it was naturally necessary to make a much larger number of actual measurements than would otherwise have been required in order to draw conclusions of equal biological validity.

7.4.3   The procedure for calculating values for the dry mass of cell inclusions

The procedure adopted is best illustrated by the sample of the results obtained shown in Table 16. The two measurable dimensions of each individual nucleolus was first measured by a micrometer eyepiece (column 2 in Table 16), and a value for the third immeasurable dimension indicating the thickness of the nucleolus was obtained by averaging these (column 3). The phase change through each nucleolus was also measured (column 4), and values for its refractive index (column 5) were obtained from this, its assumed thickness (column 3) and the refractive index of the nuclear sap, cytoplasm and matching and mounting medium (column 1) by applying eqn. 13 on p. 151 above. From this refractive index value, a value for the w/v percentage of solid material in each nucleolus was obtained (column 6) from eqn. 2 on p. 35. Values for the volume, v, of each nucleolus (column 7) was then obtained from their known dimensions, a and b, and their assumed third dimension c from the familiar equation for determining the volume of an ellipsoid:

$$v = a \times b \times c \times 0.524 \tag{15}$$

The product of these last two values, the volume and the percentage of solid material in each nucleolus, gave a value for the dry mass of each nucleolus in tenths of a picogram (column 8) and, in the cases where there was more than one nucleolus in a nucleus these had to be added together to give values for the total dry mass of nucleolus material per nucleus (column 9).

It is clear that none of these individual values for the percentage solid concentrations and the dry mass of the nucleoli can be expected to be very accurate in themselves, since they are all derived from an assumed and quite probably untrue dimension; but when a large number of such values are obtained, it is obvious that valid inferences can nevertheless be drawn from the trends which these values exhibit, since the individual departures from accuracy exhibited by the unknown thickness values will tend to cancel out. The inferences which can be drawn from such trends are, as will be seen below, quite important.

7.4.4   The accuracy of individual dry mass measurements

Furthermore, it is an interesting fact that the values which one can obtain for the dry mass of individual nucleoli by employing this approach are actually rather more accurate than the values which they are derived from. A few trial calculations will show that any errors in estimating the thicknesses of the nucleoli affect the values obtained for their volumes more than the values obtained for their refractive indices from which the values for their percentage solid content are derived,* and that these errors act in opposite directions. Thus, a slight overestimation of the thickness of a nucleolus will lead to an underestimation of its refractive index and an even greater overestimation of its volume, and conversely. Since it is the product of these overestimated and underestimated values of the volume and percentage solid content of the nucleoli that give values for their dry mass, it follows that any opposite errors that they may contain will tend to cancel each other out, although they will not do so completely. This argument, of course, applies equally truly if the dry mass of any irregularly-shaped cell inclusion is measured in this way and means that, in general, the dry mass of a cell inclusion can be measured rather more accurately than either its refractive index or its volume.

7.4.5   Results of the study of the fusion of normal myoblasts

Fig. 28 shows in histogram form the values for the total nucleolar material per nucleus compiled from individual measurements made on 150 separate nucleoli in 65 nuclei from nearly equal numbers of living

* This is not quite true. The errors in the resulting values for dry mass can be shown to be considerably less than the errors in volume measurement from which they are derived, but greater than the errors in total percentage solids calculated from the refractive index measurements (see Ross, 1967).

uninucleate, binucleate and multinucleate myoblasts. It is immediately apparent that the nucleoli in the binucleate cells have, in general,

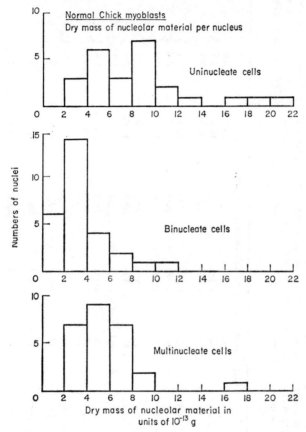

Fig. 28   Histograms showing the distributions of the total dry mass of nucleolar material per nucleus found in nuclei from uninucleate, binucleate and multinucleate myoblasts cultured from 4 chick embryos 10–12 days old.

markedly less nucleolar material per nucleus than in the uninucleate cells and that the nucleoli in the multinucleate cells give intermediate values for nucleolar dry mass. The inference which was drawn from these comparative values (by Ross, 1964) was that, during the process of cell fusion which takes place in the formation of multinucleate 'muscle strap' from uninucleate myoblasts, nucleolar material, quite probably RNA, is removed from the nucleoli at a greater rate than it can be resynthesized, and some of the nucleoli go down in mass. Subsequently, when cell fusion between myoblasts is completed, the nucleoli

TABLE 16

A sample series of measurements for determining the dry mass of nucleoli in living myoblasts

1 Refractive index of mounting medium	2 Dimensions of nucleolus (μ)	3 Assumed thickness of nucleolus (mean of 2 dimensions) (μ)	4 Phase change through nucleolus (degrees)	5 Refractive index of nucleolus (from 3 & 4)	6 % of solid material in nucleolus (from 5) (w/v)	7 Volume of nucleolus (from 2 & 3) (cu. μ)	8 Dry mass of nucleolus (from 6 & 7) (Tenths of a picogram)	9 Dry mass of nucleolar material per nucleus
			1-day explant from a 12-day embryo (15.3.63)					
1·360	3×4	3·5	36	1·376	23·0	22·0	6·0 }	9·1
1·360	2·5×3	2·75	54	1·390	35·5	10·8	3·8	
1·360	1×1	1	34	1·411	45·0	0·6	0·3	
1·360	4×5	4·5	48	1·376	23·0	47·1	10·4 }	16·7
1·360	2×3	2·5	48	1·389	30·5	7·9	2·4	
1·360	2×4	3	60	1·390	31·0	12·6	3·9	
1·360	2·5×2·5	2·5	32	1·379	25·0	8·4	2·1 }	6·0
1·360	2·5×4	3·25	32	1·375	23·0	17·0	3·9	
		1-day explant of a 12-day embryo (23.2.63)						
1·360	4×4	4	28	1·371	20·5	33·8	6·9 }	20·2
1·360	5×5	3	38	1·371	20·5	65·0	13·3	
1·360	2×5	3·5	30	1·373	22·0	18·3	4·0 }	9·1
1·360	3×4	3·5	34	1·375	23·0	22·2	5·1	
1·360	3·5×6	4·75	34	1·371	20·5	44·5	9·1	9·1
1·360	3×4	3·5	32	1·372	21·0	22·2	4·7	4·7
1·358	2×3	2·5	70	1·400	36·5	7·9	2·9 }	4·5
1·358	2×2	2	60	1·404	39·0	4·2	1·6	
1·358	1·5×2	1·75	25	1·380	25·5	2·8	0·7 }	2·0
1·358	1·5×3	2·25	30	1·378	24·5	5·3	1·3	

increase in mass again. This would account for the intermediate mean value for dry mass given by the nucleoli in the multinucleate cells because, although nearly all binucleate cells are the result of fairly recent fusions between myoblasts, multinucleate cells inevitably contain a mixture of constituents which are the product of both recent and less recent fusions.

Confirmation of this hypothesis was later provided by two separate lines of investigation: firstly, by studies with time-lapse cinemicrography which yielded evidence that many of the nucleoli in actively fusing myoblasts undergo a detectable linear shrinkage of the order of several microns and conversely a corresponding nucleolar swelling was observed in one or two cases after binucleate cells had been formed (Ross, 1965). An example of this nucleolar shrinkage is shown in the sequence of cinemicrographs at the top of Colour Plate III (p. 186) of a pair of chick myoblasts undergoing active fusion. In A the lower of the two nucleoli in the upper of the two fusing cells exhibits a smooth outline and is quite broad, while at the end of the fusion nearly $2\frac{1}{2}$ hours later it is narrower and appreciably indented. At the same time fusion has proceeded to the stage at which the granular cytoplasmic inclusions of the two cells have become intermingled. Secondly, densitometric studies of the distribution of cytoplasmic RNA demonstrated that this increased appreciably in one of each pair of actively fusing myoblasts (Ross & Jans, in preparation). It begins to look therefore as if the hypothesis outlined above may be the correct one.

7.4.6 Results of comparing myoblasts from normal and dystrophic mice

This method of measuring the dry mass of nucleoli was also used to compare the dry mass of the nucleoli in uninucleate myoblasts derived from normal and dystrophic mice. In this comparison more than 500 individual nucleoli were measured in the manner described above, and the distributions of the values obtained for the total dry mass of nucleolar material per nucleus obtained from around 45 cells each from three different genetic strains of normal mice of various ages and from three different age groups of a strain of mice exhibiting a form of muscular dystrophy were compared. These distributions are shown in histogram form in Figs. 29 and 30. Here, the particularly interesting thing is the proportion of cells with nucleoli which had a total dry mass of less than 0·75 p.g. In all the normal mice this proportion was under 4% regardless of strain and age; but in the dystrophic mice even the youngest individuals had around 15% of these cells with very lightweight nucleoli, and as the disease progressed with time, this proportion rose to over 50%

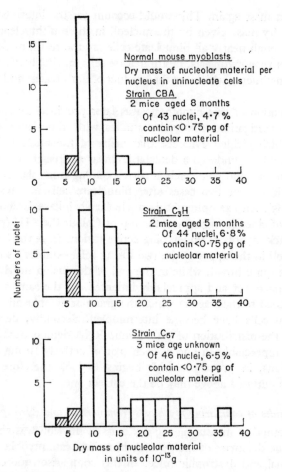

Fig. 29 Histograms showing the distributions of the total dry mass of nucleolar material per nucleus found in the nuclei of uninucleate myoblasts cultured from lesions in the adductor muscles of 3 different strains of normal mice.

Shaded areas show proportion of nuclei containing less than 0·75 pg of nucleolar material.

in the dystrophic mice over 6 months old. Muscular dystrophy is a hereditary disease characterized among other things by an inability of the muscle fibres to regenerate and differentiate normally, and this inability becomes accentuated with age. It is therefore at least a possibility that the diminution of nucleolar mass might here be a reflection of diminished RNA synthesis which, in its turn, could interrupt the implementation of the metabolic processes by which normal differentiation is

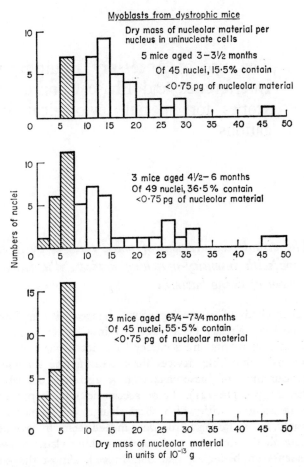

Fig. 30 Histograms showing the distributions of the total dry mass of nucleolar material per nucleus found in the nuclei of uninucleate myoblasts cultured from the muscles of the Bar Harbor dystrophic mice of different ages.

Shaded areas show proportion of nuclei containing less than 0·75 pg of nucleolar material.

effected. In any case it is at least clear that, when properly interpreted, estimations of the changes in dry mass of living cell inclusions can be of considerable biological interest, and more than justify the admittedly lengthy and tedious processes of accumulating the necessary comparative data.

8

The use of Accessory Equipment with Interference and Phase Contrast Microscopes for special Cytological Investigations

8.1   The visual measurement of phase changes by interference microscope with intensity-matching devices, illustrated by the measurement of living bacteria

Several methods of measuring phase changes with an interference microscope have already been described in Chapter 5 (pp. 97–101), but their relative merits and accuracy have not so far been discussed. Three intensity-matching devices for increasing the accuracy of the visual measurement of phase changes have also been described in the same chapter (pp. 116–121). These accessories can, if properly used, increase the accuracy with which phase changes can be measured quite considerably, but so far very little work indeed seems to have been done to evaluate all the different methods for making visual phase change measurements on biological material. Indeed, almost the only work along these lines seems to have been that of Ross (1955, 1957a, b) and latterly Ross & Galavazi (1965) in their attempts, with a Smith interference microscope and a Smith half-shade eyepiece, to obtain values for the mean widths of populations of living bacteria with an absolute accuracy greater than is normally possible by direct linear measurement. It should be emphasized, however, that absolute measurements of this kind represent a definite departure from the sort of experimental approach normally favoured by the present author, since phase change measurements by interference microscopy almost always involve systematic errors of some kind or other, and some of these are exceedingly difficult to evaluate (see Chapter 5, pp. 101–107). Consequently, as was mentioned in the Introduction (p. xvii), biological conclusions based on comparative rather than absolute measurements are usually far more satisfactory. But in the experimental work which will be described below an attempt is made both to evaluate the absolute errors in this particular instance and to throw light on the relative merits of measuring bacteria and other small microscopic objects by direct and indirect means.

The problem of measuring very small living micro-organisms is one which has interested the present writer for more than ten years. In the field of bacteriology, it is often desirable to obtain measurements of the dimensions of both stained and living bacteria with the light microscope, and many such records are to be found in the literature. By far the majority of these appear to have been made by direct measurement, either by means of an eyepiece micrometer or graticule, or by some more elegant device, such as the shearing eyepiece described by Dyson (1959, 1960), which nevertheless employs the same direct approach of making linear measurements, from boundary to boundary, of the image of the bacterium.

All such direct measurements are, however, fraught with the difficulties which arise directly from the nature of the diffraction effects that occur at the boundaries of the microscopic images formed by objects of the size and shape of bacteria, which almost always take the form of spheres, ellipsoids or round-ended cylinders with a finite thickness only a few times greater than a wavelength of light. In visible light all microscopic objects of this order of size form images with intensity gradients at their boundaries; the widths of the intensity gradients form an appreciable proportion of the total widths of the images themselves. Very formidable difficulties arise in determining which point on this intensity gradient at the edge of an image represents the true boundary of the object which forms it. This has been determined by Dyson (1960) for the edge of a broad opaque object with an incoherently illuminated straight edge. It has also been determined by Wolter (1950a) for objects of finite thickness with rectangular edges oriented parallel to the axis of a microscope, using a variety of different illuminating systems; the only comparable mathematical analysis of the diffraction gradients at the boundaries of objects of bacterial shape is that of Wolter (1950b). In this paper, which appears to be less well known than it deserves to be, Wolter concludes that, although under certain very stringent conditions, which can seldom be realized in practice, it is sometimes possible (especially with phase contrast or schlieren illumination) to determine the real boundary of such an object from its diffraction image, this image can be modified by many factors. These include the nature of the illuminating system, the numerical aperture of the objective, and the refractive index of the object itself relative to that of the mounting medium, so that, to quote Wolter, 'in ordinary microscopy these numerous limitations give rise to false diameter measurements'.

Furthermore, because of this uncertainty, there has hitherto been no generally agreed procedure for making these direct linear measurements. Those who have recorded measurements of the sizes of bacteria and other small microscopic objects have frequently, like Knaysi (1945), Dyson (1960) and Powell & Errington (1963), done so without precisely defining the points on the diffraction gradients from which the measurements were taken. Those who have defined these points have used different criteria in doing so. Dubin & Sharp (1944), Richards (1948) and Ross (1957a, b) thought it best to measure from the mid-points of the diffraction intensity gradients at the boundaries of the images. Charman (1963c) has given a valuable critical review of much of the existing literature on the measurement of test objects. He defines the 'visual size' of a microscopic object as the distance between those points on the diffraction gradients at the boundaries of the image that were just perceptibly different in intensity from that of the background field. He thus measured a somewhat larger parameter than these other workers, but found that this procedure was very convenient and repeatable. Charman's results can, however, be directly compared with the results of those who took their measurements from the mid-points, because, in nearly every case, he made a photometric record of the entire intensity gradient at the boundary of each image that he measured (p. 197).

A consideration of all these difficulties leads one to conclude that it is obviously desirable to seek alternative methods of measuring bacteria, if only to see whether the direct methods of measuring bacterial images in visible light are in fact justified. Indeed, the need for this was recognized by Pijper nearly forty years ago; he eventually devised two very ingenious methods for obtaining estimates of the comparative sizes of living bacteria without resorting to direct measurement (Pijper, 1952). The first depended on the fact that a suspension of bacteria illuminated with a parallel beam of light acts as a graticule and can be made to give rise to a series of diffraction rings with diameters that are consistently related to the mean size of the bacteria in suspension; the second method depended on differential filtration. Both methods gave accurate and comparable results in terms of the diameter of *Salmonella typhii*, but Pijper was careful to emphasize that these methods could only be regarded as comparative. Ross (1955, 1957a, b) devised a method of measuring the thicknesses of bacteria by interference microscopy, by which it was hoped that the difficulties of linear measurement could be circumvented and more reliable absolute values obtained; the work here reported conclusively demonstrates that all the measurements obtained at that time were subject to serious systematic errors because the apparatus then available for making phase change measurements were inadequate for such small objects. Ross & Galavazi (1965), however, developed a greatly improved method of making these phase change measurements, and the results which they obtained with it will now be described and evaluated, by comparing them with those obtained by other methods.

8.1.1   Material and basic experimental approach

All the measurements were carried out on typical strains of *Lactobacillus bulgaricus*. Cultures of this organism were obtained directly from the Laboratories 'Yalacta', 51 rue Lepic, Paris, for the original measurements that were made by Ross in England in 1955 and 1957, and for those made by Ross & Richards in the United States in 1958 (p. 192). For the measurements which were made by Ross & Galazavi (1965) in Holland the same organism was obtained from yoghourt bought at a Leiden creamery; as these last cultures were used to compare all the different interferometric methods which had been used previously with the one which was finally developed, any slight differences which could have occurred as a result of using a different strain did not affect the conclusions which were drawn.

In order to explain clearly the method of measurement which was finally adopted by Ross & Galavazi, it is necessary to give a brief account of the earlier methods of measuring phase changes and to describe their shortcomings.

In all the measurements the basic principle was the same; an interference microscope was used to measure the phase retardation, ϕ, of the light passing through the mid-line of a sharply focused living bacillus mounted in a saline solution with a refractive index n_m. The mean refractive index of the bacilli, n_b, was repeatedly measured by immersion refractometry, and was found to vary from $1 \cdot 398$ to $1 \cdot 404$ in different cultures. Values for the thickness of a bacillus, t, could thus be calculated from the equation:

$$t = \phi \times \frac{\lambda}{n_b - n_m} \qquad (16)$$

where λ was the mean wavelength of the light used. The great difficulty with these very small microscopic objects was to find methods of measuring the phase changes that gave repeatable results and were not subject to systematic error. Four methods were used.

8.1.2   The 'extinction point' method

The most obvious way of measuring phase changes with an interference microscope is to determine the two instrumental settings which give, firstly, a maximally dark background when monochromatic or nearly monochromatic light is used and, secondly, maximum darkness in the particular region of the object which one is measuring, i.e. by transferring the 'extinction point' from the background to the object. This, however, is the least satisfactory method, even when relatively large objects are being measured, since both instrumental settings are to some extent dependent on the subjective judgment of an individual observer as to what constitutes maximum darkness. Furthermore, it has been found that, when very small objects (such as bacteria) that give relatively low phase changes are measured by these means, most observers tend consistently to adjust the second setting of the instrument so that the bacterium appears in maximum contrast to a progressively lightening background, rather than at the position at which the bacterium is truly maximally dark. This causes the observer to make a systematic overestimation of the phase change in the light passing through the bacteria with the result that their widths are deduced as being greater than they really are (see Ross, 1957a, b, 1961b).

8.1.3   Method of matching with the half-shade strip

In the hope that the systematic error mentioned above might be eliminated if a method that did not require the observer to make subjective judgements of maximum darkness was employed, Ross in 1955 and 1957 made his measurements on the bacilli with a Smith interference microscope in conjunction with a Smith half-shade eyepiece, both of which were manufactured by Charles Baker of Holborn, Ltd. (now Vickers Instruments Ltd., Croydon). The construction and mode of operation of the half-shade eyepiece has been described and illustrated already on pp. 117–120. It consists of an eyepiece which contains a reflecting prism, on to the surface of which a very narrow strip of metallic aluminium has been deposited. This strip forms a special reflecting area which lies across the microscope field in the same plane of focus as the image of the object, but which is always out of phase with the background field by a constant amount, in the region of 120°. In monochromatic light or nearly monochromatic light the image of this strip can be used as a matching device, and phase changes through relatively large objects can be measured with a high degree of repeatability. This is done by first matching the intensity of the background to that of the strip, and then matching that part of the object that lies within the image of the strip with that which lies outside it (Fig. 25A, B).

Unfortunately, when this method was applied to measuring the phase changes that occur in bacteria a difficulty became apparent which was a direct consequence of their very small size. It was not difficult to manipulate the microscope stage so that the image of a bacterium lay partly inside and partly outside the image of the strip crossing the microscope field, but when this was done it was found to be extremely difficult to recognize the exact analyser setting at which the intensities of both parts of the image of the bacillus really matched each other. This was because the eye of the observer was misled by the markedly different intensities of the immediately adjacent regions of the strip itself. This difficulty was in fact both appreciated and discussed by the writer when he published his results in 1957. In 1961 he demonstrated the nature of this optical illusion by republishing one of his photomicrographs of an apparently matched bacillus lying across the image of the half-shade strip with the adjacent regions blocked out with pieces of white paper (Ross, 1961b). This made it very obvious that the two parts of the bacillus that appeared to match each other did not in fact do so. An even more convincing demonstration of this phenomenon can be provided by making a densitometer trace on the negative of the photomicrograph along the long axis of the bacillus and across the image of the half-shade strip. An example of this is shown in Plate 6.2, using one of the original photomicrographs (6.1) published by Ross in 1957. It is immediately apparent that the part of the bacillus a–b–c–d that lies within the image of the strip, b–c, is markedly darker than the rest of the bacillus, a–b and c–d.

As in the case of the 'extinction point' method, the error produced by this effect causes an observer to over-estimate the phase changes being measured, with the result that all the subsequent values derived from them for bacterial thicknesses are subject to a systematic error on the high side (Ross, 1957a, b, 1961b). However, since the values obtained were nevertheless appreciably lower than those provided by the 'extinction point' method, and since the half-shade eyepiece was then thought to be the best available means for measuring these phase changes, it was decided to publish the measurements obtained by these means, together with the qualification that this effect was bound to produce some degree of systematic error in the results.

The error was thought at that time to be relatively small and

Plate III   A–F—A succession of photomicrographs taken at various time intervals by time-lapse cinemicrography of two living myoblasts actively fusing in a tissue culture in the first stages of the formation of a muscle fibre. By the end of the 2 hr, 20 min of this sequence, the granular cytoplasmic inclusions in these cells have become intermingled, and the lower of the two nucleoli in the upper fusing cell has become appreciably shrunken and shrivelled. (See p. 177.)

A, o hr, o min.   B, o hr, 20 min.   C, o hr, 40 min.   D, 1 hr, 15 min.   E, 2 hr, o min. F, 2 hr, 20 min.

Plate III   G–O—A succession of photomicrographs of a group of living myoblasts growing in tissue culture taken with the space of 5 min at nine different instrumental settings of the Smith interference microscope. There is 5° difference in the analyser setting between each successive photomicrograph, which is the shift necessary to measure 10° of phase change in this instrument. In G the background is of second order red, and the cytoplasm of the cells appears purple, their nucleoli blue and the fat droplets in their cytoplasm green. In K their cytoplasm appears to have almost exactly the same colour as the background in G, which indicates that it retards the light passing through it by about 40° or $\frac{1}{9}\lambda$. In M the nucleoli appear to have the red colour of the background in G, indicating that they retard the light by about 60° or $\frac{1}{6}\lambda$, and in O this same red colour is shown by some of the fat droplets, indicating that they retard the light by about 80° or nearly $\frac{1}{4}\lambda$. (See pp. 97 and 208.) Vertically displaced 'ghost' images of the cells (see p. 93) can be plainly seen in both sets of photomicrographs.

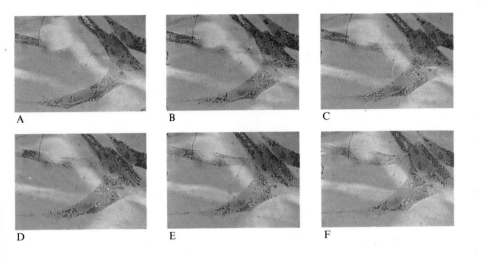

A   B   C

D   E   F

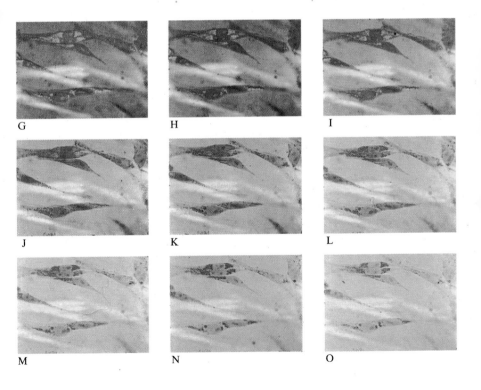

G   H   I

J   K   L

M   N   O

Printed in England by Beric Press Limited, Crawley, Sussex

unimportant, because Ross did in fact at the same time employ a second method that appeared to give very closely comparable results and seemed to serve as a check on their accuracy. This was a slightly modified version of Barer's double immersion technique (Barer, 1953b), which involved measuring by matching with half-shade strip the phase changes through bacilli mounted in two media of different refractive indices. By this means a value for the mean thickness of the bacilli, t, was obtained from the equation:

$$t = \frac{\phi_1 - \phi_2}{(n_{m2} - n_{m1})360} \times \lambda \qquad (17)$$

where ϕ_1 was the mean phase change (in degrees) in the light passing through the bacilli mounted in the medium of lower refractive index, n_{m1}, ϕ_2 was the mean phase change in the light passing through the bacilli mounted in the medium of higher refractive index, n_{m2}, and λ was the mean wavelength of the light used. By this method it was possible not only to obtain measurements for the mean thicknesses of the bacilli, but also to deduce values for their mean refractive indices from the thickness values already obtained and the phase change measurements (see Ross, 1957a, b). When this was done, it was found that the values obtained were nearly all closely comparable with the mean refractive index obtained by immersion refractometry.

The weakness of this apparent confirmation of the accuracy of the method of measurement (which was certainly not appreciated at the time when the results were reported) is that the magnitudes of the systematic errors in phase change measurement caused by the unmatched adjacent regions of the strip could, and almost certainly do, partly depend on the magnitudes of the phase changes being measured. As the 'double immersion' method depends on obtaining values for the differences between two sets of phase change measurements, these values will be misleading unless the systematic errors made in obtaining both sets of measurements are the same. In fact, it seems almost certain that when determining ϕ_2 (the smaller of the two phase change measurements) with a half-shade strip, the unmatched adjacent region of the strip will differ less in intensity from the image of the bacterium than when determining ϕ_1, the larger measurement: therefore in the former case the measurement obtained will be nearer the true value of the phase change than in the latter case. Thus, this would also tend to give values for the thickness of the bacilli which were too high.

8.1.4 The minimum 'visibility' method

A consideration of some of the difficulties involved in using the

15

method of matching with the half-shade strip led the present writer in
1958 to try out a third method of measuring the phase changes in the
light passing through the bacilli. This was by the 'minimum visibility'
method recommended in the handbook of the Baker Interference Microscope (Anon., 1954). In this method, no half-shade eyepiece was used
but phase changes were measured by the differences in the instrumental
settings required to obtain, firstly, a maximally dark background and
secondly the position at which the intensity of the interior part of the
bacillus itself matched as closely as possible the intensity of the background. In theory, this was less accurate than either of the two methods
already described, because the difference between the two instrumental
settings will only give a value for $\frac{1}{4}\phi$ instead of $\frac{1}{2}\phi$. In practice it was
found, however, that the second (matching) position of the analyser was
easier to recognize, and the reproducibility of individual measurements
was at least as good as that obtained by matching with the half-
shade strip. The results obtained were never published, but they were
closely comparable to those obtained by matching with the half-
shade strip and were thought to provide still more confirmation of their
accuracy.

However, the 'minimum visibility' method too was open to a very
serious objection, namely, that at the second position of the analyser
the image of the apparently-matched centre of the bacillus is surrounded
by the image of the edge of the bacillus, which has a markedly different
intensity. The eye is again misled into making a false judgement as to
what constitutes a true match between the centre region and the background. This is clearly demonstrated by the densitometric trace shown
in Plate 6.4 which was made across the bacillus illustrated in Plate 6.3.
The centre of this bacillus appears matched, but the trace across the
negative of the photomicrograph shows that in fact the centre is quite
appreciably darker than the background; the darker edge of the bacillus
evidently makes the centre look lighter than it really is. Thus exactly the
same kind of systematic error was inherent in this approach.

8.1.5   Method of matching with a half-shade small area

The difficulty of matching the intensities of two areas in the microscope field without an observer being misled by the close proximity of a
third unmatched area of different intensity had to be overcome in some
way. Clearly one way in which this could be done was by using a half-
shade eyepiece and reducing the size of the comparison area until one
of its dimensions was small enough for its image to be of the same size
as, or smaller than, the image of the bacterium being measured. In the

case of the Smith half-shade eyepiece this was achieved very satisfactorily by Ross & Galavazi (1965) by the simple expedient of using a specially sharpened fine scalpel to scrape away part of the metallic deposit that formed the strip across the reflecting surface of the prism so as to leave some tiny separate areas of the metalled surface. One of these, clearly indicated in Plate 7.1 and 7.2, was approximately rectangular and only just over 0·1 mm wide and, although it was imperfect through having an oblique scratch (s) across its centre, it was small enough to be completely covered by the full width of the image of a bacillus, as seen in Plate 7.1. In this position, the exact analyser setting at which the intensity of the image of the bacillus matched that of this tiny fragment of reflecting surface could be judged with much greater ease, and with much greater accuracy, than by any of the methods described hitherto.

The fact that this was so is clearly demonstrated by the densitometer trace illustrated in Plate 7.3 taken along the mid-line of the image of part of a long bacillus illustrated in Plate 7.1. No significant difference in the level of the trace can be seen throughout its length except at the Becke lines actually at the edges of the small comparison area, a and b, and in the position of the scratch, s. This could be shown even more strikingly by slightly shifting the position of the half-shade prism with respect to the microscope field without altering the setting of the analyser, as illustrated in Plate 7.2, so that the image of the bacillus lay across part of the intact and uninterrupted region of the half-shade strip. Because of the adjacent dark regions of the strip, the part of the bacillus lying across the strip, a–b, seems lighter than the rest of the image of the bacillus, but the densitometer trace (Plate 7.4) made along the long axis of the bacillus shows that this was not so and that in fact all the parts of the image of the bacillus matched each other.

This modification to the Smith half-shade eyepiece thus seems to confer a notable improvement in the efficiency of measuring phase changes through very small microscopic objects. It is no longer necessary to produce this effect by scraping since Vickers Instruments Ltd. of Croydon now supply, on request, this specially modified half-shade eyepiece with very small comparison areas already deposited on the prism and forming part of an interrupted half-shade strip.

Since the method just described, using a very small comparison area in a half-shade eyepiece, was clearly superior to any of the preceding methods, it was decided to compare it with the three other methods already described in order to try and quantify the systematic errors that had previously been obtained, and also to obtain an estimate of the individual variability of the measurements when more than one observer used each method.

For this purpose, the phase change through a single bacillus mounted in 0·9% saline (with a refractive index of 1·338) was measured by both Ross & Galavazi by all four methods. Ten separate phase change measurements were made by each observer with each method, so that the standard deviations of the measurements made by each individual could be calculated. For these measurements the microscope was arranged so that neither observer could see the analyser scale until after each setting had been made. Each observer also recorded his measurements independently of the other, and neither observer communicated his findings to the other until after all the measurements had been completed.

Table 17 records all the analyser readings made by each observer, together with the phase changes calculated from them and the standard deviations of the values for the phase changes. From the mean phase change obtained by each of us using each method it was possible to obtain a value for the thickness of the bacillus by applying eqn. 16 (p. 183). It was assumed that the refractive index of this bacillus was 1·404, which was the mean refractive index of a similar culture of *Lactobacillus bulgaricus*. The particular bacillus examined may not have had exactly this refractive index, but the thickness values so obtained provide a useful indication of the differences in the results obtained by each method when translated into terms of thickness. Furthermore, from the standard deviations obtained in each set of phase change measurements it was possible to obtain upper and lower values for each thickness measurement which represented the accuracy with which each of the methods could be used by each observer. From these values, an indication could be obtained of the accuracy to be expected when more than one observer used each method. These results are summarized in Table 17.

From these two tables some interesting facts emerge which would appear to provide numerical confirmation of many of the findings already mentioned regarding the relative merits of each method. The 'extinction point' method gave both the highest values for bacterial thickness and the greatest variability in the results. It was in fact even less accurate than the figure of $\pm 0.2\ \mu$ which is generally accepted as being possible to achieve by direct measurement on a small resolvable object in visible light. Matching with the half-shade strip and the 'minimum visibility' method gave closely comparable values for the thickness of the bacillus. The results, which were appreciably lower

TABLE 17

The analyser setting (in degrees) made by two different observers when using a Smith interference microscope to obtain 10 successive sets of measurements of the phase change in the light passing through a single specimen of *Lactobacillus bulgaricus* by the four different methods described in the text, together with the values for the phase change in degrees) mean phase change and standard deviation (S.D.) calculated from them

'Extinction point' method			*Half-shade strip matching method*			*'Minimum visibility' method*			*Half-shade small area matching method*		
Back-ground max. dark	*Bac-illus. max. dark*	ϕ	*Back-ground match*	*Bac-illus. match*	ϕ	*Back-ground max. dark*	*Bac-illus. centre match*	ϕ	*Back-ground match*	*Bac-illus. match*	ϕ

Observer 1 (K.F.A.R.)

58	91	66	49·5	72	45	61·5	70·5	36	51	65	28
60·5	92	63	50	73	46	60·5	72	46	50	65·5	31
61·5	89	55	50·5	76	51	61·5	72·5	44	50	62·5	25
61·5	91	59	51·5	75	47	62	71·5	38	50·5	65·5	30
61·5	92·5	62	51	74	46	60·5	71	42	51	64	26
58	95	74	50	73	46	59·5	71	46	50	63	26
61·5	92	61	51	75	48	61	70·5	38	50	63·5	27
60	88	56	51	72	42	61·5	71	38	50·5	64	27
59·5	88	57	50·5	72	43	59·5	71	46	50	62	24
62	88·5	53	51	75	48	59·5	72·5	52	50	65	30

| | | mean ϕ 59·6 | | | mean ϕ 46·2 | | | mean ϕ 46·2 | | | mean ϕ 27·4 |
| | | S.D. 6·3 | | | S.D. 2·0 | | | S.D. 5·1 | | | S.D. 2·3 |

Observer 2 (G.G.)

60	86	52	50	78	56	60	71	44	50	66	32
61	86	50	51	74	46	61	71	40	51	66	30
59	83	48	51	76	50	59	70	44	51	66	30
61	80	38	49	76	54	61	72	44	49	64	30
60	86	52	49	75	52	60	72	48	49	66	34
60	84	48	52	75	46	60	71	44	52	67	30
58	81	46	50	77	54	58	72	56	50	67	34
58	80	44	50	76	52	58	71	52	50	67	34
59	82	46	49	78	58	59	71	48	49	65	32
60	84	48	49	76	54	60	71	44	49	66	34

| | | mean ϕ 47·2 | | | mean ϕ 52·2 | | | mean ϕ 46·4 | | | mean ϕ 32·0 |
| | | S.D. 4·1 | | | S.D 3·7 | | | S.D. 4·7 | | | S.D. 2·7 |

than those obtained by the 'extinction point' method, showed a variability (derived from the standard deviations in the phase change measurements obtained by both observers) of $\pm 0.15\,\mu$, which was considerably less than the $\pm 0.26\,\mu$ obtained with the extinction point method. Finally, the results obtained by matching with the half-shade small area gave the lowest values for the thickness and the least variability of all, $\pm 0.11\,\mu$.

It will also be noticed that there were quite appreciable differences between the sets of measurements obtained by the two different observers. In both the methods using the half-shade eyepiece Galavazi consistently obtained higher readings for the matched position of the analyser than Ross, so that even the act of matching areas of the same intensity is to some extent affected by an individual's subjective judgement. However, even allowing for this, it was clear that matching with the half-shade small area was subject to the least instrumental error, and, as it had already been demonstrated densitometrically to have the least systematic error also, it was clearly the most accurate.

It is therefore reasonable to assume that the measurements of about $1.15\,\mu$ previously reported by Ross (1957a, b, 1961b) for the mean diameter of *Lactobacillus bulgaricus* should be amended to about $0.7\,\mu$ following the application of this demonstrably more accurate method of measuring phase changes. This revision is particularly interesting in the light of some previously unpublished work which was undertaken by the present writer and Dr. O. W. Richards in the research laboratories of the American Optical Co. at Southbridge, Mass., U.S.A. in July, 1958. Ross measured a total of 30 different specimens of *Lactobacillus bulgaricus* in four different preparations both by matching with the half-shade strip and by the 'minimum visibility' method, and obtained values for their mean diameter which varied from $1.0-1.1\,\mu$. Richards photographed the same individual bacilli under both $+$ve and $-$ve phase contrast with a quick-flash xenon lamp, and measured on the photographs the widths of sharply focused individuals, from the mid-points of the diffraction gradients at the edges of their images (in the manner more fully described by Richards, 1948). He found no differences between the dimensions of the $+$ve and $-$ve phase contrast images, and obtained values of between $0.43\,\mu$ and $0.64\,\mu$ for the diameters of the bacilli, with a mean of $0.55\,\mu$. These are, of course, much closer to the values that have now been obtained by interference microscopy by matching with the half-shade small area, but at that time it seemed as if there was a very big discrepancy between the values that could be obtained by interference microscopy and those arrived at by direct measurement.

This discrepancy did not, however, cause any very great concern to Ross at that time because, from a consideration of the diffraction gradients at the edges of images of small objects with a circular cross-section, he had been led to conclude that the dimensions of these images (measured from the mid-points of the diffraction gradients) can be expected to be appreciably less than the true dimensions of the objects that form them (Ross, 1957a, b). This view appears to accord with the conclusions arrived at in the mathematical treatment of the problem by Wolter (1950a, b), to whom all the credit for the original inception of the idea rightly belongs. It also receives partial confirmation in the recent experimental findings of Charman (1963c) discussed below. Briefly the argument can be stated as follows.

The intensity gradients across a uniformly light-absorbing object of square cross-section of the order of size of a living bacterium, seen in visible light with a 2 mm objective, will approximate fairly closely to the curve shown in Fig. 31A. C and C' represent the actual position of the edges of the square cross-section of side t. The main intensity gradients are in the zones between A and B, and A' and B'. Outside AA' a number of minor fluctuations (Airy patterns) may be visible but the largest of these, R, will have a maximum amplitude of only one fifty-seventh of that of the main gradients if there is no spherical aberration in the lenses of the optical system (Airy, 1835); its amplitude will certainly not exceed one twenty-fifth of that of the main gradients in most ordinary microscopes (Martin, 1926).

The width of the main gradient of intensity-change at each boundary h can be determined by the equation:

$$h = \frac{0 \cdot 61 \lambda}{N} \qquad (18)$$

where λ = the mean wavelength of the light used and N = the numerical aperture of the objective and condenser. The actual boundaries of the correct image of *any* microscopic object will always lie somewhere within the limits of this gradient; in the present case of an object with a square cross-section, they will be at C and C', exactly midway between A and B, and A' and B' respectively.

Thus, the true width of an object of square cross-section (lying with two of its sides parallel to the optical axis of the microscope) may be arrived at by measuring the image from the mid-points of the main

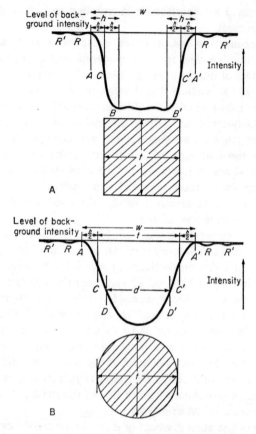

Fig. 31   A—The approximate distributions of intensity across the image, under a 2 mm microscope objective, of a uniformly light-absorbing microscopic object of square cross-section with a side t, of the size of a living bacterium. Ordinate = intensity. Abscissa = linear distance across the object at right angles to the optical axis of the microscope.

B—The approximate distributions of intensity across an image, under a 2 mm microscope objective, of a uniformly light-absorbing microscopic object of circular cross-section with a diameter t, of the size of a living bacterium. Ordinate = intensity. Abscissa = linear distance across the object at right angles to the optical axis of the microscope.

diffraction gradients at its edges. Alternatively, it may be determined from the equation

$$t = w - \frac{0.61\lambda}{N} \qquad (19)$$

where t = the true width of the object and w = the maximum width of the main diffraction gradient round the image ($=$ the length AA' in Fig. 31A).

This is mainly of theoretical interest, because very few microscopic objects have a square cross-section. There are, however, many biological objects of microscopic size with a circular cross-section and these include a great many kinds of living bacteria. The exact form of the intensity gradients across an object of circular cross-section, such as a cylindrical bacillus, is very difficult to determine exactly, but they will have a less steep slope than the curves shown in Fig. 31A, and will be, very approximately, of the shape shown in Fig. 31B. It is immediately obvious that a measurement between the mid-points of these shallower gradients (the length DD' in Fig. 31B) will *not* indicate the true width t of the cylinder, but will indicate a rather *lesser* width d. This effect will be even more pronounced if the object is not a cylinder but an ellipsoid, or a sphere as in the case of a coccus, because in these cases the gradients due to diffraction would be even less steep than in the case of the cylinder.

From this, because it is usual for an observer to estimate the width of a microscopic object from approximately the mid-points of the diffraction gradients at its edges, one is led to an important conclusion: microscopic objects of circular cross-section will tend to *appear* rather smaller than they really are.*

If, however, the present experimental results obtained by the technique of matching with the half-shade small area give truly accurate values for bacterial thickness they indicate that the errors arising from this effect of undersizing by visual measurement may not be so large, although they certainly appear to be present. From the upper value of 0·79 μ which this technique gave for the thickness of *Lactobacillus bulgaricus* (see Table 18) and the mean value of 0·55 μ obtained by Richards from the direct measurement of individuals of the same species, one can conclude that the discrepancy between the values obtained by the two different methods is unlikely to exceed 30% and would usually be appreciably less than this. However, in view of the uncertainties inherent in all methods of direct measurement it would seem, at the present time, to be inadvisable to claim an accuracy greater than ± 0·1 μ for any of the existing methods of measuring small microscopic objects

---

* Richards (1959) states that the foregoing explanation (first published by Ross, 1957) is 'inadequate'. The author readily agrees, but contends that, in the absence of a full mathematical investigation of the relevant diffraction phenomena, a geometric treatment of this kind is better than nothing at all. In the same paper, Richards continues 'the problem will only be solved when the diffraction image problems are solved for spherical and cylindrical objects'. True.

TABLE 18

The maximum and minimum values for the phase changes measured through a single specimen of *Lactobacillus bulgaricus* (obtained by two different observers using four different methods) calculated from the mean phase changes and standard deviations shown in Table 17, and the values for the maximum and minimum width (thickness) of the bacillus calculated from these assuming that it had a refractive index of 1·404. Values for the variation in the width measurements obtained with each method by both observers together are also shown

	'Extinction point' method	Half-shade strip matching method	'Minimum visibility' method	Half-shade small area matching method
Observer 1 (K.F.A.R.)				
mean ϕ	59·6°	46·2°	42·6°	27·4°
S.D. ϕ	6·3°	2·0°	5·1°	2·3°
max. ϕ	65·9°	48·2°	47·7°	29·7°
min. ϕ	53·3°	44·2°	37·5°	25·1°
max. width	1·50 μ	1·10 μ	1·09 μ	0·68 μ
min. width	1·22 μ	1·00 μ	0·85 μ	0·57 μ
Observer 2 (G.G.)				
mean ϕ	47·2°	52·2°	46·4°	32·0°
S.D. ϕ	4·1°	3·7°	4·7°	2·7°
max. ϕ	51·3°	55·9°	51·1°	34·7°
min. ϕ	43·1°	48·5°	39·7°	29·3°
max. width	1·18 μ	1·30 μ	1·16 μ	0·79 μ
min. width	0·98 μ	1·11 μ	0·90 μ	0·67 μ
Mean width (both observers)	1·24 μ	1·15 μ	1·00 μ	0·68 μ
S.D. in width (both observers)	±0·26 μ	±0·15 μ	±0·15 μ	±0·11 μ

in visible light. For this reason the present writer feels bound to express the view that claims such as that of Powell & Errington (1963) to have measured the absolute thickness of a bacterium accurately to ±0·03 μ represents a somewhat overconfident assertion which must be treated with reserve. The fact that the Dyson image-splitting eyepiece, which these authors used, has an instrumental accuracy of this order is not the point at issue, but one can legitimately ask whether the parameters which were measured with this instrument truly represented the real dimensions of the bacteria. This in no way detracts from the value of the comparative measurements which form by far the greater part of their paper, nor from the indisputable value of shearing devices of this kind for making such comparative measurements extremely accurately: it is, after all, such comparative measurements that are of principal interest in most bacteriological studies.

The recent very elegant experimental work of Charman (1963a, b, c; 1964) suggests a way in which it may soon be possible to draw more valid inferences about the true dimensions of bacteria and similar small microscopic objects from their diffraction images in visible light. This author has not only used microscopic test objects of known sizes which have been predetermined by electron microscopy, but has evolved a photometric scanning technique to record the entire intensity gradients at the edges of their visible light images. Unfortunately, his most detailed analysis has so far been confined to objects of very simple shape and negligible thickness, but it is interesting to note that, even with these, their 'visual size' is often appreciably different from their real size. Allowance must be made for the fact that Charman measured his visual sizes from the outer visible limits of the diffraction gradients and not from their mid-points, and when the latter measurements are made on his plotted intensity gradients for the images of opaque discs 0·1 μ thick there is quite a close correspondence between visual and real size. This would seem to agree with the conclusions of Wolter (1950a). Unfortunately, Charman has published no corresponding intensity gradients for the images of the polystyrene spheres, the 'visual sizes' of which he also measured, and which could have served as valuable bacterial models.

A rather similar approach, involving a comparison of the widths of air-dried *Bacillus megatherium* in light and electron microscopy, was undertaken by Dubin & Sharp (1944) who found a very close correspondence between the two sets of measurements. Unfortunately, however, this work cannot be regarded as being entirely above criticism because their electron micrographs reveal the presence of a slight surface deposit on the bacteria which could have affected their visual sizes under the light microscope (see Ross 1957b, p. 97).

8.2 Applications of microdensitometry to interference microscopy

In the measurement of living bacteria described in the preceding sections, microdensitometry was used to check the validity of the visual phase change measurements made with the Smith half-shade eyepiece accessory, by using it to check whether or not two areas of the field were precisely matched in intensity. A microdensitometer can, however, form a valuable accessory to an interference microscope as a means by which the phase changes themselves may be measured with great accuracy by recording the actual differences in intensity in the microscope field. Indeed, a considerable number of the earliest quantitative cytological investigations by interference microscopy were done with its help. The most notable example of this is the work described in the classical paper of Davies, Wilkins, Chayen & La Cour (1954); since it so happened that Dr. P. B. M. Walker, who was at that time working in the same department at King's College, London University, had just developed the first really satisfactory automatic 2-beam recording microdensitometer, and its suitability for determining phase changes by measuring the relative densities of different parts of the image of an object and of the background field was immediately apparent.

8.2.1   The basic principles of microdensitometry

It is unnecessary here to describe the optics and precise mode of operation of such a microdensitometer in detail, since this has been done by Walker (1956) and Walker & Deeley (1955). Essentially, it consists of an arrangement of glass prisms by which a beam of light from a single source is split so as to pass partly through a small area of a photographic negative lying on a glass stage and partly through a small area of a moveable glass 'density wedge'. Both beams are then made to impinge on photoelectric cells, and, by balancing circuits, the 'density wedge', which has a uniform density gradient along its length, is activated to move in the direction of this gradient one way or the other until the light passing through it is of exactly the same intensity as the light of the first beam passing through the selected region of the negative. The moving wedge is connected to a pen which will write on a piece of paper clipped on to a stage which moves at right angles to the movement of the wedge and pen. The stage carrying the paper is in its turn connected mechanically with the glass stage on which the photographic negative is placed and moves with it, so that, when both stages move, the negative is made to move across the path of the first beam and a continuous trace is made by the pen on the paper which moves under it that records the changes in optical density in the path of the beam scanning the negative. If the negative is of a photomicrograph of a cell, it is thus possible to trace out the differences of density in quite small areas of its image; it is even possible, by making a succession of contiguous traces across the whole area of the image of a cell, to obtain a figure for the overall optical density of the image of that cell or of any selected region within it (see Ross & Jans (in preparation).

8.2.2 Microdensitometry in quantitative histochemistry

A very satisfactory commercial version of this valuable instrument, which has many uses in an extremely wide variety of fields, is manufactured by Messrs. Joyce Loebl, Ltd. of Gateshead, England. In the field of cytology one of its most promising applications is in evaluating the depths of staining in fixed and stained histological and cytological preparations: for if such preparations are stained by histochemical dyeing techniques specific for certain cellular substances, and if the dyeing reaction is stoichiometric (i.e. if the depths of staining are truly proportional to the amounts of the cell substance that the histochemical reaction displays), the density trace will provide a measure of the relative amounts of that particular substance that are present in different parts of the cell. At the present time, however, not as much work has been done along these lines as might have been expected, probably because of the difficulties involved in establishing that given histochemical dyeing reactions are in fact stoichiometric: but the stoichiometric nature of the Feulgen reaction for DNA was established relatively early on by the work of Walker & Richards (1957) and others, and was used in a quantitative densitometric study of polyploidy by Leuchtenberger (1958) and others, who found that the DNA content of the polyploid cells increased by varying amounts which were always factors of 2. A more recent worker in the field was Szirmai who, with Balazs, established the stoichiometric nature of the Azure II test for polysaccharide (Szirmai & Balazs, 1958; Balazs & Szirmai, 1958) and used it with microdensitometry to determine its distribution in cartilage (see Galjaard, 1962). The potentialities of microdensitometry in this field are certainly very great, but so far this potentiality has been explored relatively little. There are so many optical difficulties to contend with before it is possible to ensure that the measured densities truly represent the amounts of the substances present in a cell that probably comparative rather than absolute measurements will be more profitable. Work in the field has been admirably reviewed by Chayen (in preparation).

8.2.3 Phase change measurements on isolated cells by 'fringe displacement'

It is, however, in conjunction with interference microscopy that microdensitometry has at the present time been most frequently used in quantitative cytological investigations, where it has been used as a means of measuring phase changes from photomicrographs of living cells. One method of doing this, which was first used by Davies, Wilkins, Chayen & La Cour (1954) has been called by Hale (1958) the 'fringe displacement' method. The interference microscope is set up, using monochromatic light, so as to give a 'fringe field' with fairly widely spaced fringes so that the image of a whole cell can be placed in a lighter region between two adjacent dark bands, but rather nearer to one band than the other, and the preparation is then photographed. Densitometric traces made across the photomicrograph negative at right angles to the

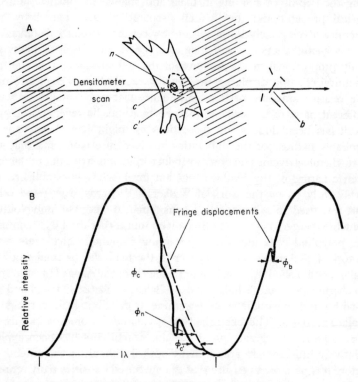

Fig. 32   Diagram (derived from Davies, Wilkins, Chayen & La Cour, 1954) showing the method of measuring phase changes on different regions of separate isolated cells with a microdensitometer by the 'fringe displacement' method.

A—Sketch of a cell and a group of bacilli in a 'fringe field' exhibiting 2 dark fringes. The densitometer scan, represented by the horizontal line, passes through the cell in the region of its nucleolus, n, and through a bacillus, b.

B—A representation of the densitometer trace across the two fringes showing the displacements caused by the cell and the bacillus in the field. The horizontal displacement of the fringe expressed as a fraction of the distance between successive fringes will indicate the phase change at any point along the scan.

direction of the fringes reveal a typical sinusoid curve, like that illustrated in Fig. 32, for the changes in density of the fringes in the background field: but if the trace crosses part of the image of a cell, such as that shown in the middle of Fig. 32A, this curve becomes distorted because of the greater phase changes in the light passing through the different regions of the cell. Such a distortion or displacement is seen in Fig. 32B and the dotted line represents the shape the curve would have taken if the cell had not been there. The amount displaced at any one point provides a direct and very accurate measure of the phase change through the equivalent point on the cell. For example, the phase change through the nucleolus n traversed by the trace in Fig. 32A is represented by the linear distance ϕn on Fig. 32B, and the two regions of cytoplasm c and c' are similarly represented by the distances ϕc and $\phi c'$ in Fig. 32B. Similar fringe displacements given by points on small microscopic objects such as that given by the centre of the bacillus b on the right hand side of Fig. 23A can be measured even more directly by the distance ϕb on Fig. 32B without it being necessary to make any reconstruction of the position of the background intensity curve like the dotted line in the middle of Fig. 32B. To convert all these displacements (e.g. the distances ϕc, ϕn, $\phi c'$ and ϕb in Fig. 32B) into actual measurements of phase change in fractions of a wavelength they must be expressed as fractions of the linear distance of the lateral displacement between two adjacent background fringes, i.e. of the distance λ in Fig. 32B.

Davies, Wilkins, Chayen & La Cour (1954) claim that an accuracy of $\pm 0 \cdot 005$ of a wavelength can be obtained by this method, which is more than twice that obtainable by any visual method of phase change measurement on cytological material. It is necessary, however, for the illumination across the field to be even, and that the cellular material should only occupy a small amount of the field. Hale (1958) has pointed out that this method can only be used in measuring cytological material that give phase changes of less than half a wavelength; with objects given greater values than this, an ambiguity arises, since a given intensity level might be related to either an ascending or a descending part of the curve depicting the changes for the background intensity. Fortunately, many cell regions in cells mounted in aqueous physiological media give phase changes less than half a wavelength.

8.2.4 Phase change measurements on continuous histological preparations

It is obvious, however, that as it stands this method is not suitable for measuring the phase changes in different cell regions in continuous sections, since in this case no portion of the background fringe field will be visible on the scan. To overcome this difficulty, Galjaard (1962) and Galjaard & Szirmai (1965) have developed a modification of the original fringe displacement method which will now be described. It is necessary to have an interference microscope capable of readily changing from a 'fringe field' to 'even field' without changing its magnification: thus the Horn microscope (which they used), the Dyson microscope, the Smith microscope and several of the Normarski microscopes described on p. 115 are suitable for this. A portion of the section is then placed in the field of the microscope and a substantial width of a free background area unoccupied by the section is also included in this field. Galjaard & Szirmai did this by photographing a region which included the edge of such a section; but this could equally well be achieved by scratching the block in the appropriate direction before cutting sections from it, as was done in a different study by Goldstein (1965) or by making holes in it, if a more interior region of the section needs to be

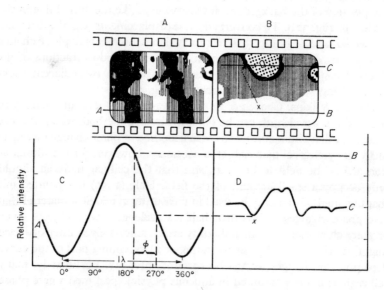

Fig. 33   The modification of the 'fringe displacement' method of measuring phase changes by densitometry developed by Galjaard (1962) and Galjaard & Szirmai (1965) for measurement on cellular regions in continuous sections.

A—Photomicrograph of a section and a clear area in a 'fringe field' showing a scan across two fringes in the clear area, A.

B—An adjacent photomicrograph of the same section and clear area in an 'even field' showing a scan across the clear area, B, and across a region of the section C.

C—The densitometer trace A.

D—The densitometer traces B and C on the adjacent photomicrograph. The horizontal displacement between B and C projected on to A expressed as a fraction of the distance between successive fringes will indicate the phase change at any point along scan C. (Redrawn from Galjaard, 1962.)

measured. Two successive photomicrogaphs of this preparation in mono-chromatic light are now taken: the first with the microscope adjusted to give a fringe field with the fringes sufficiently closely spaced for it to be possible to include two successive dark fringes in the clear background field unoccupied by the section (Fig. 33A), and the second taken with an even field microscope adjustment arranged so that the intensity of this even field in the background unoccupied by the section is equal to that given when the instrumental phase-measuring adjustment is moved by a distance equivalent to about one fifteenth of a wavelength for the position of maximum background brightness (Fig. 33B). Densitometric traces are then made at the same scale across the fringe pattern in the clear area on the first photomicrograph negative, A in Fig. 33C and across both the clear area B and the section C in the second even field photomicrograph, Fig. 33D. From these two sets of traces, Fig. 33C and D, the fringe displacement exhibited by any region x on the photo-micrograph of the section taken in even illumination, Fig. 33B, can be obtained by measuring the distance, ϕ, between the intensity it exhibits and the intensity of the background field projected on to the curve given by the fringe field background in Fig. 33C. As before, this hori-zontal distance has to be expressed as a fraction of the total horizontal distance between the maximally dark regions in two successive back-ground fringes in order to obtain actual values for the phase change (relative to the background) at the point being measured.

Since all densitometric methods depend on making accurate measure-ments of the optical density of photographic negatives, it is always ex-tremely important to ensure that the film exposure time and develop-ment times are such that each level of optical density of the preparation photographed is truly represented in a strictly linear manner by a series of equivalent densities in the negative, for it is obvious that a very short exposure or development time will give a very light negative and a very long exposure or development time will give a dark one. In either case the relative densities of the features photographed will not be linearly reproduced. Furthermore, some films will only permit such linear repro-duction over a very restricted range of densities in the subject photo-graphed, so the choice of film is important, too. In the absence of suitable film exposure and development data, it is necessary to deter-mine these by photographing different regions of a density step wedge under a microscope under standardized conditions of illumination, and measure the densities of a succession of photomicrographs taken at different exposures and subjected to different development times until one is satisfied that the densities of the subject matter being studied

16

falls within the limits of linearity provided by a selected set of conditions. Very little data on this subject has in fact been published, and that which has can only serve as a rough guide, since the intensities exhibited by different cytological material and the intensities of microscope illumination vary greatly. Galjaard & Szirmai in their study of cartilage obtained linearity with their preparations under a Horn interference microscope with a 4 mm objective by using an Ilford FP3 film exposed for 1 second and developed in 'Rodinol' (an Agfa product) for 5 minutes at 18°C, and Ross & Jans (in preparation) obtained it in their study of Toluidene blue stained myoblasts by ordinary light microscopy with a 4 mm objective by using a Kodak plus X film exposed for one fifth of a second and developed for 15 minutes at 20°C in Kodak 'Microfile'.

8.2.5 Densitometry with phase contrast microscopy

It could happen that an investigator might possess a microdensitometer of the kind described and a phase contrast microscope, but no interference microscope. Although the present writer knows of no instance of it having been done, it should be possible to measure phase changes through certain areas near the edges of cells and through small cells such as bacteria with this equipment by measuring their optical density and that of the background and relating this to intensity/phase change curves of the kind shown in Fig. 5 (p. 18). It would not, however, be possible to measure the phase changes in the more interior regions of larger cells because the 'shading off' optical artefact would falsify the intensity values, nor could the measurements obtained be expected to be very accurate owing to the fact that it is seldom possible to determine the absorption of a phase plate very accurately. Such an attempt might be worth making if no interference microscope were available, even though, because of the serious optical objections to this approach, any results obtained would be subject to error. Nevertheless, for comparative work, such results might be useful.

If such an investigation was to be combined with the immersion of the cells in a series of protein solutions, it would be possible to trace out a large part of a curve such as those shown in Fig. 5 from the different depths of optical density which the region of the cell in question exhibited in each of the different media and by extrapolation arrive at a value for its refractive index. An investigation along these lines was actually done by the present author in 1953 on some fungal spores, but without a densitometer the different appearances of the spores had to be judged subjectively and accurate quantification was not possible.

8.3 Applications of cinemicrography to phase contrast and interference microscopy

8.3.1 Cinemicrography with phase contrast microscopy

Cinemicrography has added a new dimension to cytological studies in that it enables a continuous record to be made of a wide variety of cellular activities. Many important and fundamental studies of the behaviour of living cells were made with it and even before the advent of phase contrast microscopy; for example, as early as 1917, W. H. Lewis and M. R. Lewis made their important observations on living myoblasts in tissue culture, by which they established the fact that their cells normally fused with each other in the course of the development of a fully differentiated muscle fibre, with the aid of an ordinary light microscope with a reduced aperture stop; Pijper (1957) made all his elegant observations on bacterial flagellar movements with dark-ground illumination. Phase contrast microscopy, however, gave an enormous impetus to the morphological study of living cell activities, and the important and interesting cytological problems which have been successfully tackled by its use with cinemicrography are far too numerous to enumerate or comment on here. Much of this work is, however, admirably reviewed in the articles contained in the excellent book *Cinemicrography in Biology* edited by G. R. Rose (1963). Mention has already been made (p. 26) of the pioneer study in this field by Michel (1941) with his phase contrast film of cell division during spermatogenesis in the grasshopper in which the curious peripheral movements of the mitochondria during metaphase and anaphase were first recorded: if any other studies are to be singled out for special mention, undoubtedly the studies of Bajer & Molè-Bajer (1963 and elsewhere) on the process of mitosis in wheat endosperm cells and their analysis of chromosome movements merit this distinction. The interesting haemological and other studies of Pulvertaft (1956, 1959) also deserve mention since for some reason all mention of them has been omitted from G. G. Rose's book and Professor Pulvertaft's contributions to this field have been by no means negligible.

8.3.2 Ambrose's quartz wedge eyepiece for phase change measurement with interference cinemicrography

In the field of interference microscopy Ambrose (1956, 1957b) was undoubtedly the pioneer in using cinemicrography. Initially his studies were principally of morphological changes and, for reasons that have already been discussed at some length (pp. 91–95), the morphology of living cells are in many respects more correctly reproduced under an interference microscope than under a phase contrast microscope. Later, however, he realized that it would be possible to include in the cine record a means by which the actual phase changes through different cellular regions could be measured on each frame. To achieve this, he developed an ingenious modification to the eyepiece of the Smith interference microscope with which he made his studies, so that the image of a quartz wedge occupied a small part of the field finally photographed (Ambrose, 1963). This meant that, when white light was used, the succession of Newtonian interference colours exhibited by the wedge, which were linearly related to phase change, could be matched to the colours of different regions in the cells in the rest of the microscope field. This modified eyepiece is, unfortunately, not at present marketed commercially, but Fig. 34 shows how it can be simply constructed in almost any

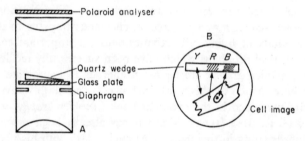

Fig. 34 A—The arrangement of the quartz wedge and polaroid analyser in a Huygenian eyepiece, modified by Ambrose, to form a reference area in the microscope field as an aid to cinemicrography. The quartz wedge is mounted on a circular disc of plain glass and placed in the plane of the secondary image, and occupies a position rather to one side of the microscope field. A piece of polaroid is conveniently placed over the top of the upper lens of the eyepiece where it can be rotated as desired to give a background field of a suitable colour before superimposing the camera.
B—A microscope field containing one cell viewed with this eyepiece. The background field has been adjusted so that it is second order yellow (Y). The yellow (Y), red (R) and blue (B) interference colours exhibited by the wedge can be matched to different regions of the cell and background, thus giving indications of the phase changes exhibited by each region.

laboratory possessing a Smith interference microscope. The quarter-wave plate and the analyser on this microscope must first be removed or placed in the 'out' position and the (Huygenian) eyepiece must be dismantled and a quartz wedge placed in the plane of the diaphragm in the secondary image plane. A polaroid analyser must then be placed in some position above this, and the most convenient place for it is above the upper eyepiece lens where it is accessible and can be rotated by hand to give optimal colour contrast. With the device Ambrose & Bajer (1960) made some most interesting studies of the variations in phase changes occurring in the regions of the chromosomes, spindle and cytoplasm during the later stages of mitosis in the endosperm cells of *Leucojum astiveum*.

8.3.3 A simple and inexpensive set-up for cinemicrography with interference or phase contrast microscopy

The present writer has used cinemicrography with interference microscopy to establish the fact that some of the nucleoli in cultured myoblasts undergo appreciable amounts of linear shrinkage during the process of the fusion of these myoblasts to form a multinucleate muscle strap (Ross, 1964, 1965), a fact which he had been led to strongly suspect from his studies of the changes in their dry mass (pp. 175, 177), and remarks based on the writer's own experiences in this field may perhaps be helpful. Much has been written about cine apparatus, massive supporting pillars, warm chambers and the like, and a great many of the recommended set-ups are very costly and elaborate (see, for example, Lefeber, 1962). The present writer has found that, provided a camera with a magnetically operated shutter is used in preference to one operated mechanically through a cable, elaborate rigid support for the camera is unnecessary. The 16 mm Scientific Camera marketed by W. Vinten Ltd., Bury St. Edmunds, England is excellent for this purpose.

A warm chamber or a warm stage is essential if living tissues from homoiothermic animals are studied and, of the two, a warm chamber completely enclosing the microscope is definitely preferable. Such a chamber built of Perspex around a Smith interference microscope by Mr. H. Taylor of Taylor Industries Ltd., Rowlands Gill, Durham, England, and based on a design first developed by Professor R. J. V. Pulvertaft, is illustrated in Plate 8.1. It is heated by two 800 ohm 0·3 amp resistance coils connected together in parallel and then placed in series with an adjustable thermostat manufactured by Sunvic Ltd., England. Even when the access doors to the chamber are opened for short periods to enable the instrument to be focused and adjusted the temperature recorded by the thermometer on the stage fluctuates by less than ± 1 °C from 37 °C. This rigid Perspex case carries the weight of the camera and film cartridge so that even the relatively small vibrations emanating from the magnetic shutter are not transmitted appreciably to the microscope. Frames taken at one second exposure or even shorter are sharp and clear and the whole apparatus relatively simple, easily transportable and inexpensive (see Colour Plate III, p. 186).

8.3.4   Recording phase change measurements on short-lived preparations by interference cinemicrography and microdensitometry

Microdensitometry can be usefully combined with the use of cine apparatus with the interference microscope to solve one otherwise somewhat intractable cytological problem. Many preparations of living cells mounted under a microscope deteriorate quite rapidly. It is not often that valid phase change measurements can be made on, for example, living cells mounted in isotonic saline/protein solutions after they have been on the microscope stage for more than half an hour. It sometimes happens that this time is inadequate for making all the individual measurements that are needed, and the investigator suffers the frustration of seeing some of the cells begin to become moribund before all the features of particular interest which they contain can be measured. One way of overcoming this, however, successfully tried by the present writer, is to take a series of exposures of the preparation on cine film with each successive frame at a slightly different instrumental setting of the phase change-measuring mechanism than the previous frame. With the Smith interference microscope the present writer set the time-lapse mechanisms to take one frame every 15 seconds; this gave ample time to change the analyser setting by, say, a degree between each shot. An example of this approach is illustrated in the sequence of cinemicrographs at the bottom of Colour Plate III, p. 186; in this case the analyser has been rotated by 5° between each successive frame, which is, of course, too great to enable phase changes to be measured with the required precision. Later this method was still further improved by first setting the analyser to give what was judged to be a nearly maximally dark background and taking alternate frames always at this setting with the intervening frames progressing by a degree at a time as before. In this way one can photograph every cell in the field at a complete recorded series of analyser settings, and at several different depths of focus, in under 15 minutes. This record can subsequently be analysed densitometrically to determine which cell feature at what analyser setting exhibited the same optical density as that of the initial background setting, which, being repeated on alternate frames, provided a readily available point of reference. This method is not only quick but very accurate, since levels of density between each degree of analyser setting (equivalent to 2° of phase change measurement with the Smith microscope) can be detected readily and the final analysis of the film by densitometer can be done at leisure.

Appendix I

Converting an Ordinary Light Microscope for use as a Phase Contrast Microscope

Modern phase contrast microscopes seldom cost less than £250, and although many microscope firms also market sets of phase contrast objectives and a special condenser with centring annuli, by which one of their standard microscopes may be adapted for use as a phase contrast microscope, such 'conversion kits' usually cost at least £75. What is not generally appreciated is that many ordinary light microscopes can be converted far less expensively to provide phase contrast of a quality which compares favourably with that given by many very expensive research instruments. The only expenditure needed is for the purchase of phase contrast objectives, and, if adequate workshop facilities are available, in some cases only the phase plates need actually be bought, at around £5 for each objective.

The present writer used such a conversion illustrated in Plate 8.2 for all his work with phase contrast microscopy between 1953 and 1963 and all the phase contrast photomicrographs in this book, except those in Plates 1 and 9, were taken with its aid.

This conversion was developed nearly 20 years ago by Dr. J. R. Baker and his colleagues at Oxford (Kempson, Thomas & Baker, 1948; Baker, Kempson & Brunet, 1949). Its principles have been incorporated in the commercial phase contrast microscope manufactured and marketed by W. Watson Ltd., of Barnet, England between 1950 and 1966. It differs from the conventional Zernike type of phase contrast microscope illustrated in Fig. 3 (p. 14) only in the positioning and relative sizes of the annuli and phase plates. The phase plates, instead of lying in the back focal plane of the objectives are placed at some distance above this plane, and this enables the annuli to be placed well in front of the front focal plane of the condenser (where they normally occupy the position of the sub-stage aperture stop). Instead they are placed immediately in front of the microscope lamp where they occupy the position normally occupied by the field-stop (Fig. 35). One effect of this is that these annuli do not need to be anything like as small or as finely made as those in the orthodox position immediately beneath the condenser and therefore they can easily be cut with scissors from black paper and stuck on to a piece of glass which can be placed in the filter holder which is often provided next to the field stop on many microscope lamps.

If objectives with a lower power than 4 mm are not used, such an annulus should not need to be greater than 1½ inches in diameter and consequently it can be used in conjunction with quite a number of standard microscope lamps which have fully illuminated aperture stops of this diameter. If 16 mm phase contrast objectives are to be used, the appropriate annulus often needs to be larger (up to 2 ins. in diameter) Designing a lamp to accommodate this presents some difficulties, and is

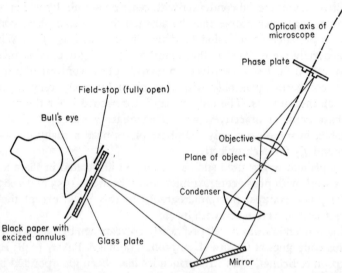

Fig. 35 The essential optics of the modified system of phase contrast developed by Kempsen, Thomas & Baker (1948) and Baker, Kempson & Brunet (1949) which can be used with many ordinary light microscopes by making a few relatively inexpensive modifications. (Drawing slightly modified from Kempsen *et al.*, 1947.) The condenser and objective are shown by single lenses and an eyepiece is omitted. (The phase plate shown here is a −ve one; normally it would be a +ve as in Fig. 3A.)

probably the principal reason why the Watson commercial version of this phase contrast system is rather less satisfactory than many homemade ones using only 2 mm and 4 mm objectives. The low power phase contrast objectives are, however, much less often required for most cytological problems than higher power ones, and can usually be dispensed with.

Kempson, Thomas & Baker (1948) describe how to make phase plates, but this requires good workshop facilities and considerable skill. It is therefore best to buy the phase plates mounted in a special cell which are still marketed by W. Watson Ltd., of Barnet, England. These can be made to fit into the back of many objectives, but are specially designed to screw into the backs of the Watson's 4 mm 'parachromatic' and fluorite 2 mm objectives, and, as these are very good optically, it is recommended that they are bought complete with detachable phase plates. Since the establishment of the Royal Microscopical Society standardization, all microscope objectives have a standard thread and are interchangeable so that these objectives may be used on almost any microscope, although some tube length correction may be necessary.

Having now got an objective with a phase plate, it is next necessary to mount an object upon the microscope stage and focus it with this objective; then, in order to be able to determine the correct size for the lamp annulus, it is necessary to be able to obtain a magnified image of this phase plate. This can be done with the 'telescope', provided as a standard piece of equipment with every phase contrast microscope to replace the eyepiece, but even this costs nearly £10. Many microscopes have, however, at the bottom of their draw-tubes a standard R.M.S. thread into which a standard objective may be screwed, and, as an alternative to using a telescope, one can use a very low power objective, e.g. 20–40 mm in this position and draw out the tube to obtain a sharply focused image of the 25% absorbing phase plate which appears as a grey ring.

It is next necessary to determine the size of the annulus suitable for this particular phase contrast objective, and for this a special measuring device must be constructed to take the place of the annulus which will be placed just in front of the lamp in or immediately adjacent to the plane of the field stop. The best device of this kind consists of a number of circles inscribed in Indian ink on a piece of tracing paper each 1 mm in diameter larger than the one immediately inside it, and with figures indicating their diameters marked on every other circle. When this is mounted centrally on a piece of glass and placed in front of the lamp, it can be focused in the plane of the phase plate by appropriately adjusting the focus of the sub-stage condenser. Small movements of the mirror will then make the images of these inscribed circles coincident with the image of the phase plate, and it can at once be determined which circles have diameters equal to the outer and inner circles formed by the image of the phase plate. The annulus for this objective then has to be inscribed on black paper so that its outer diameter is very slightly less and its inner diameter very slightly more than the diameters which would exactly correspond to the image of the phase plate. This means that when the annulus is made, all of its image can be made to lie just within the image of the phase plate which is important, since if any of it lies outside the image the quality of the phase contrast will deteriorate markedly.

One now has a phase contrast objective and an appropriate annulus, cut out of paper and mounted on glass. The latter must be placed as nearly as possible exactly on the line of the optical axis of the microscope and lamp and so a rigid filter holder should be fixed to the lamp beside the field stop to keep it in that position whenever it is dropped in place. (Alternatively a centring device for the annulus can be provided on the lamp like that shown in Plate 8.2, but this is not absolutely necessary.) To adjust the microscope the whole procedure already described is repeated.

1. Place the specimen to be examined on the stage and focus it with the phase contrast objective without the annulus in front of the lamp. (If necessary stop down the substage aperture stop to give any transparent living material some measure of visibility.)
2. Focus the phase plate at the back of the objective with the phase telescope in the place of the eyepiece, or with a low power objective screwed into a partially withdrawn draw-tube, and an ordinary eyepiece.
3. Drop in the annulus on the lamp and adjust the focus of the substage condenser (which needs to be in a lower position than that for normal microscopy) until a sharp image of the annulus is obtained in the plane of the phase plate.
4. Move the mirror carefully to and fro until the image of the annulus coincides with and all lies just inside that of the phase plate.
5. Remove the telescope or low power objective, replace eyepiece and examine the specimen.

To avoid double images, the microscope mirror needs to be surface aluminized so that light is only reflected from its upper surface. Ordinary untreated microscope mirrors are unsatisfactory, and this treatment is inexpensive. For the best results the condenser too should preferably be chromatically corrected although an ordinary Abbe condenser is quite reasonably satisfactory. If these instructions are followed out carefully, it is possible to adapt most ordinary light microscopes to give a high-quality phase contrast image. This conversion could also be done on instruments with 'built in' illumination, by placing somewhat smaller annuli on the window of the illuminator.

Suitable Microscope Illumination

A great many dogmatic statements about microscope illumination are to be found in the literature and much of this dogmatism is unjustified. Dr. J. R. Baker, in a paper which is less well known than it deserves to be

(Baker & Bell, 1951), has established the fundamental and necessary properties of an adequate microscope lamp and these are best appreciated by referring to Fig. 36 which, together with Fig. 37, is reproduced here with Dr. Baker's permission, as is the following passage from this paper.

The source of light and the quality of the lamp-condenser (if any) are irrelevant, provided that certain conditions are fulfilled. These conditions are shown in Fig. 36. The field-stop has an aperture that is focused by the sub-stage condenser in the plane of the object. Imagine that the apertures of both the field-stop and the aperture-stop (sub-stage iris) are divided into a large number of small areas. Perfect lighting should then result if these conditions are fulfilled:

(i) Approximately the same amount of light must pass through each of the small areas of the aperture of the field-stop.

(ii) From each of the small areas of the aperture of the field-stop, light must pass in approximately equal amount to each of the small areas of the aperture of the aperture-stop.

The position of the source of light should make no difference, provided that these two conditions are fulfilled.

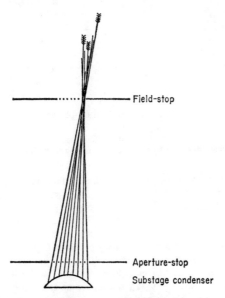

Fig. 36 The conditions that should be fulfilled by lighting systems; the mirror is omitted to simplify the diagram. (From Baker & Bell, 1951.)

The areas into which the field-stop must (in imagination) be divided must be so small that the image of the aperture of the field-stop appears perfectly structureless in the microscopical field of view. The areas into which the aperture-stop must (in imagination) be divided must be so small that there is no special tendency towards central, zonal, marginal, or oblique illumination.

There is no special virtue in focusing the source of light in the plane of the object. The source may be anywhere, provided that the conditions laid down on p. 213 and illustrated diagrammatically in Fig. 36 are fulfilled. It follows that very diverse lighting systems are permissible. Three systems especially commend themselves: the plain opal bulb (or a plate of opal glass lit from behind), the pearl bulb withdrawn some distance behind the field-stop and large-source Kohler illumination. These are illustrated diagrammatically in Fig. 37. Rays proceeding from a single small spot on the surface of the bulb are traced in each case. It will be noticed that if rays proceeding from many such spots be considered, the required conditions are fulfilled.

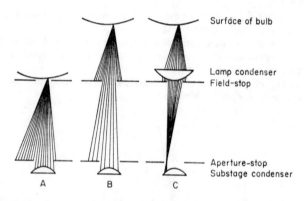

Fig. 37   Three lighting systems that fulfil the necessary conditions. A cone of rays is traced from a small spot on the surface of the bulb in each case (mirror omitted).
A—Opal bulb close behind field-stop.
B—Pearl bulb withdrawn behind field-stop.
C—Large-source Köhler illumination. (From Baker & Bell, 1951.)

A plain opal bulb with a field-stop in front of it (Fig. 37A) is a good illuminant. The fact that its surface is not flat is no drawback. It is not suitable when very high magnification is necessary, because its light is not sufficiently intense to allow the eye to work at maximal acuity. A pearl bulb throws a much more intense beam, because there is less scattering of light. It is for this reason that when one looks towards a pearl bulb, only a small part of its surface appears to be brightly illuminated. Since the surface is not structureless, it is necessary to withdraw the bulb some distance behind the field-stop (Fig. 37B), so that when the plane of the latter is focused by the sub-stage condenser in the plane of the object, the structure of the pearl surface is not seen. If the surface is placed 60 mm behind the field-stop, its image will not be visible when a 2 mm objective is used. This very simple lighting system is admirable for high-power microscopy. It is necessary, however, to be sure that the brightly illuminated part of the pearl surface is large enough to fulfil the conditions laid down on p. 213. To find this out, take a piece of cardboard and cut a circular hole in it of the size of the largest field-stop that you are likely to use in high-power work (say 7 mm radius). In another piece of cardboard cut a circular hole the size of the largest aperture of the sub-stage iris that you will need to use. Set up these two pieces of cardboard parallel to one another and 200 mm apart (the distance between iris and field-stop, via the mirror). Now look through the hole representing the iris aperture and examine the pearl bulb placed (say) 60 mm behind the aperture representing the field-stop. Use a filter to reduce the intensity of the light. Move the eye about. Satisfy yourself that in whatever direction you look through the two holes, the part of the surface of the pearl bulb that is visible appears evenly illuminated. If that is so, the necessary conditions are fulfilled.

The only disadvantage of this system of lighting is that when an objective of 4 mm or longer focus is used, the greater depth of focus results in the appearance of the pearl surface in the field of view. The easiest way to avoid this trouble is to place a lamp-condenser behind the field-stop, and to put the bulb at such a distance behind the lamp-condenser that the pearl surface is imaged in the plane of the sub-stage iris (Fig. 37C). This large-source Kohler illumination is a lighting system that we recommend as being suitable for all powers. It follows from our experiments that there is no advantage in using a highly corrected lens as a lamp-condenser when this system is used. A simple plano-convex lens is suitable. Even when a very small field-stop is used, the simple lens will not produce colour fringes at the edge of the image of the stop in the microscopical field of view (though an uncorrected sub-stage condenser will necessarily produce such fringes).

The present writer has found that the brightest and most satisfactory lamp for this large source Kohler illumination is a Phillips 'blended' 160 watt, 220–230 volt a.c. lamp, type 57270E/56. This gives a very bright illumination and is very suitable for the 2 mm phase contrast objectives. Its light has an appreciable component of ultraviolet however, and, although the glass in the microscope may be expected to absorb most of this, for absolute safety to the eyes it is advisable to use an Ilford 805Q filter or some similar ultraviolet-absorbing filter somewhere in the optical system.

Appendix II

Brief Clinical Notes on Patients with Various Blood Disorders whose Corpuscular Refractive Indices are shown in Figs. 14-16 and 17

These data were obtained and supplied to the writer by Dr. J. B. Howie* in September and October 1952. The haemoglobin estimations were made with a grey wedge photometer and the values for mean cell diameter with a Waterfield halometer.

(a) *Five established cases of iron deficiency anaemia associated with a variety of different conditions, all untreated* (Fig. 14, p. 72)

Case B.T. Blood examined 22.9.52 ♀ with bleeding haemorrhoids. Mild iron deficiency with an appreciable proportion of normal cells in the film Hb 65% (916 g)

Case A.P. Blood examined 19.9.52. ♀ with pregnancy anaemia. Moderate iron deficiency. Hb 70% (104 g)

Case C.B. Blood examined 1.10.52. ♀ with pregnancy anaemia. Moderate iron deficiency. Hb 54% (8·0 g)

Case U. Blood examined 1.10.52. ♀ with pregnancy anaemia. Marked iron deficiency. Hb 50% (7·4 g)

Case D.B. Blood examined 26.9.52. ♀ (18 years) with menorrhagia. Severe iron deficiency. Hb 41% (6·0 g)

(b) *Three established cases of untreated pernicious anaemia* (Fig. 15, p. 73)

Case B.B. Blood examined 13.10.57. ♀ P.A. established by megaloblastic marrow and characteristic peripheral blood films. Hb 52% (7·7 g). Mean cell diameter 8·2 μ. Reticulocytes 1·2%

Case A.F. Blood examined 23.10.52. ♀ P.A. established by megaloblastic marrow and characteristic peripheral blood films. Hb 48% (7·1 g). Mean cell diameter 8·0 μ. Reticulocytes 0·6%

Case D. Blood examined 13.10.52. ♂ P.A. established by megaloblastic marrow and characteristic peripheral blood films. Hb 53% (7·8 g). Mean cell diameter 8·1 μ. Reticulocytes 0·9%. This case was examined again after 10 days treatment with vitamin B_{12} (see (c))

* Then at the Department of Haematology, Radcliffe Infirmary, Oxford; present address, Department of Medicine, University of Dunedin, New Zealand.

(c) *Two cases of pernicious anaemia under treatment with vitamin B_{12}* (Fig. 16, p. 74)

Case D. Blood examined 23.10.52 (after previous examination, before treatment, on 13.10.52, see (b)). ♀ Showed characteristic response to vitamin B_{12} therapy, commenced on 13.10.52. Hb 58% (816 g). Mean cell diameter 8·1 μ. Reticulocytes 15·4%

Case A.N. Blood examined 26.9.52. ♀ P.A. originally established on 19.9.52 by megaloblastic marrow and characteristic peripheral blood pictures with Hb 45% (6·7 g). Mean cell diameter 8 μ. Reticulocytes 1%. Showed characteristic response to treatment with vitamin B_{12}, and after 7 days of treatment Hb 59% (8·7 g). Mean cell diameter 8·2 μ. Reticulocytes 37·8%

(d) *One established case of spherocytosis* (acholuric jaundice) (Fig. 18, p. 77)

Case W. Blood examined 30.10.52. ♀ Aged 6. Hb 79% (11·7 g). Reticulocytes 3·3% Abnormal fragility curve. Patient subsequently cured by splenectomy

(e) *A single case of atypical iron deficiency anaemia, in which immersion refractometry played a decisive diagnostic role* (Fig. 18, p. 77)

Case C. Blood examined 29.10.52. ♂ Originally reported as having macrocytic red cell morphology not characteristic of liver-factor deficiency (P.A.). No history of haemorrhage. Hb 68% (10·1 g). Mean cell diameter 8·1 μ. Finally diagnosed as mild iron deficiency anaemia and treated with iron for one month. On 27.11.52, Hb 101% (14·9 g). Mean cell diameter 7·3 μ. Normal film

References—Author Index

Note.—The references marked with an asterisk * are to written reports and personal communications known to the author which were not themselves printed and published.

The numbers in square brackets indicate the pages in the text on which that reference is cited and discussed.

ADAIR, G. S. & ADAIR, M. E. (1934) *Biochem. J.* **28**, 1230. [8]

ADAIR, G. S. & ROBINSON, M. E. (1930) *Biochem. J.* **24**, 993. [8, 9]

AIRY, G. B. (1835) *Camb. Phil. Trans.* **5**, 283. [193]

*ALLEN, R. D. (1958) personal communications. [38, 45 46]

ALLEN, R. D., BRAULT, J. & MOORE, R. D. (1963) *J. Cell. Biol.* **18**, 223. [122]

ALLEN, R. D., BRAULT, J. & ZEH, R. (1966) in *Recent advances in optical and electron microscopy* ed. BARER, R. & COSLETT, V. Academic Press, New York and London [122]

ALLEN, R. D. & DAVID, G. B. (1966) *Proc. R. Microsc. Soc.* **1**, 143. [122]

ALLEN, R. D., DAVID, G. B. & HIRSH, L. F. (1966) *Proc. R. Microsc. Soc.* **1**, 141. [94, 95]

AMBROSE, E. J. (1948) *J. scient. Instrum.* **25**, 134. [104]

—— (1956) *Nature* **198**, 1194. [205]

*—— (1957a) quoted by DAVIES, 1959. [xx, 129, 134]

—— (1957b) *Proc. R. Soc.* **B148**, 57. [205]

—— (1963) in *Cinemicrography in Cell Biology* ed. ROSE, G. G. Academic Press, New York and London. [206]

AMBROSE, E. J. & BAJER, A. (1960) *Proc. R. Soc.* **B153**, 357. [161, 206]

ANON. (1954) in *The Baker Interference Microscope*, p. 19, 1st ed. Charles Baker of Holborn Ltd., London. [188]

ARMSTRONG, S. H., BADKA, M. J. E., MORRISON, K. C. & HASSEN, M. (1947) *J. Amer. Chem. Soc.* **69**, 1753. [8]

BAJER, A. & ALLEN, R. D. (1966) *Science* **151**, 572. [95]

BAJER, A. & MOLÈ-BAJER, J. (1963) in *Cinemicrography in Cell Biology* ed. ROSE, G. G. Academic Press, New York and London. [205]

BAKER, J. R. (1946) *Q. Jl. microsc. Sci.* **87**, 441. [166]

—— (1966) *Jl. R. Microsc. Soc.* **85**, 231. [14]

BAKER, J. R. & BELL, A. S. (1951) *J. Quekett microsc. Club* series 4, **3**, 261. [213]

BAKER, J. R., KEMPSON, D. A. & BRUNET, P. J. C. (1949) *Q. Jl. microsc. Sci.* **90**, 323. [24, 209]

BALAZS, E. A. & SZIRMAI, J. A. (1958) *J. Histochem. Cytochem.* **6**, 278. [199]

BARER, R. (1952a) *Jl. R. microsc. Soc.* **72**, 10. [16, 17, 19, 20]

—— (1952b) *Nature* **169**, 366. [10]

*—— (1953a) personal communication. [31]

—— (1953b) *Nature* **172**, 1098. [128, 129 187]

—— (1955a) *Research, Lond.* **8**, 341. [54]

—— (1955b), in *Analytical Cytology* ed. MELLORS, R. C., Chapter 3. McGraw-Hill, New York and Maidenhead. [88, 108, 112]

—— (1956a) in *Physical techniques in biological research* eds. OSTER, G. & POLLISTER, A. W. Vol. 3, p. 30. Academic Press, New York and London. [50, 52]

—— (1956b) *The interference microscope in quantitative cytology*, supplement to *The Baker interference microscope* 2nd ed. C. Baker of Holborn Ltd., London. [124]

—— (1957) *J. opt. Soc. Am.* **47**, 545. [54, 78]

—— (1966) 'Frits Zernike—an obituary' *Proc. R. Microsc. Soc.* **1**, 185 [11]

BARER, R. & DICK, D. A. T. (1957) *Expl. Cell Res. Suppl.* **4**, 103. [124, 129, 130, 170]
BARER, R., HOWIE, J. B., ROSS, K. F. A. & TKACZYK, S. (1953) *J. Physiol., Lond.* **120**, 67P. [56, 61, 71]
BARER, R. & JOSEPH, S. (1954) *Q. Jl. microsc. Sci.* **95**, 399. [5, 6, 7, 22]
—— (1955a) *Q. Jl. microsc. Sci.* **96**, 1. [37, 41, 42, 45, 46]
—— (1955b) *Q. Jl. microsc. Sci.* **96**, 423. [54, 56]
BARER, R., JOSEPH, S. & ESNOUF, M. P. (1956) *Science, N.Y.* **123**, 24. [54]
BARER, R. & ROSS, K. F. A. (1952) *J. Physiol., Lond.* **118**, 38P. [34]
BARER, R., ROSS, K. F. A. & TKACZYK, S. (1953) *Nature* **171**, 720. [34]
BARER, R. & TKACZYK, S. (1954) *Nature* **173**, 84. [8]
BARTER, R., DANIELLI, J. F. & DAVIES, H. G. (1955) *Proc. R. Soc.* **B144**, 412. [144]
BENNETT A. H. (1946) *Sci. Mon.* **63**, 191. [33]
BENNETT, A. H., JUPNIK, H., OSTERBERG, H. & RICHARDS, O. W. (1946) *Trans. Am. Microsc. Soc.* **65**, 99. [15]
—— (1951) *Phase Microscopy, principles and applications.* John Wiley, New York: Chapman & Hall, London. [xvi, 11, 16]
* BERENDES, H. (1960) personal communications. [168]
—— (1961) *Genen Phaenen* **6**, 70. [168]
BERENDES, H. & ROSS, K. F. A. (1963) *Chromosoma* **14**, 111. [28, 54, 167]
BEYER, H. (1966) *Proc. R. Microsc. Soc.* **1**, 144. [115]
BROWN, G. L., MCEWAN, M. & PRATT, M. (1955) *Nature* **176**, 161. [9]
* VAN DEN BROEK (1961) Doctoral dissertation, University of Leiden, Holland. [27, 53]
CAPERS, C. R. (1959) *J. biopys. biochem. Cytol.* **7**, 559. [136]
CASPERSON, T. (1936) *Skand. Arch. Physiol.* **13**, suppl. 8. [102]
—— (1950) *Cell Growth and Cell Function.* Norton, New York. [102]
CASTLE, I. S. (1933) *J. gen. Physiol.* **17**, 41. [31, 32]
CHAMOT, E. M. & MASON, C. W. (1938) *Handbook of Chemical Microscopy* 2nd ed., Vol. I. Chapman & Hall, London. [133]
CHARMAN, W. N. (1963a) *J. opt. Soc. Am.* **53**, 410. [197]
—— (1963b) *J. opt. Soc. Am.* **53**, 415. [197]
—— (1963c) *Jl. R. microsc. Soc.* **82**, 81. [182, 193, 197]
—— (1964) *Jl. R. microsc. Soc.* **82**, 163. [197]
CHAYEN, J. (in preparation) in *Cell structure and its interpretation—essays presented to J. R. Baker, F.R.S.* ed. MCGEE RUSSELL, S. & ROSS, K. F. A. Edward Arnold, London. [199]
CHOU, J. T. Y. (1957) *Q. Jl. microsc. Sci.* **98**, 59. [164]
CHOU, J. T. Y. & MEEK, G. A. (1958) *Q. Jl. microsc. Sci.* **99**, 279. [165]
DANIELLI, J. F. (1954) *Proc. R. Soc.* **B142**, 146. [143]
—— (1958) in *General Cytochemical Methods* ed. DANIELLI, J. F., Vol. I, Academic Press, New York and London. [126, 144]
DAVID, G. B. (1963) *Information* **49**, 75, Carl Zeiss, Oberkochen. [91]
DAVID, G. B., ALLEN, R. D., HIRSH, L. F. & WATTERS, C. D. (1966) *Proc. R. Microsc. Soc.* **1**, 142. [95]
—— (1967b) *Jl. R. microsc. Soc.* (in press). [95]
DAVID, G. B., MALLION, K. B. & BROWN, A. W. (1960) *Q.Jl.microsc. Sci.***101**, 207. [91]
DAVIES, H. G. (1958) in *General Cytochemical Methods* ed. DANIELLI, J. F., Vol. I. Academic Press, New York and London. [6, 8, 9, 100, 101, 102, 108, 121, 124, 126]
—— (1959) *Biochim. Biophys. Acta* **32**, 228. [6, 8, 133, 135, 146, 156]
DAVIES, H. G., BARTER, R. & DANIELLI, J. F. (1954) *Nature* **173**, 1234. [125, 143]
DAVIES, H. G. & DEELEY, E. M. (1956) *Expl Cell Res.* **11**, 169. [xviii, 101]
DAVIES, H. G., ENGSTRÖM, A. & LINDSTRÖM, B. (1953) *Nature* **172**, 1041. [125]
* DAVIES, H. G. & WILKINS, M. H. F. (1951) *Physical aspects of cytochemical methods;* report of the Cytochemistry Commission for the Society for Cell Biology, Stockholm. [10]
—— (1952) *Nature* **169**, 541. [10]

17 +

DAVIES, H. G., WILKINS, M. H. F., CHAYEN, J. & LA COUR, L. F. (1954) Q. Jl. microsc. Sci. 95, 271.   [6, 7, 109, 125, 199, 201]
★ DICK, D. A. T. (1954) quoted by BARER & JOSEPH (1955a).   [41, 135]
—— (1955) Q. Jl. microsc. Sci. 96, 363.   [52, 129]
—— (1958) Proc. R. Soc. B149, 130.   [52]
DUBIN, I. M. & SHARP, D. G. (1944) J. Bact. 48, 313.   [182, 197]
DYSON, J. (1949a) British Patent spec. 676749. Class 97 (i) 16.6.49.   [108]
—— (1949b) Nature 164, 299.   [108]
—— (1959) Nature 184, 1561.   [181]
—— (1960) J. opt. Soc. Am. 50, 754.   [181, 182]
—— (1966) Proc. R. Microsc. Soc. 1, 139.   [122]
★ VAN DER EB, A. (1961) Doctoral dissertation, University of Leiden, Holland. [83]
EXNER, S. (1887) Pflüger's Arch. ges. Physiol. 40, 336.   [33]
FAURE-FREMIET, E. (1929) Protoplasma 6, 521.   [33, 46]
FLEMMING, W. (1882) Zell substanz, Kern und Zelltheilung, Vogel, Leipzig.   [26]
FRANÇON, M. (1952) Revue Opt. theor. instrum. 31, 65.   [114]
—— (1956) Hanb. des physiol. 24, 452.   [114]
—— (1961) Progress in Microscopy. Pergamon Press, Oxford, London, New York, Paris.   [108]
FREDERISKE, A. M. (1933) Protoplasma 19, 473.   [30, 31]
—— (1935a) Z. wiss. Mikrosk. 52, 48.   [87]
—— (1935b) Verh. I. Internat. Kongr. Electro-Radio-Biologie 1, 535.   [87]
FRIEDMAN, C. A. & HENRY, B. S. (1938) J. Bact. 36, 99.   [xvi]
★ GALAVAZI, G. (1963) Doctoral dissertation, University of Leiden, Holland.   [64, 78]
GALBRAITH, W. (1955) Q. Jl. microsc. Sci. 96, 285.   [30, 130, 162]
GALJAARD, H. (1962) Histochemisch en interferometrisch onderzoek van hyalien kraakbeen. Doctorate thesis, University of Leiden, Holland.
                                                          [54, 114, 144, 199, 201, 202]
★ GALJAARD, H. & ROSS, K. F. A. (1962) Testing and comparison of the Zeiss and Baker interference microscopes by visual and densitometric methods. (Unpublished report).   [110, 111]
GALJAARD, H. & SZIRMAI, J. A. (1965) Jl. R. microsc. Soc. 84, 27.
                                                      [54, 114, 144, 146, 147, 201]
GLADSTONE, J. H. & DALE, J. (1858) Phil. Trans. R. Soc. 148, 887.   [5]
GOLDACRE, R. J., EASTY, D. M. & AMBROSE, E. J. (1957) Nature 180, 1487.   [28]
GOLDSTEIN, D. T. (1965) Jl. R. microsc. Soc. 84, 43.
                                         [7, 54, 129, 134, 144, 145, 146, 148, 202]
GOMORI, G. (1939) Proc. Soc. exp. Biol. Med. 42, 33.   [143]
Handbook of Chemistry and Physics: see HODGMAN.   [9, 164]
HALE, A. J. (1956) Expl Cell Res. 10, 132.   [142, 146]
—— (1958) The Interference Microscope in Biological Research. Livingstone, Edinburgh and London.   [xvi, 4, 88, 105, 108, 116, 121, 124, 170, 199, 201]
HALLEN, O. (1962) J. Histochem. Cytochem. 10, 96.   [142, 144]
HALWER, M., NUTTING, G. C. & BRYCE, B. A. (1931) J. Amer. Chem. Soc. 73, 2876.   [8]
HENRY, B. S. & FRIEDMAN, C. A. (1937) J. Bact. 33, 373.   [xvi]
HODGMAN, C. D. (ed.) (1945) Handbook of Chemistry and Physics, 29th ed. Chemical Rubber Publishing Co., Cleveland, Ohio, U.S.A.   [9, 164]
HORN, W. (1957) in Jarbuch für Optik und Feinmechanik 1957. Pegasus-Verlag, Wetzlar.   [112]
—— (1958) in Jarbuch für Optik und Feinmechanik 1958b. Pegasus-Verlag, Wetzlar.   [112]
—— (1959a) in Jarbuch für Optik und Feinmechanik 1959a. Pegasus-Verlag, Wetzlar.   [112]
—— (1959b) in Jarbuch für Optik und Feinmechanik 1959b. Pegasus-Verlag, Wetzlar.   [112]

HURSTADO, A., MERINO, C. & DELGARDO, E. (1945) *Archs intern. Med.* **75**, 284. [82]
HUXLEY, A. F. (1952) *J. Physiol., Lond.* **117**, 52P. [88, 115]
—— (1954) *J. Physiol., Lond.* **125**, 11P. [xix, 88, 115]
*—— (1958) personal communications. [136, 137]
HUXLEY, A. F. & NIEDERGERKE, R. (1954) *Nature* **173**, 971. [27, 33, 88, 136]
—— (1958) *J. Physiol., Lond.* **144**, 403. [136]
HUXLEY, A. F. & TAYLOR, R. E. (1955) *J. Physiol., Lond.* **130**, 49P. [136]
HUXLEY, H. E. (1953) *Biochim. biophys. Acta* **12**, 387. [139]
—— (1957) *J. biophys. biochem. Cytol.* **3**, 631. [139]
HUXLEY, H. E. & HANSON, J. (1957) *Biochim. biophys. Acta* **23**, 229. [139, 141, 162]
JOHANSSON, L. P. (1957) *Expl Cell Res.* Suppl. **4**, 158. [114]
JOHANSSON, L. P. & AFZELIUS, B. M. (1956) *Nature* **178**, 137. [114]
*JOSEPH, S. (1954) personal communication. [45]
KEMPSON, D. A., THOMAS, O. L. & BAKER, J. R. (1948) *Q. Jl. microsc. Sci.* **89**, 351. [24, 209, 210]
KEOHANE, K. W. & METCALF, W. K. (1959) *Q. Jl. exp. Physiol.* **44**, 343. [38, 56, 85]
*KING, R. (1958) Annual report at the Chester Beatty Research Institute, Royal Cancer Hospital, London. [xviii]
KING, R. J. & ROE, E. M. F. (1958) *Jl. R. micros. Soc.* **76**, 168. [38]
*KLUG, A. & WALKER, P. B. M. (1957) quoted by DAVIES, 1959. [xx, 129, 134]
KNAYSI, G. (1945) *J. Bact.* **49**, 375. [182]
*KOESTER, C. J. (1958) Research report No. 4500-3-1137, American Optical Co. [104]
—— (1959) *J. opt. Soc. Am.* **49**, 560. [120]
KRUG, W., RIENITZ, J. & SCHULZ, G. (1964) *Contributions to Interference Microscopy* translated from the German *Beitrage zur Interferenz-mikroskopie.* Akademie-Verlag, Berlin 1961, by HOME-DICKSON, J. Hilger & Watts, London. [xvi, 4, 88]
LEFEBER, G. C. (1963) in *Cinemicrography in Cell Biology* ed. ROSE, G. C. Academic Press, New York and London. [207]
LEUCHTENBERGER, C. (1958) in *General Cytochemical Methods* ed. DANIELLI, J. F., Vol. I. Academic Press, New York and London. [199]
LEWIS, W. H. & LEWIS, M. R. (1917) *Amer. Anat. Mem.* **22**, 169. [136, 205]
LINNIK, W. (1933) *C.R. Acad. Sci. U.S.S.R.* new series **1**, 18. [87]
—— (1938) *Optiko-mechanitscheskaja proyschlennestj* **8**, 9. [87]
LOMAKKA, G. (1965) *Acta Histochemica,* Supplement VI. [xviii]
LORENTZ, H. A. (1880). *Wied. Ann. Phys.* **9**, 641. [5]
LORENZ, L. V. (1880) *Wied. Ann. Phys.* **11**, 70. [5]
*MCGEE, RUSSELL, S. (1963) personal communication. [165]
MARTIN, L. C. (1926) *Trans. opt. Soc.* **27**, 249. [193]
MAYHEW, I. G. & ROE, E. M. F. (1965) *Jl. R. microsc. Soc.* **84**, 235. [46]
MCFARLANE, A. S. (1935) *Biochem. J.* **29**, 407. [6]
MICHEL, K. (1941) *Naturwissenschaften* **29**, 61. [26, 205]
MITCHISON, J. M., PASSANO, L. M. & SMITH, F. H. (1956) *Q. Jl. microsc. Sci.* **97**, 287. [xviii, 38]
MITCHISON, J. M. & SWANN, M. M. (1953) *Q. Jl. microsc. Sci.* **94**, 381. [111]
MURRAY, M. R. (1960) in *Structure and function of muscle* ed. BOURNE, G. H., Vol. I. Academic Press, New York and London. [136]
NAGELI, C. & SCHWENDENER, S. (1867) *Der Mikroscop* 1st ed. Engelmann, Leipzig. [30]
NEDZEL, G. A. (1951) *Q. Jl. microsc. Sci.* **92**, 343. [145]
NORMARSKI, G. (1955) *J. Phys. Radium* **16**, 9S. [94, 115]
NORTHROP, T. G., NUTTER, R. L. & SINSHEIMER, R. L. (1953) *J. Amer. Chem. Soc.* **75**, 513. [9]
NORTHROP, T. G. & SINSHEIMER, R. L. (1954) *J. chem. Phys.* **22**, 703. [9]

OETTLÉ, A. G. (1950) *Jl. R. microsc. Soc.* **70**, 232.
OSTERBERG, H. & CARLAN, A. J. (1958) *Trans. Am. microsc. Soc.* **68**, 340.   [49]
PANTIN, C. F. A. (1948) *Notes on microscopical technique for zoologists.* Cambridge   [19]
University Press, London.
PEDERSON, K. O. (1936) *Biochem. J.* **30**, 961.   [39]
PEDERSON, K. O. & ANDERSEN, quoted by MCFARLANE, 1935.   [6]
PERLMAN, G. E. & LONGSWORTH, L. G. (1948) *J. Amer. Chem. Soc.* **70**, 2719.   [6]
PFEIFFER, H. H. (1930) *Protoplasma* **11**, 85.   [8]
—— (1931) *Z. wiss. Mikrosk.* **48**, 47.   [30]
—— (1938) *Protoplasma* **30**, 321 and 334.   [30]
—— (1951) *Cellule* **54**, 41.   [30, 31]
PHILPOT, J. ST. L. (1948) British Patent 645464 oc. 7.b.   [31, 32]
—— (1952) in *'Contraste de phase et contraste par interferences'* ed. FRANÇON, M.   [88]
Revue, Opt. théor. instrum. Paris.
PIJPER, A. (1952) *J. Path. Bact.* **64**, 529.   [88]
—— (1957) in *Engebnisse der Mikrobiologie Immunitatsforschung und Experimentellen*   [182]
Therapie ed. KIKUTH, W., MEYER, K. F., NAUK, E. G., PAPPENHEIMER, A. M. &
TOMESIK, J. Springer-Verlag, Berlin and Heidelberg.
PILLER, H. (1962) *Zeiss-Mitt.* **2**, 309.   [205]
PONDER, E. (1948) *Haemolysis and related phenomena.* Churchill, London.   [110]
[57, 62, 63, 64, 76]
POWELL, E. O. & ERRINGTON, F. P. (1963) *Jl. R. microsc. Soc.* **82**, 39.   [182, 196]
PULVERTAFT, R. J. V. (1959) *Proc. R. Soc. Med.* **52**, 315.   [205]
PULVERTAFT, R. J. V., DAVIES, J. R., WEISS, L. & WILKINGSON, J. H. (1959) *J. Path.*   [205]
Bact. **77**, 19.
PULVERTAFT, R. J. V., HAYNES, J. A. & GROVES, J. T. (1956) *Expl. Cell Res.* **11**, 99.   [205]
PULVERTAFT, R. J. V. & HUMBLE, J. G. (1956) *Revue Hémat.* **11**, 349.   [205]
REDFIELD, A. C. (1934) *Biol. Rev.* **9**, 175.   [8]
RICHARDS, O. W. (1948) *Stain. Technol.* **23**, 55.   [182, 192]
—— (1952) *Wallerstein Labs Commun.* **15**, 155.   [11]
—— (1954) *Science, N.Y.* **120**, 631.   [11]
—— (1959) *Measurement with phase and interference microscopes* Special Technical
publication number 257. American Society for Testing Materials.   [130, 162]
—— (1963) *A. O. Baker Interference Microscope Reference Manual* 2nd ed. American
Optical Co., Buffalo, N.Y., U.S.A.   [xvi, xx, 99, 101, 104, 105]
RIENITZ, J. (1964) in *Contributions to Interference Microscopy* by KRUG, W., RIENITZ,
J. and SCHULZ, G. translated by HOME-DICKSON, J. from *Beitrage zur Interferenz*
mikroskopie, Akademie-Verlag, Berlin 1961. Hilger & Watts, London.
[xiii, 87, 88, 108]
ROSE, G. C. (ed.) (1963) *Cinemicrography in Biology.* Academic Press, New York and
London.   [205]
ROSS, K. F. A. (1953) *Q. Jl. microsc. Sci.* **94**, 125.   [39]
—— (1954a) *Nature* **174**, 836.   [153]
—— (1954b) *Q. Jl. microsc. Sci.* **95**, 425.   [45, 51, 112]
*—— (1954c) *'The refractometry of living cells using phase contrast microscopy'.*
B.Sc. thesis, University of Oxford.   [40, 65, 72, 73, 74, 77]
—— (1955) *Nature* **176**, 1076.   [180, 184]
—— (1957a) *Q. Jl. microsc. Sci.* **98**, 435.   [121, 180, 184, 185, 187]
*—— (1957b) *'Some special problems involving the refractometry of living cells'.*
D.Phil. thesis, University of Oxford.   [121, 180, 185, 187, 192, 193]
—— (1961a) *Q. Jl. microsc. Sci.* **102**, 59.   [xix, 27, 53]
—— (1961b) in *General Cytochemical Methods* ed. DANIELLI, J. F. Vol. 2, Chapter 1.
Academic Press, New York and London.   [56, 184, 185, 192]
—— (1962) *Jl. R. microsc. Soc.* **80**, 171.   [viii]
—— (1964) *Q. Jl. microsc. Sci.* **105**, 423.   [53, 207]

ROSS, K. F. A. (1965) in *Research in Muscular Dystrophy* (Proceedings of the Third Symposium) ed. Members of the Research Committee of the Muscular Dystrophy Group. Pitman, England. [177, 207]

—— (1967) *Jl. R. microsc. Soc.* (in press). [174]

ROSS, K. F. A. & BILLING, E. (1957) *J. gen. Microbiol.* **16**, 418. [xvi, xix, 7, 37, 49, 130]

ROSS, K. F. A. & CASSELMAN, W. G. B. (1960) *Q. Jl. microsc. Sci.* **101**, 223. [33, 42, 141, 142]

ROSS, K. F. A. & CHOU, J. T. Y. (1957) *Q. Jl. microsc. Sci.* **98**, 341. [164, 165]

ROSS, K. F. A. & GALAVAZI, G. (1965) *Jl. R. microsc. Soc.* **84**, 13. [viii, 180, 183]

ROSS, K. F. A. & JANS, D. E. (in preparation) in *Cell structure and its Interpretation —essays presented to J. R. Baker, F.R.S.* ed. MCGEE RUSSELL, S. & ROSS, K. F. A. Edward Arnold, London. [130, 177, 198]

ROSS, K. F. A., MORRIS, I. B., HALL, F. M. & MONKS, G. K. (1958) *J. Histochem. Cytochem.* **6**, 401. [56, 61, 80]

SAGNAC, G. (1911) *Radium, Paris* **8**, 241. [87]

SCHMIDT, W. T. (1939) *Nova Acta Leopoldina* **7**, 1. [165]

SCHULTZ, A. (1924) *Zentbl. allg. Path. Anat.* **35**, 314. [166]

SCHULTZ, A. & LORH, G. (1925) *Zent.lb allg. Path. path. Anat.* **36**, 529. [166]

SENN, G. (1908) *Die Gestalts und Lageveranderung der Pflanzen chromatophoren.* Englemann, Leipzig. [30]

SIRKS, J. L. (1893) in *Handelingen van het vierd Nederlandsch Natur-en-Geneskunding Congres s'Gravenhage 1893*, p. 92. [87]

SMITH, F. H. (1947) British patent 639014, Chs. 97 (i) Group XX 5/8/47. [115]

—— (1954) *Nature* **173**, 362. [117]

—— (1955) *Research* **8**, 385. [88, 115]

★—— (1956) personal communications. [140]

★—— (1959) personal communications. [105, 121]

★—— (1966a) personal communications. [xiii, xviii, 15, 19, 22]

—— (1966b) *Proc. R. microsc. Soc.* **1**, 139. [xviii]

—— (1966c) *Jl. R. microsc. Soc.* (in press). [xviii, xix]

STENRAM, U. (1957) *Expl Cell Res.* **12**, 626. [144, 160]

—— (1958) *Expl Cell Res.* **15**, 174. [142]

STODDARD, J. L. & ADAIR, G. S. (1923) *J. Biol. Chem.* **57**, 437. [8]

SVENSSON, G. (1957) *Expl Cell Res.* Suppl. **4**, 165. [xviii]

SZIRMAI, J. A. & BALAZS, E. A. (1958) *Acta histochemica, Supplement band* **1**, 556. [199]

TAKAMATSU, H. (1939) *Trans. Soc. Path. Japan* **29**, 492. [143]

★VEERAART, J. (1962) Doctoral dissertation, University of Leiden, Holland. [154]

VERZÁR, F. (1945) in *Hohenklimaforschungen der Basler Physiol. Inst.* **41**, Benno Schwabe & Co., Basle. [82]

VERZÁR, F. & VÖGTLI, W. (1945) in *Hohenklimaforschungen der Basler Physiol. Inst.* **29**. Benno Schwabe & Co., Basle. [82]

VLÈS, F. (1911) *Propriétés optiques des muscles.* Hermann, Paris. [32]

VLÈS, F. (1921) *C. R. Soc. Biol. (Paris)* **85**, 492. [10, 31, 32]

WALKER, P. B. M. (1956) *Expl Cell Res.* **10**, 155. [198]

WALKER, P. B. M. & DEELEY, E. M. (1955) *Brit. Photoelectric Spectrometry Group Bull.* **8**, 192. [198]

WALKER, P. B. M. & RICHARDS, B. M. (1957) *Expl Cell Res.* Suppl. **4**, 97. [199]

WALTER, F. (1964) *Scientific and Technical Information.* English edition **1**, 9. E. Leitz, Wetzlar. [170]

—— (1965) *Scientific and Technical Information* English edition, **1**, 71. E. Leitz, Wetzlar. [113]

WETHERLY-MEIN, G., HUTT, M. S., LANGMEAD, W. A. & HILL, M. J. (1956) *Brit. med. J.* **4981**, 1145. [79]

WILDE, C. E. (1958) in *Cell growth, organism and milieu* ed. RUDNICK, D. Ronald Press, New York. [136]

WILKINS, M. H. F. (1950) *Discuss. Faraday Soc.* **9**, 363. [102]
WINTROBE, M. M. (1951) *Clinical Haematology*, 3rd ed. Kimpton, London. [64]
WOLTER, H. (1950a) *Annln. Phys.* **6**, Folge 7, 33. [22, 181, 193, 197]
—— (1950b) *Annln. Phys.* **6**, Folge 7, 147. [22, 181, 193]
ZERNIKE, F. (1934a) *Roy. Astron. Soc. M.N.* **94**, 377. [11, 25]
—— (1934b) *Physica*, **1**, 689. [11, 25]
—— (1935a) *Z. tech. Phys.* **16**, 454. [11]
—— (1935b) *Phys. Z.* **36**, 848. [11]
—— (1942) *Physica*, **9**, 686 and 974. [11]
—— (1946) in *Achievements in Optics* ed. BOUWERS, A. Elsevier, New York. [11]

Index